• ANNALES CRYPTOGAMICI et PHYTOPATHOLOGICI •

edited by Frans Verdoorn

Volume II

FUNGICIDES
and their Action

ANNALES CRYPTOGAMICI

et PHYTOPATHOLOGICI

(incorporating Annales Bryologici)

edited by

FRANS VERDOORN, Ph.D.

*Managing Editor of Chronica Botanica, 'A New Series of Plant Science
Books', etc.; Bibliographer, Arnold Arboretum of Harvard University;
Bot. Adviser, Board for the Neth. Indies; Hon. Sec., Bot. Section,
Intern. Union of Biological Sciences; etc.*

---

*Wij en konnen den Heer en maker van het geheel
Al niet meer verheerlijken, als dat wij in alle zaken,
hoe klein die ook in onse bloote oogen mogen zijn, als
ze maar leven en wasdom hebben ontfangen, zijn al
wijsheit en volmaaktheit, met de uiterste verwondering
sien uit steken.*

Antoni van Leeuwenhoek

1945

WALTHAM, MASS., U.S.A.

Published by the Chronica Botanica Company

FUNGICIDES
and their ACTION

BY

JAMES G. HORSFALL, Ph.D.

Chief, Department of Plant Pathology and Botany,
Connecticut Agricultural Experiment Station

Foreword by DAVID FAIRCHILD, PH. D., SC. D.

1945

WALTHAM, MASS., U.S.A.

Published by the Chronica Botanica Company

First published MCMXLV
By the Chronica Botanica Company
of Waltham, Mass., U. S. A.

New York, N. Y.: G. E. STECHERT AND CO.,
31 East 10th Street.

San Francisco, Cal.: J. W. STACEY, INC.,
244 Flood Building.

Ottawa, Ont.: THORBURN AND ABBOTT, LTD.,
115, Sparks Street.

México, D. F.: AXEL MORIEL SUCRS.,
San Juan de Letran 24-116; Ap. 2762.

Bogotá and Medellín: LIBRERIA CENTRAL

Lima: LIBRERIA INTERNACIONAL DEL PERÚ
Casa Matriz. Boza 879; Casilla 1417.

Santiago de Chile: LIBRERIA ZAMORANO Y CAPERAN,
Compañía 1015 y 1019; Casilla 362.

Rio de Janeiro: LIVRARIA KOSMOS,
Rua do Rosario, 135-137; Caixa Postal 3481.

São Paulo: LIVRARIA CIVILIZAÇÃO BRASILEIRA,
Rua 15 de Novembro, 144.

Buenos Aires: ACME AGENCY, SOC. DE RESP. LTDA.,
Bartolomé Mitre 552.

London, W. 1: WM. DAWSON AND SONS, LTD.,
43, Weymouth Street.

London, W. C. 1: H. K. LEWIS AND CO., LTD.,
136, Gower Street.

Groningen: N. V. ERVEN P. NOORDHOFF.

Paris VI: LIBRAIRIE H. LE SOUDIER,
174, Bvd. St. Germain.

Torino: ROSENBERG & SELLIER,
Via Andrea Doria 14.

Lisbon: LIVRARIA SÁ DA COSTA,
100-102, R. Garrett & 24, Poço Novo.

Moscow: MEZHDUNARODNAJA KNIGA,
Kusnetzki Most 18.

Calcutta, Bombay and Madras: MACMILLAN AND CO., LTD.

Johannesburg: CENTRAL NEWS AGENCY, LTD.,
Commissioner & Rissik Sts.; P. O. Box 1033.

Melbourne C. 1: N. H. SEWARD, PTY., LTD.,
457, Bourke Street.

Made and printed in the U. S. A.

"*I am giving here only the summary of the experiments that I have tried in order to determine the limits of the action of copper sulphate* and the manner in which it acts *when dissolved in a small quantity in ordinary water, the lengthy details seeming to me to be unnecessary. . . . . These experiments . . . . . require more time and care than one would first imagine; although in general, they yield within a few days, results analogous to those that would require eight or ten months in the field.*" — (BÉNÉDICT PRÉVOST, 1807; *from* KEITT translation, 1939.)

FOREWORD

I am happy to recall those pioneering days of the uses of fungicides to which you refer in your Historical Introduction.

I have been talking with my old friend, WALTER T. SWINGLE, with whom I was associated during those attic days in the Old Brick Building of the Department in Washington. I seem to see him poring over his microscope trying to see if there was any observable structure in the gelatinous precipitate formed when we mixed a solution of copper sulphate with a dilute "milk" made by slacking "stone lime". We did find out that the precipitate was what we learned then was a "colloid" and that when it dried it stuck fast to the cuticle of the leaf and only slowly gave off its copper and inhibited the growth of spores of various fungi; particularly the swarm spores of the Downy Mildew of the grape and the Phytophthora infestans of the potato.

IRA REMSEN had just published his "Introduction to the Study of the Compounds of Carbon or Organic Chemistry" and I had spent nights trying to understand it but since I was only twenty and the science of plant diseases was in its infancy; so young even that ALFRED FISCHER, the Berlin Botanist, denied that there were any such things as plant diseases caused by bacteria, I could do little more than stagger around in a world of rapidly growing discoveries.

But how exciting it all was! The days were too short and the nights too for we were trying to learn the languages which we felt we should need to open up the discoveries which the investigators all over the world were making.

Wars have come since then . . . . but that world of fascinating romance, the romance of chemical compounds and reactions, is still luring men's minds and leading the curious on into still vaster and more incredible things than any we fellows ever dreamed of in those attic days in Washington.

Let me congratulate you on bringing together the latest discoveries in the realm of fungicides, those remedies without which our horticulture would never have become what it now is, the source of that element which Plato declared was the most important of them all in the building of a State—food.

TO

THE MEMORY

OF

H. H. WHETZEL

STIMULATING TEACHER

AND

TRUE FRIEND

PREFACE

A scientist spends most of his time educating himself. Only thereby can he fulfill his function of advancing knowledge. The writing of this book has constituted for the author a post-graduate course on fungicidal action.

The course has been designed to consider the basic two problems in warfare, which apply as surely to fighting fungi as they do to any other combat: (1) to procure the proper materials for killing the enemy and (2) to deliver them to him in sufficient quantity when and where he is vulnerable.

The object of this book is to discuss the two problems in the light of the chemistry and physiology of toxic action and of the mechanics of application. We shall discuss materials and the techniques of delivering a killing dose to the locus of toxicity.

In general, the illustrative examples have been drawn from the field of plant pathology, but in many cases it has been necessary to tap the rich fields of wood and fabric preservation, human pathology, bacteriology, and entomology. I hope that the book may find some sympathy in those fields.

The book is no cook book. It provides no recipe for cooking railroad ties in creosote, no spray schedule for combating apple scab or potato blight. It attempts to develop the underlying theory on which the practice is based, and by which the practice may be improved.

The problem of dissecting fungicidal action has been simplified by the introduction of a fairly new tool, the dosage-response curve. We are only beginning to learn how to use this new tool, but it has the property we need of distinguishing mechanism of action from size of dose—quality from quantity.

It is a pleasure to thank my many collaborators in the Department of Plant Pathology and Botany who have been so stimulating and helpful in organizing and processing the material. Especially, must I thank NEELY TURNER, entomologist, who has helped to cultivate the interesting fence row between the toxicology of insects and that of fungi, and Dr. GEORGE A. ZENTMYER, who has contributed generously of his time in the many problems of book writing. It is a pleasure to thank also Dr. C. I. BLISS for reading the Chapter on Assessment of Data, and Dr. GEORGE A. GRIES and Dr. GEORGE W. PUCHER for helping me out of chemical trouble. None of these colleagues must be charged with any sins of omission or commission, however. That responsibility I must absorb.

May 8, 1945 CONNECTICUT AGRICULTURAL EXPERIMENT STATION
NEW HAVEN, CONNECTICUT

CONTENTS

FIGURE 1. — Typical farmhouse and vineyard in the Medoc Region of France where bordeaux mixture was born, and from whence it traveled over the civilized world. — Drawn by C. C. TEBBUTT after a photograph by W. V. CRUESS, from REED's "A Short History of the Plant Sciences" (A New Series of Plant Science Books, edited by F. VERDOORN, Vol. 7, 1942).

Chapter I

HISTORICAL INTRODUCTION

A half century has passed since 1894. That half century has seen an enormous expansion in the use of fungicides for combating the attacks of fungi on plants, on animals and on wood and fabrics. Particularly that half century has witnessed the remarkable development of sulfur and of metallic fungicides based on copper, zinc, and mercury. Bordeaux mixture and other copper materials have spread all over the world. It is almost as well known as NPK in fertilizers.

In 1894 bordeaux mixture was young. MILLARDET had only first observed its effects 12 years before. In 12 years the mixture had attained such prominence as to be the subject of innumerable research papers. It was clear that the material had a brilliant future. Nevertheless, the factors in its decline were visible a half century ago.

In 1894 young D. G. FAIRCHILD published a paper on bordeaux mixture in which he said, "Although I am inclined to agree with WÜTHRICH that no other metal will be likely to drive copper from the field as a fungicide, I am not at all certain that some of the organic compounds which exert such a powerful influence on plants may not be utilized to a greater advantage. As yet this field remains largely unexplored."

Only a few like D. G. FAIRCHILD cared for the finesse of the problem. Bordeaux mixture was messy stuff. It got on their clothes and they looked, not like scientists, but like garbage collectors. Is it any wonder that ROLAND THAXTER, working in the laboratory where these lines are being written, applied to plant pathologists the epithet of "Squirt Gun Botanists"? If one looked like a squirt gun botanist, was he blamable for being content to squirt? FAIRCHILD was no squirt gun botanist. He foresaw the present-day surge to organic fungicides.

FAIRCHILD is now retired but in the evening of his life he can take satisfaction in observing the fruition of his prediction made just fifty years ago. That field of organic compounds is now being explored vigorously, DR. FAIRCHILD. The discussion of those explorations will include a large section of this book. Before we get too far, however, perhaps it would be well to give a short historical account of fungicides and their development.

H. H. WHETZEL (1918) has published an outline of phytopathological history. Recently, E. C. LARGE (1940) has covered the field in a most satisfactory fashion, including a comprehensive discussion of the history of fungicides.

Ancient Records of Pesticides: — Powdery mildews and bunt of wheat are ancient and honorable diseases, presumably because the fungus and its effects are quite prominent. Hence fungicides for these two diseases were discovered first. The earliest reference so far found to a fungicide is the reference of PLINY to DEMOCRITUS who reported circa 470 B. C. that amurca of olives should be sprinkled on plants to prevent attacks by blight (presumably powdery mildew) (see A. F. MASON, 1928). Amurca of olives is the press cake left after making olive oil. No doubt the material contains olive oil. H. MARTIN and E. S. SALMON (1931) rediscovered some 2400 years later the fungicidal properties of vegetable oils as fungicides for powdery mildew.

Here we find an organic compound as the first fungicide. History repeats itself. We find ourselves now (in 1945) in a mad whirl to uncover new organic fungicides. Of course, it is only natural that organic fungicides should have been used first. Medicine men have been stewing up decoctions of natural products since prehistoric times. If any of the decoctions have toxicity, it should have been found.

CATO in 200 B. C. according to MASON (1928) advocated for the vine-fretter (whatever that is!) a fumigation of the plant with a smoke from amurca of olives, sulfur, and bitumen. This shows an early use of sulfur and also a coal by-product — a substance that was to produce hundreds of fungicides and bactericides by 1945. Of course, the most useful fungicide of the type in terms of tonnage is the present-day creosote for wood preservation.

Seed treatment for wheat mildew (could it have been smut?) was recommended by PLINY (see MASON, 1928). PLINY proposed that the seed be soaked in wine plus a mixture of bruised cypress leaves. Alcohol is a modern mild disinfectant. If PLINY really referred to wheat smut he was several hundred years ahead of TILLET and PRÉVOST in using seed treatments.

Wheat smut has fathered many new fungicides. About 1637 R. REMNANT in England suggested an unnamed seed treatment. The treatment was probably sodium chloride because JETHRO TULL in 1733 said that soaking seed in salt brine had originated about 1650 when wheat salvaged from a wrecked ship near Bristol grew free of smut. In 1753 lime enters the fungicidal field with a recommendation by MEYER to treat wheat with it to control bunt. Among other fungicides that sprang from the necessity for combating wheat smut may be listed with their birth dates: copper sulfate in 1761, formaldehyde in 1897, and organic mercuries in 1913.

Other new fungicides were slowly to be acquired — some to be kept — most to be discarded — some to be rediscovered.

Recently, J. G. HORSFALL and G. A. ZENTMYER (1942) have shown the interesting properties of certain basic nitrogen compounds like urea as antidotes for toxins liberated by pathogens of vegetables and trees. This was no really new proposal because J. PARKINSON, advocated it some 300 years earlier in 1629 for cankers in trees. PARKINSON spoke as follows about the canker disease: "It must be looked into in time before it hath run too farre; most men doe wholly cut away as much as is fretted with the canker, and then dresse it, or wet it with vinegar or cowes pisse, or cowes dung and urine, etc., until it be destroyed, and after healed again with your salve before appointed."

PARKINSON started something because his recommendation crops up again and again. M. TILLET (1755) suggested putrid urine as a seed treatment for wheat bunt. W. FORSYTH in 1791 recommended a paste of cow's dung and other ingredients to promote the healing of wounds on trees. Research here shows that urea will markedly improve the speed of healing of tree wounds, just as it is alleged to promote healing of animal wounds.

An infusion of walnut leaves as a pesticide crops up in old literature. SAMUEL DEANE, D.D., suggested it for canker worms in trees in New England in 1797 and E. BOURCART (1913) said it was used as a spray for aphids in 1872. The material has been used by Colonials in America for ringworm on the skin. G. A. GRIES (1943a) has shown that the material is a fairly potent fungicide. The active ingredient is juglone which is 5-hydroxy, 1-4 naphthoquinone. It is related to tetrachloroquinone, the popular seed treatment sold as Spergon.

History of Sulfur and Copper: — We have only mentioned sulfur and copper. They are so commonly in use by civilization that their fungicidal properties could hardly have been missed. Both materials seem to have been discovered and rediscovered several times. HOMER mentioned sulfur in about 1000 B. C. According to H. H. SHEPARD (1939) DIOSCORIDES, a Greek physician, about 100 A. D. used sulfur ointments in dermatology. The next reference found was written by J. ROBERTSON in 1824, who used it for powdery mildew.

Lime soon showed up in the sulfur treatment as it did in copper treatments. Hard upon the outbreak of the powdery mildew of grape in England in 1845, TUCKER tried a mixture of sulfur and lime in water (see LARGE, 1940). DUCHÂTEL soon discovered that sulfur dust applied to wet foliage was about as good as sulfur spraying, and dusting was born. Usually, GRISON, a French gardener, is given credit for boiling lime and sulfur together in 1852 (see H. S. REED, 1942). The mixture was called "Eau Grison". According to E. G. LODEMAN (1896), KENRICK, an American, boiled them together in 1833.

Usually historians credit Australians (see N. B. PIERCE, 1900) with the modern revival of sulfur. They are said to have used lime-sulfur as a sheep dip. It spread to California and was used for San Jose scale as a dormant wash. From there it spread east and was used by A. B. CORDLEY (1909) on apple foliage for scab.

P. M. A. MILLARDET is given much credit for discovering bordeaux mixture. MILLARDET had many unpleasant arguments with his colleagues about the credit for bordeaux mixture.

Actually, MILLARDET is usually given too much credit for his overpowering discovery. MILLARDET was a salesman. He should be credited with that. He definitely "sold" bordeaux mixture to the world in a buyers' market brought on by a devastating outbreak of downy mildew in the French grape vineyards.

Others had made bordeaux mixture, but they lacked MILLARDET's imagination and drive. DREISCH (1873), ten years before MILLARDET, was using lime and copper sulfate to treat wheat seed but of course a professor in a wine country could not possibly see far enough in front of his nose to notice a professor in a wheat field. Such are the limitations of crop-line distinctions in research.

MORREN in Belgium in 1845 who lived through the great potato famine caused by *Phytophthora infestans* proposed copper sulfate, sodium chloride, and lime for the disease (see JOHNSON, 1935). Unfortunately MORREN put his "bordeaux mixture" on the soil where it was not very valuable rather than on the leaves where it would have been valuable.

An amateur farmer, Judge CHEEVER, of the New York Farmers' Club was better than MILLARDET at inductive reasoning. He wrote in 1844, also during the potato famine, one year ahead of MORREN and some 40 years ahead of MILLARDET. He said, "Sulfate of copper is said to be a preventive of rust [smut] of grain. This disease [late blight of potato] is compared to rust. Cannot the science of chemistry throw some light upon the subject?" All he needed was MORREN's lime from Brussels and he would have had bordeaux mixture for the starving Irish (see JOHNSON, 1935).

Judge CHEEVER was probably referring to the work of PRÉVOST (1807), a professor in a small school in France, who discovered for himself in 1807 the magic properties of copper sulfate for wheat bunt. He was the old original laboratory worker in plant pathology. He germinated bunt spores in various solutions. Having one day prepared his spore suspensions in water from a copper alembic (vessel), he said, "To my great astonishment, these gemma [spores] either did not germinate or germinated very poorly, whereas, some others in similar circumstances, save for the copper, germinated as usual. I decided then to direct my researches principally towards copper and the copper salts." Unfortunately, PRÉVOST's salesmanship was weak in a sellers' market. He published his discovery in an obscure journal. Moreover, he was working on wheat smut, a disease which, not being new, was considered by the farmers a sort of cross that had to be borne. As a consequence his results were not immediately used. PRÉVOST, however, was widely credited with discovering copper sulfate until WOOLMAN and HUMPHREY (1924) unearthed a reference to SCHULTHESS (1761) who used copper sulfate on wheat seed for bunt some 25 years ahead of PRÉVOST. According to G. M. HUNT and G. A. GARRATT (1938), BOULTON used copper sulfate for preserving wood in 1767.

The chance to rediscover copper sulfate and sell it in a buyers' market was presented by nature in 1846 in time to alleviate some of the Irish famine that resulted from potato rot. In 1846 a newspaper correspondent in Wales (see LARGE, 1940) noted that the potato blight was not present on potatoes near a copper smelter, whereas potatoes farther away were a stinking putrid mess. Here a salesman like MILLARDET was needed. It will probably always remain a mystery why BERKELEY "missed the bus". He was a well trained mycologist and he was working on potato blight at the time. BERKELEY knew that the potato fungus was pathogenic. He should have known that copper stopped wheat bunt if an amateur in America knew it. He knew that wheat bunt was caused by a fungus as the amateur also knew.

It seems probable that BERKELEY was so busy feuding with LINDLEY, editor of *Gardener's Chronicle,* about whether or not the extrusions from a sick leaf were really fungoid, that he simply did not have energy enough left to chase down that wonderful lead developed over in Wales. Maybe he thought he could not believe what he saw in the newspapers.

At any rate the blight went ahead and demolished the Irish potato and the Irish starved despite the recommendations of MORREN and CHEEVER and despite a mountain of copper that they could almost see just across the Irish sea in Wales.

Landmarks in Fungicide History: —

1000 B. C. HOMER spoke of "the pest-averting sulfur" (see SHEPARD, 1939).
 470 B. C. DEMOCRITUS recommended sprinkling pure amurca of olives on plants to control blight (see MASON, 1928). This is probably the first case of therapy.

1629   PARKINSON recommended urine for cankers on orchard trees (see LODEMAN, 1896).

1637   REMNANT mentioned seed treatment (probably sodium chloride) for wheat bunt. This is the first case of protection.

1705   HOMBERG recommended mercuric chloride as wood preservative (see HUNT and GARRATT, 1938).

1733   JETHRO TULL described salt brine treatment for wheat seed.

1755   AUCANTE mentioned arsenic and corrosive sublimate for wheat bunt (see WOOLMAN and HUMPHREY, 1924).

1761   SCHULTHESS apparently first used copper sulfate on wheat seed.

1779   TESSIER used copper sulfate on wheat bunt but results not striking (see WOOLMAN and HUMPHREY, 1924).

1807   PRÉVOST was first exponent of laboratory testing. Rediscovered copper sulfate.

1815   WADE suggested zinc chloride as wood preservative (see HUNT and GARRATT, 1938).

1824   J. ROBERTSON said that sulfur was specific for powdery mildew of peach.

1833   KENRICK in United States proposed boiled lime sulfur for grape mildew (see LODEMAN, 1896).

1834   KNIGHT in England recommended sprinkling in early spring with sulfur and lime to control peach leaf curl.

1844   CHEEVER drew parallel between potato blight and wheat smut, suggested copper sulfate (see JOHNSON, 1935).

1845   MORREN recommended lime and copper sulfate as soil treatment for potato blight (see JOHNSON, 1935).

1846   LINDLEY mentioned action of copper fumes on potato blight (see LARGE, 1940).

1850   (circa) DUCHÂTEL invented dusting. Used sulfur on dew-dampened foliage (see LARGE, 1940).

1852   GRISON boiled lime with sulfur (see LODEMAN, 1896).

1861   RADCLYFFE recommended copper sulfate for rose mildew on basis of results with wheat smut (see LODEMAN, 1896).

1873   DREISCH safened copper sulfate on wheat seed by addition of lime (see WOOLMAN and HUMPHREY, 1924).

1880-81   MARSHALL WARD elucidated the theory of plant protection by spraying.

1882   MILLARDET made first report of bordeaux mixture (see MILLARDET, 1885).

1884   MILLARDET developed sulfatine dust, bordeaux plus sulfur.

1888   HALE in California used lime-sulfur for peach leaf curl (see PIERCE, 1900).

1888   TRILLAT, first recognized fungicidal properties of formaldehyde (see MARTIN, 1940).

1889   C. M. WEED of Ohio first mixed fungicides and insecticides together.

1894   W. SAUNDERS, S. A. BEDFORD and A. MACKAY introduced theory of seed protection.

1893   NÄGELI's startling work on action of copper sulfate printed posthumously.

1896   W. T. SWINGLE first suggested spore excretion as solubilizer for copper in bordeaux.

1897   H. L. BOLLEY first used formalin for wheat smut.

1900   A. D. SELBY introduced formaldehyde soil treatment for onion smut.

1906   Bordeaux mixture began to lose ground. Replaced by lime-sulfur on apples by CORDLEY (1909).

1913   Following EHRLICH's lead on organic arsenic for human syphilis, RIEHM introduced organic mercury for wheat smut (see MARTIN, 1940).

1917   DARNELL-SMITH introduced copper carbonate dust treatment for wheat seed (see LARGE, 1940).

1918   G. E. SANDERS and A. KELSALL introduced copper-lime dust for foliage.

1920   Crop Protection Institute founded. This opened the road for collaboration between public and commercial interests on fungicides.

1923   A. J. FARLEY proposed first wettable sulfur (but see ROBERTSON, 1824).

1927   Formaldehyde dust introduced by J. D. SAYRE and R. C. THOMAS.

1932   (circa) Bordeaux mixture began to lose out on vegetables. "Fixed coppers" introduced.

1934   TISDALE and WILLIAMS patented the dithiocarbamates. The beginning of the scramble for organic fungicides.

1934   An awareness arrived that few or no inert materials are really inert. Lime began to lose out.

1938   First research on tetrachloroparabenzoquinone. Smoked out the dithiocarbamates.

1941   HOWARD's work (1941) appears to date the modern revival of interest in chemotherapy.

Chapter II

SOME GENERAL CONCEPTS

The Matter of Definitions: — Before penetrating deeply enough into the dynamics of fungicidal action to obtain a worm's-eye view, it is perhaps best to look at the whole matter and obtain first a bird's-eye view. One is tempted to begin with a definition of a fungicide. This would be the classical approach. Right here a pair of almost mutually exclusive difficulties are encountered because definitions can both clarify and befog thinking.

It has been accepted almost categorically that definitions clarify thinking. In fact science has been considered as the grouping of natural phenomena into classes, each with its own definition. This view of science is based on the truism that an individual human mind can no more encompass at once the whole of nature than an individual stomach can digest a cow. It must be carved into chewable bites. These chewable bites are the classes of things that must be defined.

The necessity to carve the cow into chewable bites has led to a remarkably widespread view that the cow is a collection of cuts of meat. Nature is no museum of definitions. Nature operates almost entirely by smoothly integrated processes.

Those who consider the cow to be a half ton of chunks are those who hold to hard and fast species. They are those who hold that natural processes have thresholds, that point which separates action (one chunk) from no action (a different chunk). In the case of fungicidal action there is no point that separates killing a fungus from not killing a fungus. The threshold is the line carved out by the butcher's knife. It does not exist in the cow. This static concept of thresholds has delayed seriously the progress of biological science.

The channelizing and classification of facts has led rather naturally, but also unfortunately, to channelized thinking. Channelized thinking means simply — a rut. It is well known that those in a rut do not observe the movement in an adjoining rut. Hence the dynamics of pest control have been developed along parallel lines by entomologists, bacteriologists, wood preservers, and animal or plant pathologists. Obviously, where the same mistakes have been made by three or four groups, progress has been slower than might have been anticipated.

One sees heartening examples occasionally where the boundaries between these fields have been flattened, however. The Rockefeller Institute at Princeton, New Jersey, is attempting to correlate plant and animal viruses. Erwin F. Smith and later Riker and others have explored the similarities between cancer in man and crown gall in plants.

There has been a little transfer of information on bioassay of drugs and poisons between entomologists, plant pathologists and human pathologists, especially through the work of C. I. Bliss (see Bliss and Cattell, 1943). More should be done. The assay of bactericides could be improved by similar liaison.

Nevertheless, the human brain thinks best in channels. No amount of wishful thinking can void that elementary fact. On that account definitions will have to be used, but they will be concerned chiefly with describing a general category of things. Having made a definition it will have to be ignored when we arrive at border lines. Dr. G. F. Warren, Cornell University economist, once remarked in a lecture that the fence rows are the most fertile parts of a science, as well as the most fertile parts of a farm. We hope here to cultivate some fence rows.

Let it be clearly understood, however, that the flexible use of definitions is no excuse for loose thinking. Hazy thinking will always arise unless the concepts are clearly illuminated. A cow definitely has legs even if it is impossible to say exactly where they join her body.

To take another case in point, a fungicide is applied to a plant surface. The ability of the surface to hold the fungicide has been termed "retention". Retention has been used by some writers as a characteristic of the fungicide. It is not a characteristic of the fungicide. By definition it is a characteristic of the foliage.

Simply because the foliage retains a fungicide is no excuse for turning the tables and using the same term for characterizing the ability of the fungicide to cling to that surface. The fungicide adheres to the surface. The surface retains the fungicide. But why quibble? The fungicide is there. The difficulties arise when a new fungicide or a different surface is considered. Fungicides differ in their ability to cling. Surfaces differ in their ability to hold. Therefore, the two concepts are illuminated by having two definitions. Retention is the ability of the surface to hold. Adherence is the ability of the fungicide to cling.

The Committee on Standardization of Fungicidal Tests of the American Phytopathological Society has recently presented a series of definitions of fungicidal terms (1943). Since the writer is a member of that Committee he must adhere rather rigidly to these definitions but in some cases, exceptions will have to be made.

To define then a fungicide. Strictly speaking, a fungicide is a material to kill a fungus — from the Latin *fungus,* and the Latin *caedo* — to kill. This appears to be a perfectly logical class wherein to dump a group of phenomena. First we must come to an understanding as to what a fungus is, but we can settle that from books on mycology. A sufficient definition for us is that it is a low form of plant life, threadlike, free of chlorophyll.

Then we come to inquire what we mean by kill. When is a fungus dead? The elements to answer this question have been covered in texts on physiology. For practical purposes a fungus is dead when it neither grows nor reproduces. Some chemicals make a fungus look dead. It no longer grows nor reproduces. Is it dead? The chemical can be washed out of the fungus with water or acid as PRÉVOST (1807) long ago showed, and then the fungus will grow again. In this case the material is said to be fungistatic, because it keeps the fungus static. Fungistatic is a term based on bacteriostatic, a term apparently coined by J. W. CHURCHMAN (1923).

There are other chemicals such as certain phenanthrene derivatives (see R. A. STEINBERG, 1940) which permit a fungus to grow but which prohibit it from reproducing by sporulation. Are such materials fungicides? Probably not, but what are they? Possibly they can be called anti-sporulators. CHURCHMAN would call them genestatic substances.

Despite these discrepancies we will make use in general of the original definition that a fungicide kills fungi. How, why and when it does so will be considered in their proper places. For our purpose here, however, we will recognize also the discrepancies and include fungistatic and genestatic substances also in the group of fungicides.

Principles of Chemical Control of Plant Diseases: — Although we shall deal extensively with the problems of plant disease control, the principles elucidated will be equally as applicable to combating fungus diseases of animals or to the preservation of fabrics or wood. It is necessary only to substitute animal, wood, or fabric in the sentence for the word plant. Perhaps it would irk the purist to suggest that a piece of decayed wood is an infected host; nevertheless, basically that is what it is. One must distinguish between principles of disease control and techniques of disease control. Principles of plant disease control must be based on the plant's eye view, not on the fungus' eye view. The techniques of control effectuate the principles of control.

Three principles of control can be based on the plant — protection, immunization, and therapy. One of these principles, protection, involves outside treatments of the plant. The other two, immunization and therapy, involve primarily internal treatment.

Protection is the principle which involves treating a plant or its environment so that the pathogene will be destroyed before the plant becomes sick with disease. With few exceptions, the plant takes no active part in the process of protection. In animal pathology protection is called prophylaxis. Immunization is the principle of control in which a plant actively helps in warding off its own enemies or is artificially aided in warding off its enemies by introduction of chemicals. Therapy is the principle of curing a sick plant. When chemicals are used, the process is chemotherapy.

A case could be made out for lumping immunization with protection since both principles deal with the pre-disease status of the plant. They are separated here because one is mainly an internal process in which the plant itself may participate and the other is an external process in which the plant is passive.

Some will note immediately that eradication is not listed as a plant disease control principle. In general, eradication is aimed at the fungus, rather than at the host. Hence it is really a method of treatment to gain control of a disease, not a principle of control. Recently the literature has been full of eradication in the sense of killing *Venturia inaequalis* in overwintered apple leaves. This is a technique of protection or prophylaxis like the chlorination of drinking water. Others have referred to eradicating an infection of powdery mildew. This is a technique of therapy. Obviously, killing a fungus in dead tissue cannot be the same principle of plant disease control as killing a fungus in living host tissue. The fungus is killed in each case, but the plant is protected from infection in one case and cured in the other. Eradication is the fungus' eyeview of these principles in action.

Protection: — Protection is the most widely used principle of controlling diseases with chemicals. It seems probable that H. MARSHALL WARD (1880) was the first to expound this great principle of plant pathology. He held that the fungicide had to kill the fungus before it penetrated the leaf or the fungicide would be ineffective. MILLARDET (1885) rediscovered the principle a few years later.

A well known case of the commercial success of protective fungicides is the control of apple scab. In the spring the fungus blows ascospores into the air from perithecia in the old leaves on the ground. The development of these spores can be watched by extension men. When the spores are ready to blow, the word goes out over the radio to apply the first spray. The farmers pour on the first apple scab spray of the year, usually a sulfur mixture which deposits on the developing tissue. Any luckless spore that hits the sulfur deposit is killed before it can enter. The leaf is protected.

It should be emphasized that the definition of protection does not specify when a pathogene is killed. Protection merely requires that it be killed before it produces infection. For practical purposes protection covers all treatments that are external to the cuticle or other plant surface.

Sometimes the pathogene arrives in the infection court before treatment is applied as in the case of wheat bunt. Sometimes the copper carbonate applied as a control measure here is called a disinfestant. Disinfestation in this case is a technique of disease control by protection. Soil treatments to kill pathogenes are variously called disinfectants or disinfestants. These are techniques of protection or prophylaxis.

Immunization: — The field of chemical immunization has barely been touched. Past research in the field of immunization has been done by geneticists and plant pathologists interested in plant breeding. In fact, success has crowned these efforts so regularly that smugness sometimes prevails. Often one hears that plant breeding is the really polished method of plant disease control. By such lights, spraying is a crude and messy business. ROLAND THAXTER once wrote in his correspondence that bordeaux mixture is a vile substance. That it is.

If recent research in the field of a chemical immunization continues to pay, it may well be that breeding techniques will turn out to be maddeningly slow. Probably breeders succeed in many cases only in rearranging chemical processes of resistance. This can only mean that some day we shall learn to do artificially what nature does naturally.

Chemotherapy: — The process of curing sick plants, or therapy, is usually a very difficult operation because of the danger of killing the host with the treatment that kills the pathogene. Probably the first examples of curing plant disease were the surgical treatments by pruning to rid the plant of diseased tissues. An early instance found for chemical cure of disease is the control of powdery mildew of peach with sulfur as reported in 1824 by ROBERTSON.

BOLLEY's discovery of the value of formaldehyde in the chemical cure of oat seed infected with smut came more than a half century later. It is now everyday practice to treat certain cereal seeds with volatile organic mercury compounds like ethyl mercury phosphate to cure them of smut infections or infections with other organisms like *Gibberella saubinetii* and *Helminthosporium sativum.* This process is usually called seed disinfection. It is a technique of therapy.

Medical men very commonly "let Nature take its course" in the therapy of disease. Some seed-borne pathogenes like those of certain leaf diseases of celery and the foot-rot disease of squash are known to die out of infected seeds after two years of storage. Whether the celery or squash protoplasm aids in this process is not now known.

Inoculum Potential: — One of the least investigated sections of the whole fungicide problem is that of inoculum potential, the relation between the disease-producing power of the environment and the amount of fungicide required. It seems common knowledge that high inoculum potential reduces the effectiveness of fungicides but few precise data are available in the field.

It will be noted that inoculum potential is not as originally defined (HORSFALL, 1932a) just the amount of fungus material available, although that is an important element in inoculum potential. Inoculum potential may be represented as the equilibrium between number of hosts, number of spores, distance between hosts, randomness of host distribution, and weather factors as G. A. ZENTMYER et al. (1944) suggest.

If the hosts are few and scattered, the pathogene spreads slowly, the potential amount of disease is small and amount of fungicide required is small. When the hosts are congregated as in orchards, groves, or fields, they are sitting ducks to the pathogenes, the potential amount of disease is large, and the amount of fungicide required is large. One often hears his father or his grandfather say that pests are much more prevalent now than they were when he was a boy, that nobody had to spray when he was a boy. This, in fact, is a statement of the effects of inoculum potential. The hosts were fewer and hence pests were fewer and less fungicide was required.

On the other hand, if the amount of fungus produced is large, inoculum potential is high, and the amount of fungicide required is high. This is the situation at present in large orchards and in areas where production of a given crop congregates for various reasons.

Finally, if the weather favors the fungus, its chances of producing infection are increased and the amount of fungicide required is increased.

The best known field where inoculum potential receives routine attention is wheat bunt. Spore load control beginning with F. D. HEALD (1921) is standard practice in research and farmers recognize that wheat seed needs more fungicide as the spore load increases. In fact, some wheat seed may be so heavily loaded as to be discarded because no treatment is sufficiently good to reduce the smut load to a reasonable level.

Chapter III

LABORATORY ASSAY

Director SLATE of the Connecticut Agricultural Experiment Station has said that if one asks Nature a question correctly, he will receive a correct reply. It follows then that if proper techniques can be devised for asking Nature questions about fungicidal action, a proper understanding of the subject can be obtained.

Fungicides perform in the field, it is true, but we find that it is extraordinarily difficult to phrase a simple enough question in the field so that Nature can reply in words that we can understand. To obtain proper answers, we must simplify the matter by bringing it to the laboratory. Having obtained a series of answers in the laboratory, then a question can be framed in the field with some hope of an intelligible answer.

Laboratory research has paid dividends over many years, although progress at times has crept like a turtle. In 1807 PRÉVOST discovered in his home-made laboratory the remarkable fungicidal property of copper. He placed some of the granules of the dirty black dust from bunted wheat in water and found that they pushed forth protuberances which we now call germ tubes. If, however, he used water that had been standing in a copper vessel, the spores were killed—they would not germinate.

He reasoned that, that being so, the spores on the wheat seed could be killed by soaking the seeds in copper sulfate and that the wheat would grow healthy. It did.

MILLARDET also helped to firm his discovery of bordeaux mixture by germinating spores in copper solution. Following MILLARDET, there was a great rush among plant pathologists to test bordeaux mixture and then lime sulfur and other mixtures in the field on every living thing. They left the basic laboratory research chiefly to general botanists like NÄGELI (1893) and J. F. CLARK (1902) who made some of the earliest observations on the toxic properties of copper. It was not until 1911 that laboratory assay was approached seriously again by plant pathologists when E. WALLACE et al. (1911) took up the laboratory bioassay of lime sulfur.

Laboratory bioassay soon languished again, however, because few could reproduce their own laboratory data or those of any one else. Particularly discouraging was the fact that field results could not be reproduced in the laboratory with any satisfaction.

Much of the slowness in this period appears to have been due to the fallacies inherent in thinking chiefly about concentration of active ingredient. The emphasis was on the dust or spray mixture, not on the deposit that actually was responsible for the toxicity. Concentrations were controlled, therefore, very accurately, but the mixtures were applied so haphazardly that the differences in technique tended to overbalance the differences between treatments.

Workers in England, notably A. C. Evans and H. Martin (1935) and R. W. Marsh (1936) at Long Ashton, and H. B. S. Montgomery and M. H. Moore (1938) at East Malling, reopened the field by shifting the thinking to deposits. They demonstrated the significance of precision of mechanical application. They showed that spraying distance and spraying time had to be controlled with as much precision as the concentration had formerly been controlled. Tattersfield and Morris (1924) had demonstrated these facts earlier in the field of insecticides.

From this work grew the horizontal (Horsfall et al., 1940) and settling tower (S. E. A. McCallan and F. Wilcoxon, 1940) types of sprayers now standard equipment in laboratories dealing with bioassay of fungicides. J. W. Trevan (1927), W. C. O'Kane et al. (1930). J. H. Gaddum (1933) and Bliss (1935) were working in the meantime to clarify some of the statistical mysteries of using populations of spores as yardsticks of fungicidal value. This work will be discussed in Chapter IV.

The cultivation of the field was proceeding so rapidly that by 1938 a committee to assist in the standardizing of the techniques of fungicide assay was set up by the American Phytopathological Society. This Committee has just published its first report (1943), a recommended method for laboratory assay of foliage protectants.

Objectives: — The objectives of laboratory assay are many, of course. A primary objective is to understand the dynamics of the action of chemicals we call fungicides. We wish to know how and why fungi respond to various chemicals under various conditions. Sometimes the objective is to develop new fungicides. Much of the realization of this objective depends upon the realization of the first. Sometimes the objective is to control the quality of fungicides offered for sale.

Two possible types of assay have been used, chemical assay and biological assay. The stories of these two types of assay are interesting and significant.

Chemical Assay: — Bioassay is often held in contempt by chemists on the ground that it is not precise. To that charge we must plead guilty but we are moving toward precision. It seems strange that the charge is well founded despite the fact that fungous spores can often detect quantities of copper much too small to be assayed chemically. We are weighing an elephant on baby scales. The fungus may be so sensitive as to show up the sloppy technique.

Chemical assay looks simple. It is. It is both simple and precise to determine the amount of copper in a sample of tribasic sulfate. This is well treated in the cook book of the Association of Official Agricultural Chemists. It would be an easy matter to find on the market a sample of copper oxychloride with exactly the same percentage of copper in it as in the tribasic sulfate, but there would be a considerable difference in the fungicidal properties of the two samples.

To assume as the fungicide laws do that two fungicides are equal because they have identical copper contents is equivalent to thinking that two soils are equally fertile phosphoruswise because they contain the same quantity of phosphorus. Such is patently not the case and the soils people recognized it several decades ago.

This point will be discussed in more detail below under the nature of the action of various fungicides.

Fungicide research has been hamstrung by the fallacies of chemical assay. Large sums are expended annually analyzing spray residues on foliage under the assumption that the disease is controlled by the residues, but the relation between residue and disease control is often startlingly low, especially as between materials. The reason for this is that the strong reagents used for dissolving residues do not determine the effectiveness of the residues. They merely determine, "active ingredient" but give no information as to how active it is. In focusing the thinking on residues, therefore, it should be remembered that not all of the residue is effective.

Soils people first tried chemical assay of soils using generalized solvents like strong acids, but soon discovered that data so obtained bore little or no relation to soil fertility. They passed through a stage of bioassay of fertility as witness NEUBERG's technique with oat seedlings, but currently they are swinging back to chemical assay by using a selective solvent such a sodium acetate-acetic acid as an extracting fluid as devised by M. F. MORGAN (1941). This procedure assumes that the extractant simulates the extractant properties of root hair excretions.

HORSFALL, MARSH and MARTIN (1937) attempted a similar chemical assay of the copper oxides, but they obtained only a fair correlation with performance. As a result bioassay remains as the best method yet available for measuring fungicidal value.

Bioassay: — Bioassay is subject to all the manipulative errors of chemical assay plus those additional errors resulting from "biological

variation." Bioassay cannot be escaped, however, because it is difficult. Bioassay must be used in the evaluation of fungicides until the
chemistry of the process by which fungicides act is known.

Bioassay aims to reduce the properties of a fungicide to figures of
performance that can be compared with similar figures for other materials. The primary property is inherent toxicity — will it kill fungi
and how potent is it? If the material is particulate as many fungicides
are, is the toxicant liberated from the particles fast enough for killing
action to occur? Finally, how well will the protectant cling to treated
surfaces? All of these factors can be assayed biologically.

Fungicidal, Fungistatic, Genestatic: — We have already seen
that fungicides may act to kill, to prevent growth, or to prevent sporulation—fungicidal, fungistatic or genestatic, respectively. Assay techniques must be used to distinguish these. It is an interesting thing
that bacteriologists in general have developed the bactericidal techniques best whereas mycologists have developed the fungistatic techniques best. Neither has done much with techniques for assaying
genestatic properties of the materials.

In general, bacteriostatic and fungistatic techniques simply involve
  tempting to grow the organism or to germinate its spores in the
presence of the chemical. The technique just published by the Fungicide Committee of the American Phytopathological Society (1943)
is one for determining fungistatic properties of a compound. A true
bactericidal or fungicidal technique involves attempting to leach out
the chemical again before attempting to grow the organism or to germinate its spores. The phenol coefficient technique of S. RIDEAL and
J. F. A. WALKER (1903) for bacteria is essentially a bactericidal
technique. S. E. A. McCALLAN and R. H. WELLMAN (1942) have
discussed the general problem with respect to fungi.

Inhibition of Mycelial Growth: — Those interested in wood
preservatives have developed a technique through the years for measuring fungicidal value through the inhibition of mycelial growth on
agar or on wood blocks. As early as 1907 FALCK showed that the
diameter of a fungous colony was linear with time. The fungicidal
value of a toxicant could, therefore, be measured by comparing the
growth of a fungus on treated agar with that on untreated agar.

Much of the technique was developed by C. J. HUMPHREY and
R. M. FLEMING (1915) and by C. A. RICHARDS (1923). Some of the
mathematics were treated by E. BATEMAN (1933) but this will be discussed below. Briefly, the method consists in mixing the toxicant
with malt agar just before the agar solidifies. One hundred ml. of the

mixture is then poured into 500 ml. stoppered Erlenmeyer flasks. The tight flask prevents the loss of toxicant or water from volatility and it also prevents cross contamination in the incubator. Several concentrations of each material are employed.

The British could never quite agree on the agar technique. They preferred the method, more realistic to them, of permitting the fungus actually to rot wood in Kollé flasks. W. P. K. FINDLAY (1932) roundly criticized his American colleagues for holding to the agar procedure. Strangely enough FINDLAY did not criticize his colleagues for using a fungistatic technique when they needed a fungicidal one.

This agar technique has been followed in many other lines of fungicide work as for example by WALKER and his colleagues in Wisconsin (1935) who have worked on the chemicals in plants that may be responsible for resistance to disease.

Inhibition of Spore Germination: — A large literature has grown up in recent years on the subject of assaying fungicides by means of the inhibition of spore germination. This is perhaps the best technique possible for assaying the actual fungistatic power of a material because it permits the two ingredients, the fungus and the chemical to act without the operation of extraneous unknown factors. It is true that the fungicide may be asked to perform under more rigid conditions in nature, than in the laboratory, but these conditions can be superimposed one at a time and their effect measured. If the complexities are not segregated their effect can seldom be determined.

Some bacteriologists hold that bioassay of bactericides is often not very informative because proteinaceous materials are excluded. The effect of the proteinaceous materials can be studied in the laboratory, however. One need not wait for clinical experience to demonstrate that.

Fortunately, criticism of laboratory research in fungicides has quieted in recent years as it has begun to demonstrate results. We are coming rapidly now to a stage where the vagaries of disease control can be studied more thoroughly and accurately in the laboratory than in the field.

If one is interested in combating any given fungus, he usually prefers to use it as an indicator. Often this may be unsatisfactory because the fungus may be difficult to handle in the laboratory. The apple scab fungus, for instance, sporulates very poorly in the laboratory. If one is interested in fungicidal chemicals in general, he usually chooses easily handled indicators. One of these is *Macrosporium sarcinaeforme* parasitic on clover (HORSFALL, 1930). Another popular indicator is *Sclerotinia fructicola* parasitic on stone fruits. A few others like *Alternaria solani, Glomerella cingulata, Botrytis cinerea* have been used.

Different species apparently differ in their susceptibility to different toxicants. The difference seems quantitative for generalized poisons, but qualitative for many organic fungicides.

Producing the Fungus: — In chemical assay the manipulative errors are of major importance. The indicator is reasonably constant since it comes from a stock bottle. The indicator in fungus assay must be prepared for each test. Test to test variability is the bane of the bioassayist's existence. Most of this derives from variability in the fungus indicator.

One is tempted to advise growing the fungus on a synthetic medium, but until the deficiency factors are known for each fungus, such a synthetic medium may not be possible. Hence we are forced to use some natural medium like potato dextrose agar or oat agar.

This immediately raises a problem of growth promoting substances present in natural media. *Sclerotinia fructicola,* usually refuses to germinate in distilled water. In practice its germinability is governed by the amount of nutrient extracted from the media. McCALLAN and WILCOXON (1939) suggested that all extraneous growth promoters be removed by washing and centrifuging and that orange juice be introduced as a standard. M. C. GOLDSWORTHY and E. L. GREEN (1938) suggested coenzyme R as a growth promoter. Coenzyme R is now known to be biotin.

Macrosporium sarcinaeforme is not nearly so sensitive about growth promoters. It germinates without supplementary growth factors. If orange juice is added to the spore drops of *M. sarcinaeforme,* the spores are rendered more resistant to toxic action as A. E. DIMOND *et al.* (1941) have demonstrated. Spores lose resistance to fungicides as they grow older as W. L. DORAN (1922) and W. BROWN (1922b) first showed. This is the opposite effect of that from growth promoters and it suggests that growth substances leach from the old spores and that old spores need growth promoters more than young spores. In our laboratory we try to keep spore age constant within two days.

We shall see that response varies with the log. of the dose. This presupposes a constant number of spores. J. H. SMITH (1921) showed that the number of spores is related to performance. HORSFALL *et al.* (1940) have shown that response varies with the log. of the number of spores. Hence the number of spores must be held constant. A haemocytometer has been suggested by McCALLAN and WILcoxon (1939), but the errors of this instrument are larger with big spores than with bacteria. The number of spores in a low power field of given size is probably a more accurate measure than provided by a haemocytometer. Spore drops should be applied rapidly to treated surfaces to prevent sedimentation in the pipette. Moreover, they should be so applied as to spread to a uniform area, or else they will cover more or less toxicant than expected. The error of spore drop size is more serious than commonly considered.

Manipulation: — The equipment and its manipulation is of prime importance but after "know how" has been acquired, manipulation should be of small importance in duplicating results. Protectants are applied to surfaces. The surface, therefore, must be standardized. Glass is preferred by many workers but its wettability varies. EVANS and MARTIN (1935) have suggested a cellulose nitrate surface on glass. This is applied a day before use by dipping the glass in a 0.25 per cent solution of cellulose nitrate in butyl acetate.

The technique of applying materials is important, of course. Slides may be dipped in the spray material but the amount that clings will vary with the surface tension of the liquid as MONTGOMERY and MOORE (1938) suggest. Dipping, however, in general should give a film type distribution of material over the surface.

Different materials spread to different degrees on the same surface, however. Moreover, spore drops subsequently spread to different sizes on surfaces treated with different materials. MONTGOMERY and MOORE (1938) suggested that this source of error can be avoided by etching 15 mm. circles on glass slides. Drops of known volume are pipetted to these areas. The etched line is supposed to prevent overrun, but actually it seldom does. P. D. PETERSON'S (1941) method is superior. He pipetted drops of toxicant onto 15 mm. cover glasses which were affixed to slides with petrolatum. This usually prevents overrun. For many purposes so-called culture slides can be used. These have a single well 15 mm. in diameter cut out of them. Such slides are satisfactory for soluble materials.

The investigator of protectants is drawn toward the spray technique of application, however, probably because he fears a variable in the other approaches that will be unknown to him.

A study of the sprayer itself was made by HORSFALL et al. (1940). They showed that distance, air pressure, nozzle size, spraying time, relative humidity, and stray air currents affect deposition. A simple sprayer has been devised to control these variables (Fig. 2). At first, a drug store atomizer (de Vilbiss no. 28) was used. Recently the atomizer has been improved as O'KANE et al. (1941) have suggested by substituting an artist's air brush (no. KXM, made by the

Wold Air Brush Company, Chicago, Illinois). The spray stream is aimed down the center of a four-inch section of a cast iron sewer pipe 30 inches long. The sewer pipe protects the spray stream from lateral breezes and eddies, but there is doubtless some turbulence within the pipes as POTTER (1941) has shown.

WAMPLER and HOSKINS (1939) showed that an electrostatic charge is generated by the friction at a spray nozzle as it shears a water column into droplets. When the droplets hit the walls of the pipe, they charge it as POTTER (1941) has suggested. The charge on the pipe appears to repel succeeding spray droplets bearing a like charge. This adds to the turbulence, but the effect can be nullified by grounding the pipe to bleed off the charge.

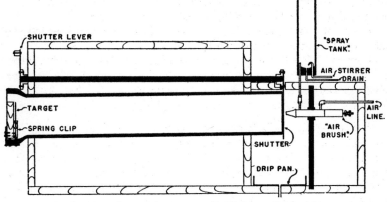

FIGURE 2. — A precision sprayer for bioassay of fungicides.

The target, a glass microscope slide coated with cellulose nitrate, is attached by a friction clip to a piece of wood hinged into the bell end of the pipe. The frontal area of the wood block exposed to the spray stream is slightly less than the difference in cross sectional area of the main body of the pipe and the bell end, so that the spray stream can part and flow around the target with no bottleneck and attendant eddying.

The speed of the spray stream and therefore the rate of spray deposit is a function of the unobstructed area of the nozzle end of the pipe. The opening is so adjusted that the sprayer gives a deposit of 20 milligrams of spray fluid per square inch per second on the slide.

Spray droplets tend to evaporate more or less in transit to the slide, depending upon the dew point of the air. This source of error is eliminated by enclosing the nozzle end of the tube in a humidified box and by bubbling the compressed air for the atomizer through water.

McCallan and Wilcoxon (1940) have designed a settling tower and they conclude that their tower is more precise than a horizontal sprayer of the vintage then available to them.

Dose can be regulated by varying the spraying time as Horsfall, Marsh, and Martin (1937) did or by varying concentration. The former is much the more rapid, because only one sample need be weighed and dispersed. The type of deposition and results obtained with the two methods are different, however. This will be discussed in more detail in Chapter VII on coverage.

J. W. Heuberger and N. Turner (1942) have described a settling tower for dusts that permits precision dusting. A given charge of dust is "whooshed" from a tapered cartridge into and upward in a settling tower by a blast of compressed air. The particles are then permitted to settle out on cellulose nitrate-coated glass plates.

Drops of spore suspension are placed on treated slides and incubated over night in a moist chamber at proper temperature.

Prévost in 1807 discovered that toxicants are more potent at temperatures away from the optimum than at the optimum. The time at which counts are made is also important as shown by Dimond et al. (1941) and Wellman and McCallan (1942).

Taking Data: — Data are taken by inspecting 50 spores in each of two drops for each dose and recording the number failing to germinate. Wellman and McCallan (1942) suggest a simple correction for non-viable spores. The check is counted first. Then half as many extra spores are counted in each drop as the check is short of 100. This number is then deducted from the ungerminated results.

Some workers prefer to measure germ tube growth, but this is probably superfluous because percentage germination and germ tube growth are highly correlated. J. M. Hamilton, D. H. Palmiter and G. L. Mack (1943) hold, however, without presenting data, that "the relative length of germ tubes is a better criterion of the inhibitory action of the sulphur than the percentage of the spores germinated." Nevertheless, determinations of germ tube length are tedious, and probably will not be used extensively except in special cases.

The Dosage-Response Curve: — If the dose is varied, the spore inhibition will be varied, of course. If these two variables are plotted against each other, a dosage-response curve is generated. The statistical theory underlying the dosage-response curve will be discussed in the next chapter. It is sufficient here to say that the use of this curve as a tool has accelerated greatly our speed of learning the dynamics of fungicidal action. The usefulness of the tool is increasing every day as we study the implications of it.

Dimond et al. (1941) suggested several factors that it can measure: spore age, nutrition level, coverage, type of compound, purity of compound. The tool can be used by a manufacturer for quality control of a new fungicide which cannot yet be assayed chemically. One can tell whether a material is decomposing in storage. If it is deteriorating, he can often determine whether the decomposition product is inert, or is a different chemical. The tool is useful in measuring the significance of the interactions between ingredients in a mixture— whether they react chemically or simply to affect the physics of use.

The dosage-response tool can be used to measure differences in inoculum potential; *i.e.,* the effect of the differences in amount of fungus inoculum or differences in the impact of environmental factors on fungicide performance.

We shall refer and refer again to this tool as we dig deeper into the mechanisms of fungicidal action. It is our best method of studying the dynamics of the problem.

Standard Fungicide: — The use of a standard fungicide has an appeal as a means of reducing test to test variation. S. Rideal and J. F. A. Walker (1903) set up phenol as a standard for bactericides. The phenol coefficient is the ratio of the killing dose of phenol to that of the unknown. H. C. Young and E. H. Cooper (1917) modified the procedure to cover fungi. They used copper sulfate as a standard. Horsfall *et al.* (1940) used bordeaux mixture as a standard and they used the ratio of LD 50 values as "bordeaux coefficient."

A standard fungicide should always be carried in tests as it informs the experimenter as to whether his manipulations are normal and in order. Ratios of LD 50 values of standard and test material give a rough approximation of relative performance, but these should not be trusted too implicitly as C. I. Bliss and H. P. Marks (1939) have pointed out.

Foliage Tests: — Marsh (1936) was not satisfied with the low precision of laboratory assay of the time. He sprayed single leaves, added spores, and placed his leaves to incubate each in its private moist chamber. He found that slides flattered the fungicide — because it was more potent on glass than on the leaves. L. W. Nielson (1942) demonstrated the same effect.

J. M. Hamilton in New York has embarked on a still bigger and better campaign to test materials on leaves as a half-way station between glass slides and the field. He sprays potted apple trees on a turntable with field type equipment. The leaves are then sprayed with spore suspensions and incubated in large moist chambers. No evidence has been adduced yet that this procedure is more precise or reproducible or indicative than modern methods using the much simpler equipment for spore germination.

Burial Tests: — The burial test is an interesting method of testing fungicides, especially protective fungicides, that has been given insufficient attention. It is a better test of fungistatic than of fungicidal value. If treated material is buried in the soil, it is constantly exposed to leaching, base exchange, inactivation by organic matter, and to action by many microorganisms. These are the factors that impinge on it in most conditions where fungicidal action is required. Even foliage sprays may be exposed to base exchange if the leaves are exposed to dirt that is either splashed by rain or blown by the wind to them. The technique has been developed perhaps farthest by those interested in wood preservatives. The standard procedure is to treat strips of wood and bury one end in the soil, using the other end for writing the labels. J. LEUTRITZ (1939) has proposed to bury small chunks of wood. The smaller the volume of wood the greater the surface area exposed to decay and hence the more rapid the test.

The war has stimulated enormously the testing of fabric preservatives. Perhaps the best laboratory test in this field is to bury the fabrics according to E. C. BERTOLET (1943).

In our laboratory we have resorted for some time to a burial test of promising new fungicides. Pea seeds are treated and planted in soil. The protective properties of chloranil (Spergon) were so discovered.

Assay of Tenacity: — Of course, protectants must resist weathering if they are to succeed and therefore their tenacity must be determined in understanding them.

No one has made any adequate analysis of the best weathering techniques. It is "Pay your money and take your choice." The only processes currently described deal with resistance to water action. MARSH (1936) leached the sprayed slides in water for an hour. R. C. WILLIAMS (1929) sloshed them and HEUBERGER (1940) swished them for 20 times through a dish of water. McCALLAN and WILCOXON (1938) showered them with "artificial rain" and MONTGOMERY and MOORE (1938) swished them through water with a mechanical oscillator.

J. W. HEUBERGER (1940) proposed a "tenacity coefficient" which is the ratio of the LD 50 of the washed and not washed slides. Useful as this statistic is, it gives only a static picture of the rate of wash off. It would seem worth while to investigate the slope of the wash-off curve. The rate of washing would be expected to follow a logarithmic course.

Chapter IV

SOME PROBLEMS OF DATA ASSESSMENT

We have just seen the manipulative procedures for testing fungicides. It is now necessary to consider the ways and means for producing with these tools a dynamic picture of fungicidal action. This is not a chapter on statistical calculations, but rather a brief discussion of the principles of data assessment. Recent general discussions of the field of statistical treatment of bioassay are given by BLISS and CATTELL (1943) and by L. C. MILLER *et al.* (1939).

Toxicity data the world around may be handled by similar techniques. Inhibition of spore germination appears to follow the same laws as the killing of insects, goldfish, cats or red blood cells. In fact, J. IPSEN (1941) has recently published a book on the treatment of toxicity data using the red blood cell as the "guinea pig." It is not surprising, therefore, that data on mycelial inhibition and control of disease in the field are also treated in a similar fashion. One suspects, in fact, that the killing of the enemy in war-time follows the same laws.

Response for a Single Dose: — The approach to toxicity measurement that the pioneers in the field have favored is to measure the effect of a single dose of a fungicide. They are likely to ask how many spores will a "standard" dose kill, how much disease will a standard dose control or how long will a standard dose preserve wood or fabric. Then they will ask what is the performance of an equal dose of an unknown material. The difference, they think, is the difference in toxicity between the two materials.

This approach is particularly favored in field research on fungicides. It serves as the yardstick of performance in hundreds of publications on the subject. This simple looking experimental pattern has probably fathered more fallacies in our knowledge of fungicides than any other single factor.

The reasons for this will develop shortly.

Dose for a Given Response: — A more suitable measure of toxicity is to ascertain the amount of material necessary to produce a given level of response, as J. H. SMITH (1921) first showed.

Using death as the type of response desired, one can imagine a theoretical microtechnique by which a given toxicant could be injected into a single spore until it is killed. Pharmacologists use just this technique for drugs, but they use animals that they can handle easily

— cats or dogs or rabbits. The amount of toxicant necessary to kill the individual is called the lethal dose. Toxicants can be compared through the size of their respective lethal doses.

Even if his spores were as big as cats, the fungicide experimenter would have difficulty in knowing when his spore is dead, however. He usually compromises on an arbitrary definition, as, for example, when it is so decrepit that it cannot put out a tube longer than the spore diameter.

A more serious difficulty is that spores vary widely in their susceptibility to being killed. This means that the lethal dose for one spore might not kill the second spore, and it might be an overdose for a third spore.

The obvious answer to this difficulty is to draw a random sample of spores and to determine the lethal dose for each spore by the hypothetical injection technique. With the data one can determine the dose necessary to kill the average spore. The dose so found will be big enough to kill all the spores that are below average in resistance but it will not be big enough to kill those that are above average in resistance. This dose will now be called LD 50 after TREVAN (1927) because it is the lethal dose for 50 per cent of the spores.

The LD 50 level of response is widely used in toxicological work. Two compounds can be compared in terms of the dose of each that is necessary to kill 50 per cent of the spores. It should be remembered, however, that low LD 50 means high toxicity.

In practice, LD 50 for spores or even for insects cannot be determined so easily as postulated, because of the manipulative difficulty of dealing with individuals. In practice, as we have seen in the previous chapter, a uniform population of spores is suspended in water, drops of which (subsamples of the population) are placed in contact with different doses of the test fungicides and the percentage of spores inhibited by each dose is determined.

This simple but necessary change in the technique throws a serious complication into the problem because we can no longer determine directly the lethal dose for the average spore. We can determine only the *percentage* of spores affected by each dose. Each dose kills not only the spores to which it is just lethal. It kills also all those that are even easier to kill.

We must infer the average lethal dose from calculations of various experimentally determined LD values above and below LD 50. Except by merest luck we shall not find a dose that will kill exactly 50 per cent of the population so that we shall have to interpolate graphically or statistically for LD 50.

Foibles of the Percentage Scale: — This brings us hard against a peculiar property of percentages when they refer to proportions of populations.

Unfortunately for this discussion, there are two kinds of percentages. One is as firm and inflexible as yardsticks should be. The other is rubbery. The use of the first type is learned in fourth or fifth grade in school. A typical example might be cited in the case of food adulteration.

If a person takes 100 pounds of coffee and substitutes five pounds of chicory for five pounds of the coffee, he has five per cent chicory. If he doubles the amount of chicory to ten pounds he doubles the percentage of chicory. Hence this type of percentage is a firm yardstick. These percentages can be added and subtracted with arithmetical ease.

Such is not the case with percentage response of biological populations to toxicants. The same dose increment produces different degrees of response at different percentage levels. As a matter of fact the percentage scale bellies out grotesquely in the middle. Some illustrative data can be taken from DIMOND *et al.* (1941, fig. 6). From their curve it can be shown that the first and third 0.05γ of copper oxychloride each inhibited about 10 per cent of the spores, but the second 0.05γ killed about 25 per cent of the spores. Obviously, percentage does not give a uniform measure of dose as it does of adulteration.

Here, then, lies the prime fallacy in the experimental design of comparing two fungicides at single doses. Results depend upon the level of response obtained, so that the difference in toxicity is not necessarily the difference in per cent response.

As a result of the rubber nature of the yardstick a simple arithmetic plot of dosage-response data gives a beautifully curved relation. To some this represents the "curved symmetry of nature." Actually it shows the inability of the percentage yardstick to be accurate towards the floor and towards the ceiling of response. In other words it shows the beautiful curvature of the yardstick and how beautifully inaccurate it is.

The curvature of the dosage-response curve stems back in part to the fact noted earlier that spores differ in their resistance to a toxicant. A few of the spores are killed by a very low dose, the "middle class" is killed by a middle dose and a few of the spores require a very heavy dose. This begins to sound like the normal curve of variation so dear to the hearts of statisticians. About sixty years ago GEPPERT (1889) suggested that microörganisms vary normally with respect to what we now shall call lethal doses.

The reason why any given moiety of dose will not and cannot

kill a very big percentage of spores at the lower or at the higher level of response is because the percentage of available individuals is small at either end. The same moiety of dose will kill a big percentage in the middle range, however, because most of the spores are in the middle range. This is the same as saying that the height range from 5′ 8″ to 5′ 9″ will include a big percentage of the soldiers in an army but the height range of 6′ 5″ to 6′ 6″ will include only a small percentage of the soldiers.

These facts can be stated also in reverse. Instead of saying that only a few per cent of the spores are killed by units of dose at either end, and that many are killed in the middle range, one can say that equal percentages of spores represent large units of dose at either end and only a small unit in the middle.

Actually, percentage responses indicate the probability that the spore will be killed. A firm probability scale is needed which will read in equal probability units. Such units should then read the effects of equal dosages equally. HAZEN (according to G. C. WHIPPLE, 1916), an engineer, first devised such a probability scale. Using the normal curve of error, he first determined how badly the results were distorted by the percentage scale. He compensated the distortions by shrinking the bulges and expanding the shriveled areas. He cut off the hills and filled in the valleys.

O'KANE et al. (1930) first demonstrated that HAZEN's probability scale is useful in the bioassay of poisons.

GADDUM (1933) derived HAZEN's probability units from a consideration of biological phenomena. GADDUM called the units "normal equivalent deviations" which carried the plus sign above the 50 per cent level and the minus sign below 50 per cent. BLISS (1934 and 1935) derived these independently, but he simplified calculations and presentation by adding five to each to get rid of minus signs and by labelling them probits. His trade-mark has stuck and probits they still are. Unfortunately, it is not possible to read response directly in probability units. The procedure is to determine the percentage values and convert these to probability units. This procedure has been called "transformation". To many, this smacks of unethical juggling of figures from "original units". This argument is weak, however, because even percentages are not "original units".

BERKSON (1944) has recently published a paper in which he proposes to substitute the logistic curve for the normal curve in bioassay. He says that the logistic curve has found use in studying growth. Presumably, therefore, he deduces that it should be useful in determining death. In order to check the usefulness of the logistic curve, he applied it to data where the normal curve had already been used and he concludes ". . . . that on the basis of the comparative χ^2 values either the results are practically the same, or there is an advantage in favor of the logistic. In no case did the normal curve appear the better of the two." BERKSON claims that the logistic curve ". . . . may have a better theoretic basis than the integral normal curve" because ". . . . it applies to a wide range of physicochemical phenomena . . . ." The statement is unconvincing, however, because he has not shown how it is more applicable to a population that varies in susceptibility. No doubt toxicity is a physicochemical phenomenon, but it must be studied with a variable population. Perhaps the statisticians should devise a formula to include both.

Dose Relations: — One of the oldest laws of nature is the law of diminishing returns. The first mouthful of apple pie à-la-mode has a delectable flavor but the flavor decreases as more is eaten. At low light intensity the eye can distinguish differences of small magnitude, but as the intensity increases the visual acuity decreases rapidly. Likewise the first pound of yellow copper oxide in 100 gallons of spray fluid will give striking control of some foliage disease, but the second and third pounds return much less additional in the form of disease protection.

The law of diminishing returns is said to be hyperbolic. Sometimes the law is said to be geometric or logarithmic. One might say that to increase a response of nature arithmetically, we must increase the treatment geometrically. Usually we must increase the dose logarithmically. The problem of understanding this effect must be superimposed upon that just discussed under probability.

Many biologists, A. J. CLARK (1933), for instance, a pharmacologist, have attempted to explain the phenomenon as biologic, but it is of much more general importance. As the speed of any given airplane is increased, the gasoline consumption goes up logarithmically.

It seems probable that the law of diminishing returns is due to the increasing operation of limiting factors as the response is upped. As the speed of an airplane increases, factors become operative that were negligible at lower speeds. At low speeds probably the major proportion of the gasoline is used for propulsion. As the speed increases internal friction in the engine increases. At higher speeds the large frontal surfaces like engine cowlings begin to impede air flow. At still higher speeds, smaller projections are important, and then still smaller projections like rivets, etc. Each of these consumes gasoline at all speeds, but the importance increases with speed.

Likewise, it is easy to kill the first spore with a barrage of particles of cuprous oxide, but to chase down and kill the last spore is very difficult. It is equivalent to looking for the proverbial "needle in a haystack".

This logarithmic aspect of the dosage-response relation is important when dosage-response is to be used as a yardstick. We have seen how the percentage scale is made of rubber and how it must be converted to a probability scale to firm it for measurement purposes. The arithmetic dosage scale is also rubber. Graphically it appears to give an inverted J-shaped curve, which is the curve for the law of diminishing returns. The dosage scale can be firmed by using the logarithms of the dose units, or by plotting on logarithmic paper as O'KANE *et al.* (1930) suggested.

In summary of this section it may be said that neither axis of the graph on the common arithmetic grid gives us a proper picture — the x-axis must be changed to logs. and the y-axis to probits.

Logarithmic-Probability Paper: — For most assay work a simppler procedure is to use logarithmic-probability paper which will accept raw data and convert to a straight line without further ado. This procedure was introduced to the fungicide field by WILCOXON and McCALLAN (1939).

We are now in a position to determine the LD 50 value for a toxicant. The results from a series of doses are plotted on log.-probability paper and the LD 50 is read directly by interpolation which is possible on a straight line — dangerous on a curved line, the shape of which is uncertain.

Slope of the Dosage-Response Curve. — Now that we have established the dynamics of the log.-probability straight line, we find that it has useful properties at first unsuspected. These properties help to justify the mental labor necessary to understand the procedure. The regression line provides two types of information, LD 50 (or LD 95) and slope. These properties of the regression line will be very useful as we go deeper into the dynamics of fungicidal action. We have discussed the usefulness of LD 50 in appraising the performance of a fungicide. LD 50 gives only a static picture, however.

Slope provides a dynamic picture. Farmers frequently assume that if a little fungicide will do good, a lot will do more good. Slope tells just how much good the lot more will do.

Different fungicides have different slopes to their dosage-response curves. Hence slope helps to differentiate among fungicides. If different fungicides have different slopes, the curves will cross, especially if the LD values are at all similar. If the slopes cross, one fungicide will be superior to the other at certain doses, but the reverse will be true at different doses. The crossing of dosage-response curves shows another big fallacy in the theory of testing fungicides at single doses. The first fallacy as already discussed earlier is that response depends upon the level of operation. The crossing of dosage-response curves has been discussed at some length by DIMOND et al. (1941) and by N. TURNER (1943).

The same fungicide will produce different slopes with different organisms. Old spores give flatter slopes than young spores and in general the more nearly optimum the conditions for the fungus, the steeper will be the slope of the dosage-response curve.

A very startling development of the recent study of slope is that coverage affects the slope. This will be discussed further in Chapter VIII on coverage.

LD 95: — Practical experimenters justifiably wonder why LD 50 is so widely used as a comparison point rather than some higher and more practical value like LD 95 or even LD 100. The spores provide the answer. The larger number of spores in the middle classes reduces the variation. Hence LD 50 can be determined more precisely than LD 95. LD 95 can be determined with as great precision as LD 50, only if about three times as many spores are counted in each test (BLISS 1935b).

Moreover, LD 50 can be determined usually by interpolation on the regression line. Seldom is extrapolation necessary. Interpolation is safer than extrapolation. Often LD 95 can be determined also by interpolation provided that enough high doses have been used. In this case the precision is reasonably accurate because it is governed not only by the high relatively unprecise points, but also by the more precise points in the lower ranges. LD 95 can be determined by extrapolation without too much danger if there are several points above 50 per cent.

Often LD 95 is more useful to the practical man than LD 50 even if it may not be determined with quite as much precision. In fact, the trend is toward LD 95 and away from LD 50 despite the groans of some of our statistically minded brethren.

We have seen how slopes of dosage-response curves may cross. It is obvious therefore that LD 95 is a much more significant level of response than LD 50 in cases of differing slope.

Non-Linearity of Dosage-Response Curves: — At intervals a dosage-response curve shows up that is non-linear. Non-linearity obviously can indicate one of two alternatives, that the theory of the yardstick is invalid, or unexpected events are occurring which are not accounted for by the technique used. WADLEY and SULLIVAN (1943) have held for the first explanation. McCALLAN *et al.* (1941) also were somewhat dubious about the theory when they found several non-linear curves. Neither of these papers gives much consideration to an alternative hypothesis.

Such a large number of linear curves have been found and for such a wide range of poisons and organisms, that one is strongly inclined to suggest that the explanation for non-linear curves had better be sought first in the manipulative technique, in the mode of action of the toxicant or in the dose actually reaching the organism, rather than in the theory underlying the linear dosage-response curve. The fact that organisms usually follow normal frequency distributions seems so well established that an exception would have to be investigated in its own right. Likewise, the fact that organisms respond with the logarithm of the dose follows so well the general law of diminishing returns that any apparent exception should be checked as an exception.

That exceptions exist is plain to any toxicologist. It seems equally plain that exceptions could be explained as aberrations in one axis or the other or possibly in both. That is they could be due to inadequate knowledge, either of the dose actually operating at the locus of toxicity, or of the percentage of mortality actually resulting from the operation of that dose.

Curvature Due to Dose Factors: — Experience has suggested that perhaps the most common type of non-linear curve is the J-curve that flattens at the bottom with low doses. In a large number of cases the curve is associated with a special type of assay technique in which the organisms are treated for a given time and then removed to a poison-free environment. In entomology such curves occur when the insects are treated with pyrethrum or nicotine. F. TATTERSFIELD and C. T. GIMINGHAM (1927a) sprayed aphids (*Aphis rumicis*) with nicotine plus saponin and H. H. SHEPARD and C. H. RICHARDSON (1931) dunked aphids in nicotine. WADLEY and SULLIVAN (1943) sprayed flies with pyrethrum. In all three cases the animals were placed in a poison-free environment. In all three cases the data give J-shaped curves.

J. H. SMITH (1921) dunked spores of *Botrytis cinerea* in phenol solutions for various time intervals and then placed them in phenol-free broth. His curves are J-shaped. Bacteriologists frequently publish data of the same type as those of J. H. SMITH and the curves are frequently J-shaped.

In searching for an explanation for this phenomenon one is struck by the similarities in technique among the experiments noted. In all cases the organisms are removed after treatment to a toxicant-free environment. It seems a safe assumption that death does not occur at the instant of treatment, certainly not for all members of the treated group. Hence the toxicant has an opportunity to escape before it completes the killing.

From the laws of diffusion, it follows that the amount of toxicant that diffuses out of an organism in a given time is a function of the amount in it. Hence the lightly dosed organisms will lose relatively less poison than those more heavily dosed, or rather that they will retain relatively more than those heavily dosed. For that reason they will be killed in larger proportions than expected and the slope will therefore flatten. Stated otherwise, suppose we start with the highest dose which will presumably diffuse out the fastest. If the next lower dose diffuses less, then the kill will be higher than expected. If the third dose diffuses still slower, then its kill will be still higher than expected. As a result, if the points for kill are connected, the line will show flattening at the bottom.

BLISS (1939) suggested that the concave curvature is due to the action of two poisons; that is, that it is a special case of dose factors. Accordingly he fitted two straight lines with different slopes, one to accommodate the steep portion, one to accommodate the flat portion.

The picture in actual practice is probably more complex than indicated. First the killing time varies among organisms and it may not vary equally among them as does the killing dose. Therefore these two are confounded. They may serve to cancel each other, complement each other, or antagonize each other. If those killed by high doses die most rapidly, the J-tendency will be aggravated. Second, the percentage kill varies with the log. of the dose, but the diffusion varies with the log. of the amount in the organism. These two variables tend to cancel each other, thus tending to straighten the J-curve.

One would expect, therefore, to find cases of essentially linear curves where similar techniques were used. McCALLAN and WELLMAN (1942) showed curves for various toxicants used for dunking spores of fungi. In general the curves are linear especially for heavy metals, but the curve for crystal violet (their fig. 4) is strongly J-shaped, if one ignores the point at 1 per cent kill.

Logarithms will usually correct the ordinary J-tendency of curves. Bacteriologists have straightened their curves fairly well by using the logarithm of the percentages on the y-axis.

They have rationalized this approach on the basis of the usual approach of the chemist who plots time-reaction curves as log. of percentage completion against time. The analogy of the time-reaction curves of the bacteriologist with that of the chemist is faulty in that the reaction may not be completed when the bacteria are removed from the toxicant and placed in a toxicant-free medium.

Using such an empirical straight line obtained from log. of percentage killed, RAHN (1929) has drawn the indefensible conclusion that bacteria do not vary or that they are killed when a single molecule is inactivated.

O'KANE et al. (1934) similarly have attempted to remove the J-ness from dosage-response curves for nicotine on aphids by using the logarithm of the probability units on the y-axis. This appears to give a reasonably good correction but Dr. C. I. BLISS in conversation has pointed out, however, that the five added to all probits is an arbitrary number and that if some other factor had been used, it would give a different value for the logarithm.

Tinkering with the y-axis is unsatisfactory, too, on a philosophical basis, because the error probably lies in the x-axis. Since the difficulty seems to be due to uncertainty about the dose actually in the organism, it seems worthwhile to determine the dose chemically and use this figure rather than to use a figure that may be considerably in error because of outward diffusion.

A. F. PARKER-RHODES (1942) has observed a series of different curves from convex to concave J-curves. He has attempted to correct these statistically by treating the x-axis. His statistics are a bit thick, but he seems to be headed in the proper direction. BLISS (1935b) also has made some effort to correct J-curves by tinkering with the x-axis.

This explanation for J-curves needs, of course, experimental support. The best support currently in the literature can be derived from J. H. SMITH himself. As already noted, his data (1921) from soaking in and subsequent removal of Botrytis spores from phenol shows a J-curve. In a similar experiment where he treated his Botrytis spores with heat (1923), his data plot a beautiful straight line.

The major portion of his technique, then, is sound. The heat differs from the phenol in that the spores killed by heat can take little advantage of a time lag. The time lag in heat escape is not appreciably different between 60° C. and 50° C. Hence no differential escape, no J-curve.

Sometimes the dosage-response curve shows a double maximum, as in that for tetramethylthiuram disulfide published by DIMOND et al. (1941). This curve is reproduced on page 125 as Figure 8. The explanation offered by the authors was that one maximum of toxicity might be due to action of the molecule, and that the increase of toxicity in the lower range of concentration might be due to action of the ions. A similar set of curves may be found in the paper by LIN (1940) who showed that antagonism between copper sulfate and certain electrolytes is periodic with at least two maxima of toxicity. NIELSON (1942) has published similar curves for the potency of silver nitrate in a metallic sulfate-lime mixture where the proportion of one ingredient was varied. Other double curves could be cited. LIN and NIELSON explained their results on the basis of the dose of toxicant reaching the organism to be killed. In effect the same could be said for the explanation of DIMOND et al. (1941).

When these explanations are considered in the light of the explanation offered above for certain J-curves, one is forced to deduce that often curvature can be explained as a dose factor, specifically the dose that actually penetrates to the locus of toxicity.

Curvature as a Response Factor: — It seems likely that the curvature can be due to response factors also. J. H. GADDUM (1933) suggested that the concave curvature could be due to an admixture of strains of the test organism, one fairly uniform strain and one fairly susceptible strain. Conversely, any convex curvature could be due to a mixture of a resistant strain with the usual strain.

The import of "natural mortality" as a response factor is not at all well understood. It appears to result in flattening of the curve at low levels of response. If further research shows this to be true, then it would offer a rationalization for tinkering with the y-axis. The significance of mortality in the checks will be discussed in the next section.

Natural Mortality: — One of the most treacherous aspects of research on toxicology is what is called natural mortality. Natural mortality means the dying or inhibition of the non-treated organisms. We have already noted the relatively simple correction for non-viable spores as introduced by WELLMAN and McCALLAN (1942). In effect they determine natural mortality in the checks first and then simply assume that these individuals do not exist.

ABBOTT (1925), an entomologist, derived a formula in which he attempts to eliminate the "naturally dead" individuals from consideration. His correction is applied after the data are collected rather than before as in the case of WELLMAN and McCALLAN. ABBOTT's formula is as follows:

$$p = \frac{p_o - p_c}{100 - p_c},$$

where p_o, p_c, p are respectively the observed, control, and adjusted percentages.

ABBOTT's formula is very widely used especially in statistical calculations. Undoubtedly it is satisfactory as the first approximation to an answer, but it still seems unsatisfactory to a "practicing toxicologist". Both corrections appear to involve the assumption that all the individuals dying "naturally" are normally distributed with regard to the log. dose of the toxicant. It seems more logical to assume that they represent weaklings and that they comprise that segment of the frequency distribution that is most readily killed by the toxicant.

If they do, then we are dealing with a truncated frequency distribution, but using probits based on a normal distribution. Is it any wonder that many dosage-response curves flatten at the bottom? That is the range in which the truncation is apparent.

This problem would appear to warrant some serious attention by toxicology statisticians. FINNEY (1944) has recently looked into the problem. He recognized that ABBOTT's formula is valid only "when the poison and the natural mortality operate independently: any interaction between the two causes of death destroys its validity." Assuming no interaction, FINNEY then set forth to erect a gorgeous structure of weighting coefficients to improve the estimate of error. It seems unfortunate that he did not first attempt to make an improvement on ABBOTT's correction before expending so much effort based on the assumption that it is accurate.

The Threshold: — It seems hardly worthwhile to leave the subject of dosage-response curves without discussing further the so-called threshold. This matter was discussed earlier (Chapter II) in general terms. Sometimes log.-probability dosage-response curves have been criticized on the basis that zero-response means zero-dose and that 100 percent response means infinite dose.

The latter, of course, is difficult to check because of the difficulty of obtaining an infinite number of experimental spores. D. F. STARR (1944) has discussed the point and concluded that "The toxicologist may apply the probit transformation without reservation that the linear relationship must fail at some high mortality." The zero-response zero-dose idea is said not to be in accordance with accepted ideas of a "threshold dose of toxicity".

The fallacy of the threshold dose of toxicity has the resilience of a tree made of rubber. It cannot be pushed over. GADDUM (1933) probably thought he had demolished it by saying, "The conception of a minimum lethal dose implies that a dose can be found which is just sufficient to kill all animals of a given species, while a slightly smaller dose would kill none. In practice this conception has no value, because of the wide variations in the sensitivity of the individual animals". Perhaps the best 1945 answer to those who propose that populations have thresholds of toxicity is "Bosh".

The Little Matter of Error: — However precisely the manipulations are done as discussed in the previous chapter, errors will still exist in bioassay. This residue of error is called the error of random sampling.

Statisticians are based on the errors of random sampling. If there were no errors of random sampling, there would be few statisticians. They have labored long to devise procedures for calculating error and for ascertaining whether the error in any one experiment is due to manipulative technique or to random sampling. The intricacies of this had best be left to courses in statistics but a few procedures might be useful to those who use bioassay as a tool in studying fungicides.

WILCOXON and McCALLAN (1939) have prepared an excellent discussion on the subject in which they showed that most of the usual calculations can be made graphically from the logarithmic-probability curves already mentioned. If two materials are to be distinguished, the limits of error for LD 50 and LD 95, say at odds of 20:1, should be known.

Lambda (λ) is the standard deviation of the population of spores with respect to the dosage of the material in question. One λ of dose below 50 per cent will give 16 per cent response and one λ of dose above 50 per cent will give 84 per cent response. That for 84 per cent should be divided by that for the LD 50, and that for 16 per cent should be divided into that for the LD 50. The average of the quotients is the mean value for λ. WILCOXON and McCALLAN (1939) give a table to determine the $19/20$ limits of error from the mean of λ and the dose ratio (*i.e.*, ratio between doses).

The width of the zone of error about LD 95 is wider than that about LD 50, but simple instructions are given also for that. χ^2 test is also obtainable graphically from a nomograph by using the percentage kill for each dose as determined and as interpolated for on the dosage-response curve.

Inhibition of Growth: — Much less research has been done on methods of assessing data on inhibition of growth than on inhibition of spore germination. BATEMAN (1933) has published the best paper in this field. The basis for the evaluation of the data is that mycelial growth is directly proportional to time whether toxicants are present or not.

BATEMAN proposed that growth in toxic media be determined at some given level of growth in the checks — say 100 mm. The difference in growth in mm. is equal to percentage retardation. By obtaining the percentage retardation from several concentrations of a given toxicant, he could plot dosage-response curves which are hyperbolic on an arithmetic grid. He was able fairly well to correct the curvature by using logs. of the dosage and logs. of the percentage retardation. He found, however, that "The departures of several of the points . . . . from the lines averaging the series to which the points respectively belong are somewhat greater than can be attributed to experimental error. Most of these points occur at the lower concentrations."

BATEMAN suggested that the lower concentrations acted differently from the higher ones. Actually the departure of the points for the lower concentrations from linearity appear to be due to his use of logs. of percentage retardation. If the data are plotted on semi-log. paper using logs. of dosage, the fit is better for the example given (his Fig. 13) than where the plot is log.-log.

Nevertheless, one may obtain a linear dosage-response curve from data on mycelial inhibition. Such a curve provides the same type of information in the form of position (LD values) and slope as is provided by similar curves for spore inhibition.

Assessing Field Data: — It is true that most of the discussion so far has dealt with laboratory data on fungicidal action; nevertheless, DIMOND et al. (1941) have shown that field data are amenable to the same sort of approach. It is necessary, of course, to apply materials with all the precision possible, and a series of doses are needed. Since the slopes of field curves are almost always flatter than those for the laboratory, a dose factor of three or even four may be desirable at times (see also p. 80).

The control of disease must be converted somehow or other to percentages.

HORSFALL and HEUBERGER (1942) have studied the usefulness of a grading system in the classifying of disease. They found that a grading system is both accurate and rapid. When this grading system was published, they were using five grades of disease, arithmetically spaced. $0 =$ no disease, $1 = 0$ to 24 percent of leaf area affected, $2 = 25$ to 49 percent affected, $3 = 50$ to 74 percent affected, $4 = 75$ to 100 percent affected. Each experimental plant was graded and the frequency of each category was weighted by the category number.

A summation was made and divided by 4, the maximum possible. This gave a mean percentage of disease for the treatment.

Use of the system improved precision of field assay, because it accelerated data taking to a usable level. HORSFALL and BARRATT (1945) have shown that the system has several faults that need correcting. The method of calculation gives an abnormally high mean. For example, if all plants for a treatment were to fall in group one, then the mean would show 25 percent disease, whereas, obviously it might well be less. Moreover, the grades are so broad that it is difficult to show differences especially at low or high levels of disease. Finally, the grades do not represent equal ability of the grader to distinguish disease severity.

A new grading system was worked out. It is based on the Weber-Fechner law which states that visual acuity depends on the logarithm of the intensity of the stimulus. In grading plant disease, the stimulus changes at the 50 percent level. Below 50 percent, the eye sees the affected tissue, but above 50 percent it sees the healthy tissue.

Starting at 50 percent, the grades in percentage are altered by a factor of two in either direction, based on diseased tissue below 50 and on healthy tissue above 50. The grades in percent (in rounded numbers) are: 0, 0 to 3, 3 to 6, 6 to 12, 12 to 25, 25 to 50, 50 to 75, 75 to 87, 87 to 94, 94 to 97, 97 to 100, and 100. This makes eleven groups in all.

Although it hardly seems possible at first that one can read differences of three percent at the end of the scale as easily as a difference of 25 percent in the middle, experience shows that such actually is the case just as predicted from the Weber-Fechner law. Since each grade, then, has equal weight, the calculations are simplified. To determine the mean grade, it is necessary simply to sum the grade readings and divide by the number of readings.

A calibration graph must be set up as shown in Figure 3. This graph must show the grade numbers on an arithmetic x-axis. It must show the percentage of disease on the y-axis with a special treatment of the logarithmic scale. The paper must show one and one-half log. phases which read from either end up to 50 percent. This gives the graph the aspect of arithmetic-probability paper. The graph between grade and percentage of disease is now straight, but, of course, it tapers below 3 percent and above 97 percent, because no intermediate grades have been put there for practical reasons. The figure for the mean grade can be converted to percentage of disease by interpolation on the calibration curve.

Having arrived at the mean percentage disease for each experimental dose, the data can be treated in the same way as laboratory data. A linear dosage-response curve should be generated. If the curve is not linear, then it is necessary, as in the laboratory, to look for aberrations in dosage. Dose in field research is usually calculated on

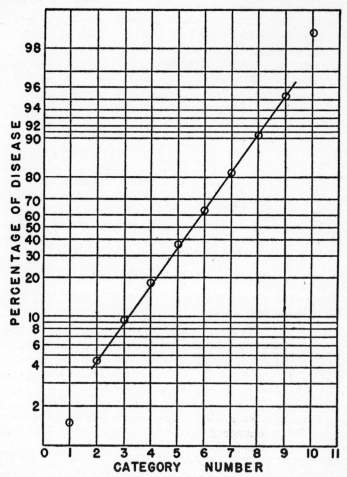

FIGURE 3. — Calibration curve for converting graded disease readings into percentage.

the basis of what is in the spray tank. This may not represent the dose on the leaf that is effective, however. Run-off may cause loss. The new application may be applied to a previous deposit of unknown size. The interrelations of all these factors will be discussed later in the chapters on deposition, coverage, and tenacity.

The fact that plant disease intensity advances with the season suggested to BARRATT (1945) a new method of treating data on disease control with fungicides. He reads his plants at frequent intervals as the season advances and plots the percentage of disease as probits against logarithm of time and obtains a straight line. From this he can interpolate for the time to give any level of disease. In effect he considers time as a dose factor and expresses his data for comparing materials as time for equal disease development. Obviously, the longer the time the better the fungicide. This method merits further research.

Chapter V

PRINCIPLES OF CHEMICAL PROTECTION

Since, in general, a sick plant is very difficult to salvage, the prevention of plant disease receives more attention than the curing of sick plants. Therefore, the major share of fungicides is used as a protectant rather than as a curative.

Fungicides are used the world around to protect seeds against decay, stems against cankers, leaves against blights, mildews and spots, and fruits against blotches and scabs, to say nothing of anthracnoses, scurfs, rusts, stripes, blasts, and molds. Outside the agricultural field protective fungicides are used to preserve wood and fabrics against decay. This phase of fungicidal protection has been stimulated greatly by the war on account of the need for protection of wood and fabrics in the tropics.

Chemicals used in protection may be applied; (*a*) to a sick host to prevent sporulation of the fungus or to kill spores after they are formed, (*b*) to the environment to kill organisms there, or (*c*) to the host or substance to be protected.

Protection by Preventing Sporulation: — In the rush to stabilize the control of disease by the application of protective sprays to the infection court, we have neglected other important measures. One of these is the use of chemicals to prevent sporulation.

In 1940 Steinberg showed that several phenanthrene derivatives of propionic acid would depress sporulation of *Aspergillus niger* without seriously affecting growth.

It is very difficult to trace the origin in the literature of any proposal to combat diseases by the process of preventing sporulation of the causal organism. Any reference to it usually has been hidden under many other things. C. E. Yarwood (1937) suggested that lime-sulfur and rosin lime-sulfur may prevent sporulation of *Peronospora destructor* on onion and later (1941) he suggested that the effect on the same fungus of the malachite green-cuprous oxide mixture of F. P. McWhorter and J. Pryor (1937) might be due also to a depressive action on sporulation.

If Yarwood did indeed discover this important fact, or someone before him, the basic significance does not seem to have been grasped generally during the eight years since it was presented. A few people appear to be aware of it however. Plakidas (1938) probably arrived at the conclusion independently. He suggested that bordeaux depressed the conidial sporulation of *Mycosphaerella fragariae* on strawberry. R. LEACH (1940) offered the same suggestion for *Cercospora musae* on banana. Quite recently DUNLAP (1943) has shown that sulfur in the soil may inhibit the formation of sclerotia of *Phymatotrichum omnivorum* with "no apparent effect on mycelial growth." One of the theories of the action of the new sulfa drugs in animal pathology is that they prevent reproduction of the bacteria so that phagocytosis can handle the population.

The panorama of unexplored territory in the area of plant disease control that has been opened by these few papers is almost breathtaking. It is now possible to look for organic compounds that may be effective as anti-sporulators without being protoplasmic poisons. In the future development of fungicides, therefore, emphasis may well shift at least in part to this field.

No satisfactory explanation has been made yet for the action of benzene and paradichlorobenzene in controlling downy mildew of tobacco caused by *Peronospora tabacina*. *p*-Dichlorobenzene is definitely not very toxic to ordinary fungi because it is standard mycological technique (see I. H. CROWELL, 1941) to kill mites in cultures by dropping a crystal into each tube. Tests in this laboratory have indicated no toxicity of the chemical to *Macrosporium sarcinaeforme* and *Sclerotinia fructicola*.

It seems probable for several reasons that *p*-dichlorobenzene prevents sporulation of the fungus. Fumigation must be repeated at frequent intervals. If the chemical actually cures the tissues by killing out the fungus, such frequent treatment would not be necessary, but if it exerts only a transitory retarding effect on sporulation, treatment would have to be repeated often. YARWOOD (1941) has shown that *Peronospora* damages the host chiefly during sporulation. Presumably therefore, as long as the tobacco fungus does not sporulate, the plants appear to be free of disease.

J. A. PINCKARD and R. McLEAN (1940) recognized that "prevention of sporangial formation" is due to treatment but apparently they did not quite appraise the significance of their observation because later they say paradichlorobenzene "causes changes in parasite or host, resulting in destruction, or prevention, of parasitism without causing significant harm to the host."

It may well be also that E. E. CLAYTON's (1937 *et seq.*) results on cuprous oxide-cottonseed oil mixtures for downy mildew of tobacco are also due to a depressive action on sporulation, especially by the action of the cottonseed oil. E. O. MADER (1943) says that the chemicals that depress sporulation of *Agaricus campestris* appear to be unsaturated hydrocarbons. Cottonseed oil is an unsaturated glyceride oil. The molecule of the malachite green of McWHORTER and PRYOR (1937) also contains unsaturated double bonds.

BERGER *et al.* (1944) treated root tips of onion with benzene. Root tips are similar in many ways to fungous hyphae. They found that benzene inhibited spindle formation in mitosis. Diplo-chromosomes are formed and tetraploid cells result. It is possible that benzene or *p*-dichlorobenzene has a similar effect on the nucleus of downy mildew fungi and that the disturbance is great enough to prevent sporulation.

Protection by Eradication: — If the spores are not prevented from forming they may be killed at some stage before they penetrate a new host. The treatments may be applied to the environment of the host to be protected or to the host or part of the host that is serving as the source of inoculum. Such treatments provide protection by eradication of the pathogene, and the fungicide itself is called an eradicant.

The term, eradication, has been booted around vigorously among pathologists. They seem to agree that eradication is an active process directed against the pathogene. Professor H. H. WHETZEL would have it as one of the four principles of plant disease control in which it refers to the removal of a pathogene from an area. I. E. MELHUS and G. C. KENT (1939) would consider eradication as control through removal of hosts as, for example, barberry eradication. G. W. KEITT (1935) used eradication in the sense of killing the apple scab fungus in old leaves on the ground. YARWOOD (1943) used eradication in the sense of curing a sick plant by killing out the fungus already producing disease as in the powdery mildews. PLAKIDAS (1938) used the term to cover the concept of killing the pathogene in the lesion where it is produced.

This agreement on "eradicating the fungus" but disagreement on where and how suggests that eradication is a method of control in which the pathogene is pushed around, not a principle of control. If the invader is killed at the outpost before he storms the citadel, it is protection by eradication. If it is necessary to oust the invader after he gets in, it is therapy by eradication.

Eradicant treatments can be applied to three different segments in the annual life cycle of the pathogene — at the source of inoculum, in the environment, or after the pathogene arrives at the infection court but before infection is established. The last comprises what usually is called disinfection or disinfestation. Actually, it is a part of protection.

Treatment at Source of Inoculum: — In 1922 DORAN suggested that a part of the effect of fungicides applied to foliage is to kill spores as they are being formed. PLAKIDAS (1938) showed a similar effect for the control of *Mycosphaerella fragariae* on strawberry.

G. W. KEITT and E. E. WILSON (1926) used a slightly different approach with their research on killing *Venturia inaequalis* on the living apple leaves in the late autumn before they fall from the trees. In each of these cases, however, the aim has been to kill the pathogene at the site of production. This is strategic bombing.

KEITT seems to have abandoned this approach to plant disease control partly because of injury to the trees, partly, no doubt, because the technique misses the leaves that die and fall early from the trees. Nevertheless, it was a fresh approach to the matter of chemical control and it has developed further in another direction, but more of that later.

E. M. STODDARD and J. W. HEUBERGER (1943) showed how this eradicative effect of spray materials could be separated from the direct protective effect. They sprayed leaves on small vigorous apple trees that were infected with *Venturia inaequalis*. They germinated conidia from the treated lesions and measured the percentage kill. The trees were then permitted to push out sprouts that were not sprayed. The control of infection on the unsprayed leaves varied with the proportion of spores that were killed by the eradicative treatment.

This research shows further, however, that the eradicative treatment is rather inefficient. The percentage of dead spores was increased from 36 in the check to 100 in the most effective treatment, but the percentage of control of infection increased only from 70 to 92.

Treatment of Environment: — The newest approach to protection by eradication is the spraying of orchard floors to kill the perithecia of *Venturia inaequalis*. This eradicative procedure also was introduced by KEITT (1935). It is receiving much attention just now. This is a case of treatment of the environment. It aims to prevent primary infection and by that to prevent secondary infection.

Perhaps the biggest case of environmental treatment is the treatment of soil to prevent root-rot and damping-off. Eradication by heating the soil in various ways is outside the scope of this book.

GIFFORD usually receives credit for introducing formaldehyde as a soil treatment. Actually SELBY (1900) first used it in the soil for onion smut. GIFFORD used it as a soil drench applying a gallon or more per square foot. It was learned empirically by SAYRE and THOMAS (1927) that the gas could be incorporated on an adsorbent, dry carrier and used as a dust which L. J. ALEXANDER *et al.* (1931) found was superior to the drench as a soil treatment. C. E. F. GUTER-

MAN and L. M. MASSEY (1935) then showed that the dust had no magic properties — that equal results could be obtained by applying the same amount of formaldehyde in a minimum amount of water. It is now plain that the formaldehyde is much more effective as a gas than when dissolved in water.

Chemical fumigation of soils is very widely used. Chloropicrin is introduced into the soil in measured doses evenly spaced over the surface. It travels by diffusion through the soil killing the pathogenes as it goes. Its present success is ascribed to this destruction of pathogenes, but the recent work of G. A. GRIES (1943b) on the toxicity of putrefied organic matter in reduced soils suggests that chloropicrin may act also to oxidize some soil toxins and thus to permit better plant growth than otherwise. The newest soil fumigant for nematodes and possibly for fungi is a mixture of dichloropropane and dichloropropylene as first suggested by W. CARTER (1943).

The treatment of storage houses is a matter of treating the environment to prevent disease. This treatment usually consists of formaldehyde fumigation or a paint or a spray of some common disinfectant like formaldehyde or copper sulfate.

Post-Inoculation Treatment of the Infection Court: — Sometimes good eradication treatment follows the advice of the military expert who said, "Don't fire until you see the whites of their eyes." That is, withhold treatment until attack is certain. This principle is widely used in the case of eradicative treatment of wheat seed for bunt. The seed does not have to be treated unless and until it is known to be contaminated with spores, i.e., until the spores arrive in the infection court. In fact, it is even possible to determine the dosage required from the magnitude of spore load on the seed.

The treatment of wheat seed for bunt is the earliest case on record of protection by eradication. Apparently PLINY had the treatment in mind when he suggested that wheat seed be soaked in wine plus crushed cypress leaves.

The treatment of contaminated seed constitutes also the largest case of eradicative treatment applied to the infection court. The fact that the seed is "contaminated" should be emphasized. If the seed is already infected, the principle of control is therapy by eradication which will be discussed later in Chapter X.

Relation of Biology of the Pathogene to Eradication: — A survey of the most successful cases of protection by eradication shows that the pathogenes in general have only one generation per year — wheat bunt, peach leaf curl, for example. The reason for this is statistical. The spores that are killed are not the important ones. It is the spores that are not killed; it is the spores that are "left for seed" that are important. Few, if any eradicative procedures kill all of the spores. Therefore a residue is left to multiply. Each spore that escapes can multiply more rapidly after treatment than before treatment because most of the competition has been killed off. As a result, if several generations per year are possible, the disease at the end of the season may be almost as heavy as if no eradicative treatment had been given.

The spores that escape a treatment for peach leaf curl may infect a few per cent of the leaves, but the damage is negligible because the chance to infect again will not come for another year.

Eradicatory control of aphids fits the same picture. The aphid on *Viburnum* overwinters as eggs on the twigs. After one generation on *Viburnum* it moves to another host. One well-timed eradicative spray, therefore, gives excellent control of the pest. Potato aphids or pea aphids that breed by geometric progression during droughts may be almost impossible to control under favorable conditions for breeding by the same eradicative treatment that gives good control of the viburnum aphid.

Ground spraying for apple scab resembles the case for single generation pathogenes because apple leaves become highly resistant as they grow older. Hence later generations of spores find a less favorable pabulum than early generations. On account of this fact eradicative treatment of the apple scab pathogene is much less successful in practice than that for peach leaf curl. It comes near enough to success to stimulate further research in the field, however.

Specifications of a Protective Eradicant: — Eradicants differ from protectants applied to the infection court in that they are generally soluble and penetrative so that they can enter into places where the pathogene lurks. Sodium dinitro-*o*-cresylate (Elgetol) as proposed by KEITT (1939) for ground spraying for scab fits these specifications precisely. Since eradicants are seldom applied to living plants, they may be and usually are much more phytotoxic than protectants. Usually also the effect of an eradicant is transient. The formaldehyde or chloropicrin treatment of soil is a matter of fumigation. As soon as eradication is complete, the chemical must escape so that plants can then be put into the soil. Under some conditions the chemical escapes less readily than expected and intense injury of the crop occurs.

Finally, an eradicant must be unusually effective because serial application cannot be depended upon to supplement the first application and kill the spores that escape the first application.

Pre-Inoculation Treatment of the Infection Court: — The protection of plants from disease by pre-treatment of the infection court has been pursued so vigorously that it is widely considered as the only phase of chemical protection. The type of chemical necessary for this job differs so widely from that used in eradicative protection that it is called a protectant. Although the distinction is not strictly valid it will be maintained because of general usage. A chemical that kills the fungus when applied is an eradicant. A chemical that must lie in wait for the fungus is a protectant.

The biology of the pathogene is important in this view of protection, too. Protectants are applied to the infection court to stop pathogenes which travel and infect in the same operation timewise. In effect, this means that protectants are directed at pathogenes which travel and infect during rain periods. Outstanding examples in plant pathology are the pathogenes of apple scab and late blight of potatoes. In the same category of things are wood-rotting fungi and mildews on textiles.

The specifications for a protectant are governed, of course, by its duties. Since its duties are exercised during wet weather, the prime specification is that the chemical be resistant to removal by rain. This usually means that the material must be nearly insoluble in water.

The rating of the protective ability of any given chemical is called protective value. Protective value or the field performance of any given fungicide rests on two legs, the spore-inhibiting qualities of the material and the quantity on hand in each infection court. Apparently, some cases of protective action are due to some other factor, as yet only glimpsed, that may discourage penetration.

Quantitative Aspects of a Protectant: — The quantity of fungicide that exists at any given moment in any given infection court is concerned with the dynamics of deposition, coverage, and tenacity. Deposition is the application of the protectant to the surface. The deposit is the amount of material initially applied. The size of the initial deposit is governed by the technique of application, by the ability of the protectant to adhere to a treated surface (adherence) and by the ability of the surface to retain the protectant (retention, see E. FAJANS and H. MARTIN, 1937).

Adherence and retention are difficult to put separately under scrutiny. Nevertheless, there are all grades of adhering ability among fungicides, and all grades of ability among surfaces to retain materials.

Coverage depends on the density and uniformity of distribution of the deposit over the surface. It is so considered in the paint industry and often it has been so defined. In the case of plant protectants, a bigger concept is necessary and apparently it has not been carefully enough distinguished. Plant protectants must be applied to innumerable surfaces like all the seeds in a bushel or all the leaves on an apple tree. The application of a protective layer over all these discontinuous surfaces has been called coverage also. Although the need for two terms is pressing, coverage will be considered here to apply to both concepts — uniformity of distribution over a single surface and over the multiple surfaces encountered with plants.

Protectants are subjected to weathering which whittles away the quantity on hand; dissolution by gentle rains and dews, baking by the hot sun, and lashing by thunder showers, or inexorable leaching from treated seeds or wood in soil. The resistance of protectants to weathering may be termed "tenacity", as defined by FAJANS and MARTIN (1937). As soon as deposition is completed, weathering sets in and the amount of protectant left at any stage of weathering is called residue. The weather writes checks against the deposit, leaving a residue.

The development of the background theory of protective action has been hampered by the far flung fallacy of thinking in terms of concentration of ingredients in a spray tank. We speak so glibly about using bordeaux mixture, 8-4-100, for the control of potato blight. Bordeaux mixture, 8-4-100, has never prevented any potato blight. Bordeaux mixture is a tank full of blue slime. Before protective action begins, the 100 part of the formula (water) has evaporated and the slime is no more. The 4 part of the formula (lime) has carbonated, and the 8 part (copper sulfate) has been converted into a complex double salt of copper.

When the farmer saves his potato crop from an epiphytotic of potato blight by spraying with bordeaux mixture, it is because he has placed a toxic deposit of the complex copper salt in a sufficient number of infection courts. There the material has lain in wait and has killed off the conidia of *Phytophthora infestans* as they have arrived. To use the paint slogan: "He has saved the surface and he has saved all".

To understand how he does this will involve an interesting study of applying the materials, of making them stay in as near continuous films as consistent with large enough deposits, and of making them resist lashing by rain or solubilization by dew.

Qualitative Aspects of a Protectant: — A good protectant, obviously, must have the ability to kill or inhibit the spores or mycelium that are trying to invade the tissue. The rating of the ability of a chemical to prevent fungous growth is fungicidal value. Fungicidal value must be clearly distinguished from protective value. High protective value demands high fungicidal value, but high fungicidal value may not confer high protective value if tenacity is weak.

The comparative fungicidal value of chemicals is governed by two factors, availability and inherent toxicity. The two concepts have been distinguished by HORSFALL, MARSH, and MARTIN (1937). They must be considered in the study of any fungicide.

Presumably fungicides can act either by chemical reaction or by catalysis. The evidence for the latter is skimpy but G. VILLEDIEU and Mme. VILLEDIEU (1923) have contended that copper acts by catalyzing oxidation. The method by which fungicides act is concerned with inherent toxicity. If they perform by chemical reaction, they presumably must be soluble or become soluble to some degree. The method and magnitude of solubility is concerned with availability.

Cupric sulfate, being very water soluble, is more highly available to the fungus than cupric oxide which is very insoluble. Availability is a term that has been taken over from the soils people who use the term to distinguish between the total phosphorus in the soil, for example, and the phosphorus that can be utilized by the root hair.

Protectants must be very insoluble in water, of course, if they are not to be leached away by rains. Zinc chloride is more soluble than creosote and hence it is less effective in the long-time preservation of wood. GOLDSWORTHY and GREEN (1938) seem to look upon availability in the sense of the amount of water-soluble toxicant initially carried on the particles of protectant. After the initial amount is used up, no more is formed. HORSFALL, MARSH, and MARTIN (1937) consider availability in the larger sense as the ability of the protectant to liberate soluble toxicant in response to any stimulus such as water or excretions from the spore or host. Therefore, the available toxicant is that which exists in the spore drop in such a state that it is capable of reacting with the fungus to kill or inhibit it.

The availability of toxicant in any fungicide is governed, therefore, by its water solubility or by its solubility in the chemicals that exist in the spore drop. The factor of speed of availability cannot be ignored. If the toxicant becomes soluble in toxic quantities too slowly, the spore will have germinated and entered the tissue before action occurs.

Therefore, availability is a function of the surface area that is exposed to reaction. This is called specific surface. Obviously, the greater the surface that is exposed to reaction, the more rapid the reaction will be. Specific surface per unit weight of toxicant is increased, of course, by comminuting the particles. This phenomenon has long been appreciated but it has been studied in some detail recently by McCALLAN and WILCOXON (1931) for sulfur protectants and by HEUBERGER and HORSFALL (1939) for copper protectants.

The nature of the particle surface is important in availability. An angular particle exposes more surface than a spherical particle of equal weight.

Apparently, availability is governed also by the nature of the solubilizing agents. Water is sufficient to solubilize some protectants. Others are so insoluble in water that filtrates are non-toxic.

W. T. SWINGLE (1896) suggested some 50 years ago that spore excretions solubilize copper protectants. This theory has been strongly supported by research of the Cornell University school of thought led by WHETZEL (see WHETZEL and McCALLAN 1930) and McCALLAN and his co-workers (1930 et. seq.). Some of the agents involved in the solubilization of copper will be discussed later in Chapter XI on copper.

BARTH (1894) thought that host excretions also play a part in making the copper available. This also will be discussed in more detail in the chapter on copper.

The nature of the excretion and its volume no doubt varies from fungus to fungus and from host to host. Such variations may account for the differences in degree of susceptibility among fungi to being killed. In a great majority of cases the differences among organisms seem to be quantitative rather than qualitative. That is, the question is not whether the fungicide will inhibit the fungus but rather how much is required. Such a situation probably is more likely to exist with general protoplasmic poisons like heavy metals or sulfur than with specific inhibitors like some of the new organic fungicides. Qualitative differences seem to exist among these. That is, some compounds may act on one organism and not on another.

This brings us to inherent toxicity which may be considered as the ability of the substance to kill, assuming equal availability. Inherent toxicity deals with the mode of action, rather than the amount of material available for action. Other things being equal, inherent toxicity governs the slope of the dosage-response curve and availability governs its position. Presumably, therefore, if two chemically related compounds have the same slope but different LD 50 values, it may be deduced that that with the high LD 50 value is the least available.

If, however, the slope is different, it may be deduced that inherent toxicity is different. The significance of slope in this connection has just been discussed by H. MARTIN, R. L. WAIN, and E. H. WILKINSON (1942).

Wood Preservation: — Wood preservation constitutes a huge field for fungicides. This subject has been covered so well recently by HUNT and GARRATT (1938) that it needs no extensive treatment here. HUNT and GARRATT say that in 1936, 155 million gallons of creosote, 23 million gallons of petroleum and 4 million pounds of zinc chloride were used in the business. Creosote is forced into wood under pressure by the Bethell process. In fact, it is the Bethell process that serves today as the basis for most wood preservation. Creosote is a mixture of hydroxy compounds such as phenol and naphthol, heterocyclic nitrogen bases, and hydrocarbons such as naphthalene, anthracene, benzene, and toluene. Some of these are discussed later in Chapter XIV under organic fungicides. Being mostly insoluble these materials leach so slowly from the wood that they serve well as protectants.

Zinc chloride is widely used for wood preservation, but being soluble, it tends to leach out of the wood and to lose its protective qualities, especially in wet soils. Innumerable other materials such as arsenic salts and chromates, have been suggested. It appears to be difficult to introduce competition for the standard treatments because adequate field tests take years to complete. Among the best of the modern introductions are ethyl mercury phosphate (Lignasan) and the chlorinated phenols (Dowicides).

Mildew Proofing Fabrics: — The war has greatly stimulated research into mildew proofing materials because of the necessity for sandbag preservation and because much of the action in the war has been in the tropics where the weather is very favorable to fabric decay. Unfortunately no inclusive monograph of the subject of mildew proofers has been written.

Salicylanilide was developed in England by R. G. FARGHER et al. (1930) but it seems less popular now than such substances as copper naphthenate and phenyl mercuric derivatives.

Chapter VI

DEPOSITION

Deposition is the process of applying a fungicide. We will be concerned chiefly here with protectants. In its stark essence, deposition is the process of transferring efficiently a quantity of chemical from the manufacturer's package to the plant tissues to be protected.

The discussion of deposition must concern itself with methods, the necessary equipment and its operation, the capacity of protectants to cling to surfaces when applied (adherence), the capacity of the surface to retain the protectant (retention), and the effect of the necessary diluents on both.

There appear to be three major methods for applying protectants to surfaces, dipping, brushing, and spraying. Barbed wire is dipped into molten zinc to protect it against moisture penetration and rust. Small items are often dipped in paint to coat them evenly and completely. Dipping is standard practice, too, in applying preservative treatments to wood and fabrics.

Since it is impossible to dip an apple tree or even a potato plant in a fungicide, this method is seldom used in plant protection, although occasionally a window box farmer will dip an ivy plant in spray material.

Brushing is very widely used in the paint industry. Brushing can be made to yield a continuous film. MILLARDET made his original bordeaux mixture very thick, so that it could be brushed onto the grape vines. His method, however, was never popular in applying plant protectants, because the leaf surfaces are not rigid like a board on a barn. The leaves give way in front of the brush and coverage is poor.

Spraying soon displaced brushing in the application of protectants. In fact it might be said to antedate brushing because in 1824 ROBERTSON recommended that sulfur be applied by "dashing it vigorously against the tree". It is not far from dashing to spraying. Spraying has only recently been taken up by the paint people and metallurgists for applying protective coatings.

The principles involved in dusting appear to be homologous to those involved in spraying, and hence dusting is sometimes called "dry spraying". The discussion below will be confined to spraying and dusting.

Proper spraying in the field is a method of mixing a liquid with leaves by means of air and a prayer. The prayer is really a hope that all the leaves will receive a toxic load of protectant before the outer ones are overcovered.

Deposition on Single Surfaces: — This problem will be simplified by considering first a single surface treated in a fixed position with a known volume of air and spray. Two basic types of liquid sprayers are used in deposit studies with single surfaces. The hydraulic variety pumps and discharges the liquid under pressure through a field-type nozzle. This is essentially a glorified field sprayer. The type is in use by W. M. Hoskins and his colleagues (1936) and by A. W. Cressman and his colleagues (1934) who have done classic researches on deposition of insecticides.

The proponents of the hydraulic sprayer hold that it copies field equipment and therefore that it introduces fewer possible sources of error than other types. The nozzle of a field sprayer in normal operation produces a hollow cone, the defects of which are overcome by moving the nozzle. This means that in an experimental set-up either the nozzle or the target must move in relation to each other or the deposit is uneven. To overcome these defects, the nozzle on experimental models may be fixed to throw a solid stream, a type of application seldom used in the field except to reach the tops of tall trees. The solid stream impinges with more force on the target than the typical spray stream in the field. In short, one wonders whether the transplanted field sprayer accomplishes what is claimed for it.

The other type of experimental sprayer used in deposition studies is the atomizer. Our model is illustrated in Figure 2 on p. 21. The cone of the spray is not hollow, and this admits of fixing both the nozzle and target with respect to each other. In the atomizer sprayer a moving column of compressed air sucks the spray liquid up by the Bernoulli principle and into the spray stream. The sprayer differs chiefly from the hydraulic types in that the carrier stream is air and not liquid. In the hydraulic sprayer each droplet is pushed by another behind. In the atomizer each drop floats in the air column. Hence the atomizer has a much softer stream than the hydraulic sprayer.

Frear (1944) held that the coefficient of day-to-day variation is much less for the atomizer type than for the hydraulic type.

R. H. Smith (1926) used a hand atomizer in his pioneer work on deposition of leaf arsenate. Exponents of the atomizer as a laboratory model argue interminably on the merits of horizontal versus vertical spraying. Evans and Martin (1935) and Horsfall et al. (1940) used horizontal types with fixed nozzles and fixed targets. Dosage of fungicide can be regulated with a horizontal sprayer by

varying the spraying time or concentration or both. McCALLAN and
WILCOXON (1940) use the settling tower, holding that it is more
precise and reproducible. It is certainly much slower and its action
does not approximate the coverage that is obtained from the build-up
of continuous spraying.

Laboratory dusters likewise are aimed at mixing dust with air.
Possibly they depart less radically from the field types than most
laboratory sprayers. Here also one finds exponents such as J. D.
WILSON and F. IRONS (1942) and E. B. HASTINGS and J. H. PEPPER
(1939), of using actual field models. The more common type is the
settling tower such as used by HEUBERGER and TURNER (1942). In
this type a given charge of dust is placed in a cartridge and blown
into the tower with a given volume of air. A settling tower is not very
different from a field duster in which small amounts of dust are
brushed periodically into the air stream which carries the dust particles over the plant. The operator hopes they will settle in the
proper places. The settling tower assures that they will settle on the
surface to be studied.

Operational Factors: — The conditions under which equipment
is operated obviously affect its performance and they affect different
equipment differently. Treatment time is important. For horizontal
sprayers, deposition of spray fluid and suspensoids prior to run-off
bears a linear relation to spraying time (EVANS and MARTIN, 1935,
HORSFALL et al., 1940). Presumably the same relation holds for the
solid-stream water pressure sprayer, but no data have been found.
G. S. HENSILL and V. J. TIHENKO (1939) measured deposition of an
oil-emulsion on beeswax after run-off. Calculation of their data shows
that deposition varies as the logarithm of spray time. Apparently, the
oil continues to deposit itself, but ever more slowly beyond the stage
of inital run-off. Calculation of data by D. ISELEY and W. R. HORS-
FALL (1943) show that if spraying of lead arsenate continues to in-
cipient run-off, deposit varies as the logarithm of concentration. This
has been confirmed here with yellow cuprous oxide.

Deposition of dust and spray in a settling tower varies with the
logarithm of the settling time. This is associated with elutriation
phenomena. The largest droplets or particles of dust settle first, followed in ever decreasing speed by the smaller droplets and particles.

One of the laws of illumination is that the intensity of illumination varies as the square of the distance from the source of light. The
same has been shown to hold true for the deposition of spray fluid by
an atomizer prior to run-off (HORSFALL et al., 1940). HENSILL and
TIHENKO (1939) again working beyond the run-off stage found with

the solid-stream type of sprayer that deposit of oil varied directly with distance. Of course, run-off and distance are confounded in this type of test and apparently they balance each other.

Since air currents interfere seriously with the operation of the atomizer type of sprayers and of all dusters, they must be enclosed (HORSFALL *et al.*, 1940). Air currents are said not to interfere seriously with the operation of the solid-stream sprayer (HENSILL and TIHENKO, 1939), but air currents are said to interfere with the hollow-cone type of field sprayer (NIELSON, 1942). Air humidity has been shown to be a factor in the atomizer (HORSFALL *et al.*, 1940). Low humidity causes the spray droplets to evaporate in transit to the target so that they lose their load of toxicant. This has been overcome by humidifying the air through which the spray passes.

The pressure at which the sprayer is operated affects deposition. In the case of the atomizer type, deposit prior to run-off increases as the logarithm of air pressure (HORSFALL *et al.*, 1940), but the deposit of oil after run-off increases directly with air pressure in the solid-stream type (HENSILL and TIHENKO, 1939). Here again run-off and pressure have been confounded. H. L. CRANE (1919) has shown that the field nozzle discharges spray fluid according to the pressure.

Effect of the Diluent: — Except possibly for materials used on seeds, fungicides must be extended or diluted in some fashion in order to obtain distribution. This means that knowledge of protective action must encompass not only a knowledge of fungicidal action, but also the diluent as well, whether it be water in a spray or talc in a dust. The dynamics of the mixtures are hardly the same as the dynamics of the separate ingredients although it is not always possible to distinguish the ingredients. The chemical interactions are discussed later in Chapter XV on synergism and antagonism.

The immediate problem here is how do diluents affect deposition. In the case of sprays, water is the diluent. Water collects into droplets as it travels through the air. The force that causes the droplets to assume the ball-shape is called surface tension.

Surface tension arises because of a gregarious tendency of molecules in liquids. The forces involved in this mutual attraction, of course, tend to operate over the shortest possible routes and these routes are the radii of spheres. Hence spheres are formed because the liquid can flow into that shape. The drops remain as spheres unless acted upon by some external force.

The forces acting inwardly on the radius of a sphere inevitably produce strain at the surface of the sphere similar to that produced by forces acting on an arch. This tends to crush the surface molecules more closely together than in other parts of the sphere. This actually produces a skin-like thickening of the surface which is often observed.

In moving through the air, spray droplets encounter friction which varies inversely with surface area of the droplet, according to Stokes' law. As the surface area of the droplet is proportional to the cube of the radius, the surface area in a gram of water increases enormously as the droplet size decreases.

Hence a gram of liquid discharged as fine droplets such as produced by an atomizer moves much less rapidly than a gram of liquid discharged by a solid stream because the frictional resistance is so much greater. This is the basis for the claim advocated for atomizers that the spray stream is velvet smooth and therefore much less likely to produce foliage injury. Likewise, however, such streams move much less distance than solid streams, and therefore reach fewer leaves in the field. Because of the friction of the small droplets, an atomizer produces less deposit per unit of time than those sprayers which do not break the liquid up so fine.

For various reasons as discussed later in Chapter VII on coverage, materials are sometimes added to sprays to reduce surface tension. The effect of such materials is to reduce droplet size. Friction, therefore, should be increased and deposition should fall. FAJANS and MARTIN (1938) give data showing that deposition rate does fall when a material is added to reduce surface tension. Recent research in this laboratory as well shows that deposition prior to run-off is reduced when depressants of surface tension are added to the spray fluid.

Generally, deposition of dusts is a matter of settling on surfaces. Stokes' law is useful here too. Dusts settle through air according to the surface area exposed by the particles, and, therefore, the smallest particles settle the least rapidly. In fact surface area of dust particles is determined experimentally by a process that depends on this fact. The process was first applied to pesticides by E. L. GOODEN and C. M. SMITH (1940). In practice the air is forced through a column of dust rather than the dust through a column of air, but the dynamics of the frictional forces involved are identical.

HEUBERGER and TURNER's (1942) settling tower offers a simple tool for investigating the settling of dusts. Different diluents and toxicants settle at different rates, of course, because of differences in specific surface, i.e., the amount of surface per gram of particles. Hence, elutriation of a dust mixture may occur. HASTINGS and PEPPER (1939) have shown that sodium arsenite settles at a different rate from some common diluents that it may be mixed with. Apparent density of the diluent has little effect. IRONS (1943) has found that the centrifugal action in the fan of a rotary duster will fractionate the dusts. The heavier ingredients will be concentrated toward the periphery of the fan housing like milk in a cream separator. If several nozzles take off from a single fan, one nozzle may contain the most of the toxicant, and the other nozzles may contain very little.

The method of mixing ingredients affects settling rate. HEU-BERGER and TURNER in unpublished work have found that dry ball-milling may increase the settling rate, presumably by inducing aggregation of the particles.

Retention by the Surface: — The problems of deposition are not over until the material is on the surface to stay. Consideration will now be given to the problems involved in retention of fungicides by surfaces and adherence of fungicides to surfaces.

HENSILL and HOSKINS (1935) would like to conceive of a primary and a secondary deposit of sprays on surfaces. As they view the matter, the primary deposit of suspensoid "builds up" as spraying proceeds until the surface is covered with liquid. After that the "continuous film of water prevents more insecticide from coming in contact with the solid". The secondary deposit "occurs when the water of the film evaporates". Apparently, a secondary deposit is a primary deposit without water. Few protective sprays develop that "continuous film". It induces drain-off with attendant reduction in deposit.

The mutual admiration of the spray fluid molecules for each other may receive a rude shock when the droplet of spray impinges on a leaf. First the drop is flattened by impact. Then it may be restrained from reassuming the spherical shape by a strong surface tension of the leaf to which it is applied. In fact these forces may be so strong, as on a potato leaf, for example, that the cohesiveness of the liquid molecules may be almost completely overcome. The droplet is then pulled out quite thin over the leaf.

We say that such a leaf is wetted because it has a greater attraction for the molecules of the spray fluid than the molecules have for themselves. Additional water applied to a wetted leaf flows along the leaf and off the edge if the leaf is inclined or vertical. EVANS and MARTIN (1935) call this "drain-off".

Some leaves have no liking for water. They do not attract the molecules of the liquid particularly, so that the molecules are free to resume their mutual attraction. As a result the liquid stands in tall drops over the leaf. This phenomenon has been seen by everyone who has observed raindrops on young rose or cabbage leaves. Such tall drops project so far from a sloping or vertical leaf that their center of gravity is out of line and they roll off. EVANS and MARTIN (1935) call this "run-off," as distinguished from "drain-off".

Obviously drain-off and run-off affect deposition. A surface that is easily wetted usually will retain much less of a spray material than one that is not. In other words drain-off is associated with smaller deposits than run-off.

Adherence of the Fungicide: — Materials vary enormously in their ability to cling to surfaces when being applied. This is most simply demonstrated by thrusting a dry piece of wood or a knife blade into a drum of material. Arsenate of lead, red copper oxide, and lime are particularly well known for their capacity to adhere under these circumstances. Copper sulfate monohydrate and most "fixed copper" protectants like copper phosphate and copper silicate cling poorly.

It seems a striking phenomenon that most metallic oxides possess this attribute of high adherence. It can be observed in iron oxide, zinc oxide, aluminum oxide as well as in the cuprous oxide and calcium oxide noted above. Other salts of these metals like nitrate, chloride, or sulfate do not adhere as well.

The reasons for this adherence are poorly understood. The oxides tend to be amorphous rather than crystalline and yet amorphous graphite and amorphous sulfur adhere less well, if anything, than the crystalline forms. Apparently, no glue-like adhesion is involved. Copper resinate adheres well from this apparent cause, but the other salts do not seem to. Unctuousness might be advanced as a reason why crystalline graphite adheres better than amorphous graphite and yet zinc stearate is much more unctuous than zinc oxide, but it adheres no better if as well.

In any case the adherence is a quality of the material itself. In general the initial adherence of dusts does not seem to be improved by any additives except oil which appears to have been discovered by GINSBERG (1927). Mineral oil seems to be preferred now to glyceride oils. E. N. KOZLOVA (1935) showed that the optimum amount of oil required for adherence is a function of the specific surface of the particles of dust. SAZONOV (1937) observed that adherence of oiled dusts to dry foliage is superior to that of non-oiled dusts, but that the reverse is true for wet foliage. Presumably water on the leaf repels an oily dust.

The adherence of materials after extension with dust diluents or water appears in most cases to assume the adherence capabilities of the diluent. Cuprous oxide dust, for instance, extended with clay seems to adhere as poorly as the clay carrier and when sprayed in water onto a leaf or other surface, it clings only as well as the water. When the excess water runs off or drains off, the suspended cuprous oxide goes with it. R. H. SMITH (1926) showed the same phenomenon for arsenate of lead and FAJANS and MARTIN (1938) showed it for cuprous iodide. The run-off water not only carries off the suspended material, but it also may take off most of the drops with their suspended material that lie in its path.

E. R. DeONG et al. (1927) demonstrated an exception to this generalization. They found that an oil emulsion may adhere while the water runs off. This preferential adherence of oil is favored by an emulsion that will "break" easily as soon as it is applied, so that the oil phase rather than the aqueous phase will "wet" the leaf first. This has been described as "oily wetting". In this case the water that runs off is poorer in toxicant than that which is applied.

J. MARSHALL (1937) showed that lead arsenate wetted and carried by the oil would remain on the leaf with the oil while the water runs off. This fact was confirmed independently by FAJANS and MARTIN (1938). E. E. WILSON (1942) showed that cotton seed oil improves adherence of bordeaux if spraying is continued beyond the run-off stage.

W. MOORE (1921) developed the intriguing theory that electrostatic charge may be involved in the adherence of lead arsenate. He suggested that the leaf on a plant, being attached to the earth, bears a negative charge. MOORE deduced from his experiments that arsenate of lead bearing a positive charge adheres to a leaf in larger quantity than arsenate of lead with a negative charge.

Spraying a leaf is like stroking a cat in the wintertime. An electrostatic charge is developed on the leaf. Similar charges are developed in waterfalls. LENARD (1915) has shown that the energy to produce the charge is developed by the shearing action of the water as new spray drops tear into those already present. This phenomenon interested E. L. WAMPLER and W. M. HOSKINS (1939) in the light of MOORE's researches on the effect of charge on the adherence of arsenate of lead.

They confirmed other work that droplets leaving a nozzle carry a positive charge which is given up to the target, thus positively charging it. WAMPLER and HOSKINS attempted to measure the effect of this charge on deposition of lead arsenate on a beeswax-coated plate. They concluded that the charge had no effect, but their technique leaves many questions unanswered. (1) The spray was directed vertically at the target. (2) Spraying continued beyond run-off. (3) The excess liquid was shaken off before the lead arsenate was determined.

Presumably the plate became initially charged like the spray droplets. If so, it could hardly have repelled oncoming new droplets because it would be operating against gravity. Conversely, when they charged the plate oppositely, it had little chance to attract more droplets because they were falling on it anyway. In other words it is not proved that charge on the target does or does not affect deposition.

G. T. Brown and W. M. Hoskins (1939) made a significant study of pH in relation to adherence of oil and water beyond the run-off stage. When used alone, the amount of water that adheres increases with the OH ion. This situation is reminiscent of the adherence of dry oxides and hydroxides of metals. The effect of pH on adherence of oil depends upon the emulsion. If sodium oleate or triethanolamine oleate is used, the adherence falls between pH 2.5 and 7.5, but then rises up to at least pH 10.0. If hemoglobin is used as an emulsifier, the adherence of the oil increases with pH from 2.5 to 10.0.

Deposition on Multiple Surfaces: — The deposition of spray fungicides on multiple surfaces like leaves and seeds follows much the same rules as those for single surfaces except that run-off is important on exposed surfaces, not so important on hidden surfaces.

Experimental evidence so far in hand shows clearly that deposition on the average leaf in the crown of a big plant like an apple accumulates according to the logarithm of the gallonage, whether the gallonage is increased by spraying time or by nozzle size. This can be demonstrated from the data of R. H. Smith (1928) for arsenate of lead on apples and from the data of G. G. Taylor (1939) for lime on apples. Also deposit accumulates according to the logarithm of concentration according to data of S. L. Hopperstead et al. (1943) on bordeaux mixture.

The probable explanation for the gallonage effect is that while material continues to accumulate on the deeper ranks of foliage with increased gallonage, it runs off the exposed ranks of foliage. The reason why it increases with logarithm of concentration appears to be that as concentration increases the time to run-off decreases. Hence as concentration goes up, the deposition does not go up as rapidly as expected because it is lost through run-off more easily.

In any event, the results mean that to increase control by increasing gallonage or concentration defeats its objective somewhat because much of the increased amount of toxicant shows up on the ground, when spraying is completed, rather than on the foliage where it counts.

Chapter VII

COVERAGE OF SINGLE SURFACES

The literature of plant pathology and entomology is full of illusions to "good coverage", dictated by the assumption that protectants will not protect if the treated surfaces are not well coated. The researches devoted to unscrambling the factors that influence coverage are startlingly few. Coverage is confounded with almost everything in the cookbook of plant pathology. For that reason, current knowledge asks more questions than it answers.

Coverage is the third link in a chain of events involved in the application of pesticides. Dosage is the amount of material applied, i.e., sprayed or dusted toward the plant. Deposit is the amount that arrives. And coverage is the uniformity and completeness of distribution of the deposit over the areas to be treated.

The words, uniformity and completeness, in the coverage definition should be noted. Completeness may be restated as density of particles of protectant. Density is concerned with the number of particles in the areas covered. Uniformity is concerned with the randomness of particle distribution over the surface.

In paint terminology coverage is called "hiding power". In the application of fungicides hiding power is important on single surfaces like single leaves or seeds, but in practice good coverage also involves distribution over multiple surfaces. The problems of coverage on single surfaces are many. The problems of coverage over multiple surfaces involve many more. The Committee of the American Phytopathological Society on the Standardization of Fungicidal Tests (1943) wrestled with the problem of defining the two concepts. Finally, they compromised on *coverage* as the "Distribution of a fungicide deposit over a discontinuous area, such as the leaves of a tree, or seeds." They used the word *spread* as the label for the "uniformity and completeness with which the fungicide deposit covers a continuous surface, such as a single leaf or seed."

Probably the most nearly perfect way of covering a leaf to protect it against fungus attack would be to wrap it in copper foil. If the copper foil is broken into small bits and applied as bordeaux mixture, a coverage problem immediately arises. Even if the same amount of copper be used, the coverage with bordeaux will be inferior to that of the foil because some of the particles will pile on top of others, leaving spaces where they should have fallen. The more piling up there is, the larger will be the number of areas left with no cover. How big can these uncovered spaces be and still obtain disease control? Spores, being particles too, may fall in the spaces between the particles of protectant. Presumably a direct relation must exist between the inter-spore distance and the interparticle distance. As the distance between spores increases the distance between particles can increase also for equal inhibition.

Whether any given spore is poisoned involves a pair of probabilities. First, what are the odds that the spore will be hit by the toxicant, and second, what are the odds that it will be killed with what hits it? The matter is analogous to the greased pig contest at agricultural fairs. What are the chances that a contestant will be able to catch the greased pig? If he catches the pig, what are his chances of hanging on?

In combating *Phytophthora infestans,* the potato farmer tries to load both sets of odds in his favor. He tries to improve his chances of hitting the spore by applying enough gallonage through the proper number and arrangement of nozzles designed to keep the uncovered foliage at a minimum. And he tries to be sure of killing the spore by using a fairly concentrated and powerful fungicide.

Phytophthora infestans can load the odds only one way. It produces just as many spores as possible, hoping that a few will alight on uncovered potato foliage.

A proper study of coverage, then, must involve a knowledge of these probabilities and how they are interrelated. The whole story must involve not only a knowledge of the density and uniformity of distribution of the fungicide. It must involve also a knowledge of density and uniformity of the spores over any given surface.

It should be admitted at the outset that our knowledge of coverage is sketchy in the extreme. This discussion, therefore, is more in the nature of an exploration of our meager knowledge than as a summary of a field.

As already mentioned insoluble protectants are thought to poison spores by a sort of suicide mechanism. Spores germinating in water excrete by-products that are capable of solubilizing the protectant. These by-products must diffuse from the spore to the protectant. Then the solubilized protectant must diffuse back to the spore. The speed of killing in any given set-up is governed by this relay race over the distance between the spore and the particle of protectant and back again. During the time the race is being run the spore is germinating. If the relay race is finished and the spore dies before germination is complete, it does not establish contact with the leaf. If the spore can send a germ tube into the leaf before the race is finished, protection is not accomplished.

Obviously the time for completion of the relay race is governed by the distance between spore and particle. If the particles are too far apart, *i.e.,* if coverage is poor, infection will occur. This is not all. Given two cases of equal coverage and one with twice the number of spores as the other, protection is poorer with the two spores than with one, because if the solubilized protectant does return in time, it now has two spores to kill instead of one, and there may not be enough of it to kill two spores.

Methods of Obtaining Coverage: — At present only two methods of obtaining coverage are available — spraying and dusting. These differ more radically, it seems, than usually assumed. For example, the diluents — water and dry powder — probably do not perform the same function in the process. Both serve to meter the pesticide into the distributing machine but there the similarity ends. After the pesticides leave the nozzles, the spray water continues to carry the particles of pesticide, but the dust particles separate and travel almost if not wholly independently. It is well known even to laymen that dusting gives more uniform coverage than spraying. This is most easily observed in the dust that settles on a car in a dusty garage. If the same amount of dirt is thrown at a car in the form of mud as in the form of dust, the coverage is splotchy, *i.e.,* the density is not uniform.

WILCOXON and McCALLAN (1931) have shown statistically what laymen knew from experience. They showed that dust particles settle on single surfaces at random according to the Poisson distribution. This is because the particles travel independently. Therefore, they arrive on the surface independently. It follows that the uniformity of dust distribution cannot be improved, provided, of course, that the settling has not been disturbed by wind currents or other extraneous forces. The density of coverage can be improved, obviously, in two ways, by increasing the concentration of active ingredient in the dust or by increasing the number of pounds per acre or the charge that is introduced into a dust tower. These procedures should not change the randomness of distribution.

Particles of fungicides applied in sprays do not travel independently. They travel together in little vehicles called spray droplets; hence they arrive in groups on the surface, and hence they give blotchy coverage in which the density is not uniform. The spray droplets themselves presumably travel at random at least from an atomizer. Presumably, therefore, they arrive at random onto the surface. They do not maintain this random arrangement long, however, because succeeding droplets pile into them and cause them to grow. As a droplet grows it engulfs nearby smaller ones and thus changes the distribution.

Presumably it is possible to increase in sprays not only the density of coverage as in dusts, but also the uniformity of coverage. The density of coverage can be increased within the spray droplet by increasing the concentration in the spray tank, but this will not affect the coverage in the interdroplet spaces. The amount of interdroplet space and, therefore, uniformity of coverage can be changed only by doing something to change droplet distribution.

Measurement of Coverage: — Three procedures for measuring coverage are available — chemical assay, pictorial recording, and bioassay.

Considerable data have been published on the estimation of coverage by chemical analyses. Many of these data are useful only for estimation of the magnitude of deposition. Chemical solvents will demonstrate the total amount of toxicant over an area, but not the pattern of its distribution. Nitric acid is the usual solvent for copper protectants. It will dissolve all the copper on a potato leaf whether the deposit occurs in ten big lumps or in 1000 small ones.

Inasmuch as improved coverage presumably assures that equilibrium is reached more readily, it seems possible that selective solvents may one day be devised for measuring the speed with which equilibrium is reached. HORSFALL, MARSH and MARTIN (1937) explored this possibility. WAIN and WILKINSON (1943) have pursued the matter still further.

Pictorial records of deposit distribution are excellent for visual demonstration. O. C. BOYD (1926) made camera lucida drawings of bordeaux membranes on a surface. F. M. BLODGETT and E. O. MADER (1934) made records of distribution of copper materials by pressing moist filter paper previously treated with potassium ferrocyanide against the treated foliage. G. F. MACLEOD and H. F. SHERWOOD (1937) photographed sulfur-treated foliage with soft (*i.e.* long) X-rays. Recently, photographs of sprayed glass have been made here with monolateral light to take advantage of the Tyndall effect. The proportion of area covered can be estimated from these pictorial records. Boyd, for example, scissored the covered areas, weighed them, and compared them with the weight of the whole area.

Bioassay may be used to determine the effectiveness of coverage. Since the precision of bioassay has been improved so much recently, the data it gives are reasonably precise. Bioassay, in general, has already been discussed in Chapters III and IV. It is well for the purposes of this discussion to recall that samples from a given spore population are exposed to deposits of variable size and then the percentage of spores inhibited is recorded for each deposit. Graphically a straight line is obtained by plotting the log. of the dosage against the probability of response.

HORSFALL and McDONNELL (1943) have investigated coverage by means of the dosage-response tool. LD 50 or LD 95 locates the position of the curve which measures amount of material available for killing the spores, *i.e.*, it measures the density factor in coverage, much as a chemical assay would. The position of the curve appears to measure the probability of killing a spore with what hits it.

Slope will measure uniformity of deposit. Statistically slope is a measure of variability, because when the x-axis is held constant slope is governed by standard deviation units on the y-axis. With constancy in size and distribution of deposits, slope is a measure of variability in the spore population. With uniform spore population and size of deposit, slope is a measure of variability in distribution of deposits. When variation is small, and hence when the standard deviation is small, the slope is steep. On these *a priori* grounds the more nearly random are the particles over the surface, the steeper will be the slope.

The experimental treatment of these postulations will be discussed later. It follows from the discussion here and in Chapter IV that the position of the dosage-response curve may be used in research on coverage to measure the number of particles available for reaction, provided the variability in distribution is kept constant. On the other hand, if the number of particles is kept constant, slope should measure the variability or randomness of the distribution of particles.

The Density Factor in Coverage: — It will simplify matters to present the discussion on coverage under its two components — density and uniformity or randomness. The density factor can be considered in terms of the distance between particles, but this cannot be considered completely without a discussion of the distance between spores as well.

Effect of Distance between Particles: — In studying the distance between particles, it is best to begin with dusts where distribution of particles is random. Perhaps the best data so far available for studying the number and density of particles and the distance between them is that published by WILCOXON and McCALLAN (1931) on sulfur dusts.

They used three samples of dust differing in mean particle diameter. Each was dusted onto glass slides to give differing amounts of sulfur. The number of particles per area was determined. They then determined the effectiveness of the sulfur by using a uniform suspension of spores of *Sclerotinia fructicola*.

Of course, for equal weights of sulfur more spores were killed on slides dusted with small particles on them than on slides dusted with large particles. This is because the slides dusted with small particles were more densely covered than those dusted with large particles. The densely covered slides should form more fungicidal sulfur than those not so densely covered. Hence the same percentage of spores should have been killed with fewer milligrams of sulfur in small particles than in large particles. This means that the LD 50 should be displaced leftward. It was. The LD 50 values were about 1.5 mg. per slide for particles that were 18.0μ in diameter, 4.2 mg. for particles that were 22.4μ, and more than 32 mg. for particles 26.5μ in diameter.

It is obvious that the chances of killing the spore were increased as would have been expected by increasing the density of the deposit because the distance for the relay race was reduced.

Since the randomness of coverage presumably was not changed in these dusts, the slope should not have been changed. It was not. The three slopes are seen to be parallel when the data are plotted on log.-probability paper. This means that the chances of hitting the spore have not been changed, only the chances of killing it with what hits it.

WILCOXON and McCALLAN replotted their data on the basis of number of particles per area and they found that the curves faded into each other to give a single curve (their Fig. 4). These data can be recalculated for our purposes here in terms of interparticle distance assuming that the mean distance between particles is the square root of the area per particle. When such data are plotted, of course, they show that the percentage of spores killed (as probits) decreases with the logarithm of the distance between particles.

HEUBERGER and HORSFALL (1939) investigated with a spraying technique the particle size for cuprous oxide. Replotting their data on log.-probability paper shows that the LD 50 is displaced leftward, as the density of deposit is increased with small particles and the different particles seem to give parallel slopes as a rule.

Even though particles are not distributed at random in sprays, it is clear that an increase in density of particles has the same effect in sprays as in dusts. It increases the chances of killing a spore but does not increase the chances of hitting it.

Effect of Distance between Spores: — Spores generally appear to settle out of spore drops at random. This may not be strictly true in the case of drops that stand high on account of high interfacial tension. The spores tend to be drawn to the center in such drops.

Data from HORSFALL *et al.* (1940) are useful in calculations of the effect of distance between spores. Spore suspensions of *Macrosporium sarcinaeforme* were made up so that the density varied from 5,000, through 10,000, to 20,000 and up to 40,000 per cc. Drops of these spore suspensions each containing $\frac{1}{20}$ cc. were placed on cellulose nitrate-coated slides sprayed to apply a constant deposit of 6.20γ of yellow cuprous oxide per square centimeter. Each drop of spores spread to 7.5 mm. in diameter or 44,179μ^2. In the light of these facts the data in their Figure 4B also can be recalculated in terms of mean distance between spores. It is clear that the response is a function of the logarithm of the interspore distance with LD 50 coming at 8.3μ mean distance.

What this means is that a coverage that is sufficient for 5,000 spores per cc. of infection drop is woefully inadequate when the number increases to 40,000 per cc. In fact the kill in the tests cited dropped from about 88 per cent to 7 per cent. Is it any wonder that "recommended concentrations" of protectants fall down in years of high inoculum potential? One often hears of "adequately covered" leaves. Adequacy is a relative term. In this experiment 6.4γ of yellow cuprous oxide per square centimeter was "adequate" for 5,000 spores per cc. where they were 13μ apart, but it was distinctly inadequate when the spores were crowding each other with less than 4μ between them.

DIMOND *et al.* (1941) investigated this problem one step further and showed that increasing the density of spores in the drop pushes the LD 50 value to the right, *i.e.*, reduces toxicity, but it does not change the slope. It follows that the chances of killing a spore are decreased as the density of spores is increased, but that the chances of hitting the spore are not altered. It is noteworthy that the effect of density of spores is the same as the effect of density of deposit of fungicidal particles.

From this discussion we conclude that, with inoculum potential a constant, the kill is a function of the logarithm of the distance between particles of protectant. With number of particles a constant, the kill is a function of the logarithm of the distance between spores.

Distance, therefore, is a dosage factor and it acts just like any other dosage factor in the killing of spores. Recently ZENTMYER *et al.* (1944) have shown that distance acts as a dosage factor in the local spread of plant diseases just as it does in the killing of spores by fungicides.

The Randomness Factor in Coverage: — Obviously, randomness of distribution cannot be studied with dusts because they are already distributed at random. It must be studied with sprays where particles are not distributed over the surface at random.

If a true picture of randomness or uniformity of coverage is to be studied, it must be clearly distinguished at all times from density of coverage. At the present stage of knowledge, this has turned out to be most difficult, as will be shown a few paragraphs later.

Randomness of distribution is governed by the surface to be sprayed, by the spreaders present in the spray fluid, by the interaction between concentration and volume, and by serial application.

Effect of Surface: — Some surfaces wet so poorly that many bare areas occur between spray droplets. To cover them with spray is like trying to paint a wet board. However much material is applied, it still remains scattered over the surface. YARWOOD (1937) holds that downy mildew of onion cannot be controlled by bordeaux, not because the fungus is resistant to copper, but because the surface is not covered by the spray material. Potato foliage on the other hand is very easy to wet. Bordeaux holds downy mildew on potato (late blight) very well.

Three procedures suggest themselves for putting materials on the bare spots between spray droplets. (1) Use spreaders to increase the spread of the spray droplets over the surface and thus reduce the size of the uncovered areas. (2) Increase volume of spray. This should give more droplets a chance to land on the uncovered areas. (3) Apply the materials serially and permit the previous deposit to dry in the meantime. This should act much like increased spray time except that the parasitizing of small droplets by big ones should be reduced.

Effect of Spreaders: — A spreader is a substance added to a spray fluid to increase the area of drop spread, *i.e.,* coverage. A large quantity of research has been done in the field of spreaders since SWINGLE's (1896) work on soap in bordeaux. As a matter of fact ROBERTSON (1824) suggested using sulfur with soap in 1824, but he probably was more interested in wetting the sulfur than the plant. A spreader is a so-called surface active agent. That is, it acts at the surface of a liquid, at the liquid-air interface and at the liquid-solid interface.

A spreader is usually a large molecule. One end of the molecule is lyophilic (*i.e.,* liquid loving). Often this is a sulfonic acid grouping. The other end is lyophobic (*i.e.,* liquid hating). This end is often oily in nature. The action of a spreader may be visualized thus: The lyophobic or oily end of the molecule migrates away from the water, and takes up a position at the edge of the drop. The water loving end tends to migrate away from the edge, so that at equilibrium, one can visualize the periphery of the drop as being composed of a palisade layer of spreader molecules, so oriented that the insoluble end of each is out and the water soluble end is in.

When a drop of liquid containing such a system is placed on a surface, the oily end lubricates the surface so that the drop slides outward and becomes thinner and broader. It spreads.

A similar lubricating effect occurs within the drop itself. The cohesion between the surface molecules is less than that between pure water molecules. That means that at the nozzle the free forming drops of liquids containing spreaders are smaller than those without.

As already discussed under deposition the small drops containing spreaders travel by Stokes' Law more slowly in a spray stream than the larger ones without spreader.

When a droplet of spray strikes a surface, it flattens and spreads from the force of impact as W. M. UPHOLT and W. M. HOSKINS (1940) have pictured. Of course, the magnitude of such spread depends upon the speed of droplet travel. If spreaders reduce the speed of droplet travel, they will reduce the initial spread due to impact. S. F. HERANGER (1935) contends that coverage with high pressure sprayers is poorer than from a sprinkling pot because of poorer spreading of the small droplets.

As the margin of the droplet advances, it forms an angle with the surface, the so-called advancing contact angle. As soon as the kinetic energy is expended, the surface tension tends to pull the margin back. As the margin recedes, it forms the receding contact angle.

Since spreaders reduce interfacial tension, they reduce the contact angles. Experts still seem not to agree as to which angle should be used to measure spreading action. EVANS and MARTIN (1935) arrived at a British compromise and took the mean of the two.

Since spreaders reduce the size of the droplet, but increase the spread of that formed, the problem in specific cases is to determine the final coverage. Does the spreading action of a small droplet containing spreader offset the fact that the droplet is smaller to begin with? This point has not received specific attention.

The answer to the question will depend primarily on interfacial friction, hence it will vary with the type of spreader, concentration of spreader, and surface. YARWOOD (1937) found that a spreader improved the performance of bordeaux on an onion leaf which is exceedingly difficult to cover. Spreaders have not been enthusiastically acclaimed for many surfaces, however.

Under the hypothesis of coverage, the addition of spreaders should steepen the slope of the dosage-response curve by improving uniformity of distribution. A few of them have been tried with "fixed" copper materials. Ultrawet was found to steepen the slope of yellow copper oxide as expected. Ultrawet is a water soluble sodium sulfonate of petroleum hydrocarbons averaging 16 carbon atoms according to CUPPLES (1943). Cottonseed oil emulsified with B 1956 has spreading properties. B 1956, according to the manufacturer, is a mixture of phthalic glycerol alkyd resins. It was found to steepen the slope of yellow copper oxide (Cuprocide), copper oxychloride (Copper A), and a type of basic copper sulfate (Oxobordo). In two tests it did not affect slope of copper silicate (Coposil). Soybean and wheat flour act as spreaders but these had no effect on slope of copper oxychloride or yellow cuprous oxide. As yet no adequate explanation is available for these discrepancies, but it seems certain that spreaders may steepen the slope of the dosage-response curve.

SHEPARD and RICHARDSON (1931) treated aphids by dipping in nicotine solutions. When their data are plotted, the dose-response curve for nicotine plus the spreader, saponin, was steeper than the curve for nicotine alone.

Interrelations Between Concentration and Volume: — We have seen that ramdomness of particle distribution in dusts cannot be improved because the particles travel independently. In order to move toward randomness of particle distribution in sprays it is necessary presumably to apply the particles in a larger number of droplets. Since the spray droplets seem to travel independently, the theoretical ideal would be to apply enough droplets so that each one carries only a single particle of fungicide.

To accomplish the objective two alternatives seem possible: (1) to break up any given volume of liquid into finer droplets, (2) to reduce the concentration in any droplet and to increase the number of droplets. Neither of these is without manipulative difficulties.

The volume of liquid can be broken into finer droplets by reducing the size of the nozzle orifice or by increasing pressure. By either method the finer droplets travel and deposit more slowly than expected. FREAR (1944) gives confirmatory data for the effect of pressure. Neither method has been tried in research with coverage on single surfaces.

The second alternative of reducing concentration and increasing the number of droplets can be attained by increasing the spraying time.

J. G. HORSFALL and A. D. McDONNELL (1943) have reported briefly on experiments with coverage of single surfaces where concentration and spraying time have been varied concomitantly. This gives a series of deposits, each of which was obtained by reducing concentration as time was increased and *vice versa*. As a result, each deposit was varied from one with a few concentrated droplets per unit area to many dilute droplets per unit area. This has produced much the same effect as a series of steps in the process by which a painter "brushes out" his paint. He thins the thick areas in order to thicken the thin areas. This type of experimental design should serve to distinguish the effect of thick and thin areas from uniformly thin areas.

In all the experiments so far conducted, the deposits applied with long spray times have shown steeper dosage-response curves than those applied with short spray times. This has been true for sulfur, copper, and several organic fungicides. Curves are given in Figure 4 which illustrate this effect for *Macrosporium sarcinaeforme* with yellow cuprous oxide and for *Sclerotinia fructicola* with wettable sulfur. From these experiments it follows that long spray time reduces the heterogeneity of the distribution of the particles of insoluble protectants.

It follows that increasing the number of droplets has helped to make the coverage more nearly random. The chances of hitting the spore have been increased. At the present stage of thinking on the problem, however, the situation is confused with regard to the chances of killing the spore with what hits it. Presumably, the chances of killing the spore have been reduced at the same time that the chances of hitting it have been improved. If so, the researcher in the field appears to find himself on the horns of a dilemma. If he attempts to correct by holding the concentration uniform while increasing the number of droplets, he is increasing both the chances of killing the spore and the chances of hitting it. Perhaps it is best to leave him there to find his way down. Possibly he cannot get down because concentration and volume may be so interrelated as not to be distinguishable.

The statisticians have tackled the problem of handling a pair of variables simultaneously. D. J. FINNEY (1943) has pioneered this field as it applies to coverage. FINNEY plots the regression lines for both variables on the same logarithmic-probability grid and he obtains a *probit plane*. He worked with data on concentration and deposit of pyrethrum in oil in its effects on the confused flour beetle. The data seem to show parallel lines for the various methods so that his probit planes are parallelograms.

Since the dosage-response curves for the different variables in the data of HORSFALL and McDONNELL (1943) were not parallel, different statistics will probably be needed. To make matters worse, there is some evidence of curvature in some of the lines.

Effect of Serial Application: — If the problem is one of covering uncovered areas, serial applications should be useful. Suppose a four-point dosage-response curve is desired. It can be obtained by apply-

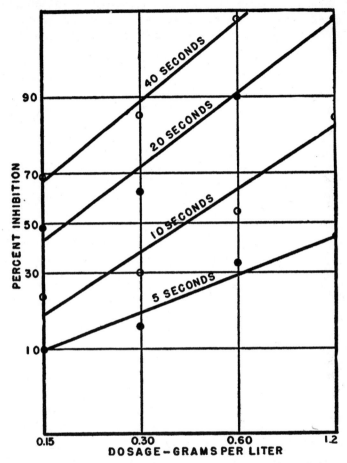

FIGURE 4. — Effect of spraying time, *i.e.*, coverage, on slope of dosage-response curve. Fungicide is yellow cuprous oxide. Fungus is *Macrosporium sarcinaeforme*.

ing four concentrations, each for a given spray time; by applying one concentration for four spray times, say 5, 10, 20, and 40 seconds; or by applying one concentration with 1, 2, 4, and 8 applications of five seconds each, permitting the surfaces to dry in between. The first two methods of application were compared in the previous section to distinguish spray time from concentration and it was shown that increasing spray time would steepen the slope. The last two comparisons have been made many times. They give identical slopes within the limits of error at least for cuprous oxide, which shows that increased spray time without drying between accomplishes the same results as if serial applications were used with drying in between.

Chapter VIII

COVERAGE OF MULTIPLE SURFACES

The coverage of all the leaves on an acre of potatoes, all the leaves on a 30 foot apple tree, or all the pea seeds in a bushel offers many interesting problems. They are not the same problems as those involved in covering the side of a barn with paint, and they are not the same problems as those involved in covering a single leaf. The surface to be covered is broken into a shimmering mass of innumerable little surfaces called leaves and fruits. They offer little firm backing for a driving spray or dust stream.

Some of the leaves are on the outside of the crown and thus they are beautifully exposed to coverage. Behind these are other leaves that are more or less screened, and behind these are still other leaves even more heavily screened by those in front, and so on for several ranks.

How is the farmer to cover all these with spray? Early in the history of spraying protectants, he was advised not to over spray, not to permit the foliage to drip. As already discussed under deposition, the objective of this advice was to prevent run-off with attendant lowering of deposit. On first thought this seems a sound recommendation, but the facts hardly warrant such an over simplification.

Since the outer leaves get wet first, the run-off stage is reached soonest there. If the crown of foliage is dense, as it often is in a potato field about to be attacked by blight, the inner leaves may receive little or no material before run-off sets in on the outer leaves. Hence the inner critical leaves may escape protection altogether even though the outer leaves are well covered.

Conversely, if the farmer continues to spray until the inner leaves are covered, the outer ones may be greatly oversprayed. In the case of apple scab or potato tip-burn where the disease occurs largely on the outer leaves, the disease may be less well controlled than otherwise.

Little information is available on the dynamics of covering multiple surfaces. Nevertheless, most researchers and recommenders have recognized the importance of complete coverage. In a 1943 brochure treating of potato blight and its impact on war time food production, coverage is said to be of utmost importance, but it receives only two lines advising the farmer to obtain good coverage. He is provided with no instructions as to how to procure that good coverage.

The information on the amount of surface to be covered in an acre of crops is almost as scanty as the information on the dynamics of

covering it. The grower is advised to increase the amount of spray
or dust as the season advances and foliage grows, but no one seems
to know how much extra spray is required. FORBUSH and FERNALD
(1895) subsampled two apple trees approximately 20 feet high and
found a mean foliage area of 3,200 square feet per tree. This means
approximately 2.2 acres of foliage per acre of land. In some preliminary studies of the problem here we have found that potatoes in full
leaf covering the ground produce from 2.5 to 4 acres of foliage per acre
of land.

S. F. POTTS (1939) estimated that the area of foliage in canopy
of a hardwood forest varied from 4.5 to 8.4 acres per acre of land.

Machinery Design as a Factor in Coverage: — During the 60
years since MILLARDET swabbed his grapes with a broom dipped in
bordeaux paste, big strides have been made in developing spray machinery and attachments. As soon as bordeaux mixture was thinned
down a little, it was applied with garden syringes in which the liquid
passed through a plate full of holes.

Hydraulic Pressure Sprayers: — Sometimes pumps were used
to put pressure on the liquid so that it traveled farther than before
and was broken up better into droplets than before by the impact of
the liquid on still air. The operator might put his thumb over the end
of the hose but this soon was replaced by a mechanical thumb-over-
hose contrivance, now known as a nozzle. It was a stopcock with a
deflector.

According to G. H. CUNNINGHAM (1935) the basic nozzle idea
used to this day was developed early, 1880, by BARNARD. It is now
called a cyclone nozzle. The nozzle aperture is a small hole in the
center of a thin metal disc. Immediately behind the plate, BARNARD
fashioned a bulbous base, an eddy chamber which started the liquid
to rolling.

This rolling continued as the liquid passed through the hole in the
disc. The centrifugal action threw the liquid outward like water thrown
from a flywheel. This gave a spray pattern with a hollow cone. The
liquid also was separated into droplets by the whirling action.

The only significant change in the basic design was the whorl
plate developed by the Goulds Pump Company in 1906 (see G. H.
CUNNINGHAM, 1935). The whorl plate is a thick ($\frac{1}{8}$") metal plate
spaced about $\frac{1}{8}$ inch behind the disc. It contains two or more holes
bored at an angle to the surface near the edge. These holes chan-
nelize and stabilize the whirling action so that it is smooth and precise.

The actions of this basic nozzle can be deduced from its design and its actions then can be altered by altering its design. There are six elements in its design that can be altered—size of disc aperture, diameter of apertures in whorl plate, number of apertures in whorl plate and angle of apertures in whorl plate. Then, too, the pressure on the liquid can be altered at the pump.

The first thorough investigation of these factors was that of CRANE (1919). He was followed by C. W. B. WRIGHT and R. M. WOODMAN (1932), C. DAVIES and G. R. B. SMYTH-HOMEWOOD (1938) and G. G. TAYLOR (1939).

Any factor tending to increase the speed of the swirling of the spray as it passes through the nozzle aperture will increase the centrifugal action and thus widen the angle of the cone and decrease the size of the droplets. Pressure, of course, increases the discharge and hence the speed of swirling. The flatter the angle in the whorl plates the less likely the liquid is to be forced out through the aperture and hence the faster it swirls. If the aperture in the disc is increased in size, the swirling is less confined and the angle is increased although droplet size is unaffected.

The "carry" of a nozzle, the distance to which it will throw a spray stream, or the depth to which the spray stream will penetrate into the crown of leaves is the factor really concerned in deep coverage. The carry is improved by increasing the volume of liquid passing through the nozzle. As all six nozzle factors but one are increased and pressure too, the rate of discharge and the carry are improved. The lone exception is angle of aperture in the whorl plate. As this angle is flattened the speed of swirl is increased at the expense of discharge rate, and therefore at the expense of carry.

TAYLOR (1939) gives a table that summarizes these effects very well.

INFLUENCE OF NOZZLE STRUCTURE ON SPRAY APPLICATION (AFTER TAYLOR, 1939).

INCREASE IN	VOLUME	"CARRY"	EFFECTS ON ANGLE OF SPRAY CONE	SIZE OF SPRAY DROPLETS
Pressure	increased	increased	increased	decreased
Diameter of aperture in whorl plate	increased	increased	decreased	decreased
No. of apertures in whorl plate	increased?	increased	decreased?	decreased?
Angle of apertures in whorl plate	decreased?	decreased?	increased	increased
Depth of whorl chamber	increased	increased	decreased	decreased
Disc aperture	increased	increased	increased	not affected
Disc thickness	not affected	increased?	decreased	decreased

All the spray delivered, obviously, must move through the disc aperture. Many investigators beginning with CRANE (1919) have studied spray nozzle delivery, which varies, not with area as expected from hydraulic theory, but with orifice diameter. TAYLOR's data (1939) indicate that the diameter of the spray pattern increases arithmetically with diameter of disc aperture. As the diameter increases the cone becomes more hollow, however.

TAYLOR's data (1939) indicate also that diameter of spray pattern decreases arithmetically with diameter of whorl plate openings and, of course, the cone tends to be more infilled.

The construction of pumps and other items of spray equipment is outside the scope of this discussion. Recently, O. C. FRENCH (1942) has covered this subject quite well.

Air Pressure Sprayers: — Since the objective in spraying is to mix liquid with air, inventors soon saw that to throw water under pressure into still air was equivalent to throwing air under pressure into a water stream. From this idea was developed the Liqui-duster, a device for injecting water into a blast of air from a blower. This device never really worked well in the field because it lacked the carry and hence the coverage of sprayers using hydraulic pressure.

FRENCH in California (1934) developed the so-called atomizer into a field machine. The atomizer is the familiar gadget used for perfumes. A stream of compressed air passes across the open end of the liquid line. It may pull the liquid into the air stream by the Bernoulli principle, or the liquid itself may be under slight pressure.

FRENCH improved the Liqui-duster principle by using oil as the carrier for concentrated solutions of soluble toxicants. Thus he saved weight, using 5 or 10 gallons per acre instead of 150 or 200. The oil evaporates less in transit than a water carrier and hence it maintains better "carry". The final advantage is, as S. F. POTTS (1940) pointed out, that the oil droplets spread much better upon contact with the leaf than the water does. This results in better coverage. These machines have not been widely used, possibly because of lack of sufficient carry.

The concentrated spray-in-oil has perhaps its best possibility in airplane or helicopter applications because the oil evaporates less than the water in the slip stream of the plane.

Dusters: — Dusters for foliage have not been changed much in design recently to improve coverage. The general principle has been to dump the material through a metering slot into an air stream which delivers it through a series of nozzles to the plants. Occasionally the dust is dumped into the air stream after it leaves the fan, but this does not break up the aggregates very well. Another and perhaps superior method is to discharge the dust from the hopper into the center of the fan so that aggregates are beaten by the fan blades. At least one manufacturer introduces the dust into a hammer mill before it enters the fan at the axle.

F. IRONS (1943) discovered that the fan may fractionate the toxicant and the carrier by centrifugal force, so that the heavier of the two migrates around the periphery of the fan housing and into the first tube or two of a multiple tube duster. This may result in throwing most of the toxicant onto one or two rows and the carrier onto the other rows.

The usual nozzle is simply a flared and flattened end for the tube. One manufacturer has made the nozzle into a very shallow truncated cone which passes along the top of a row crop. The air is introduced tangent to the inside of the cone. The air then travels around the inside slipping down and out as the cone widens. The air stream thus swirls as it leaves the nozzle. The whirlpool motion sucks the foliage upward and deposits the dust on the underside of the leaves (so the manufacturer claims).

Explosives may offer a field for applying dusts. Several years ago we worked on the possibility of shooting a charge of dust from a shot gun into a tree, but the work was abandoned because it was difficult to discharge a large enough volume with equipment available. Dust bombs have been tried in the field treatment of rubber plants in Ceylon (see Anon., 1936), and the Russians have experimented in the same field. GLASGOW and BLAIR (1944) have recently reported on the use of mortars for distributing dusts.

Much the most effective seed duster is a tumble barrel type which rubs the seeds back and forth on each other, thus distributing the dust. This is a batch treater, of course. Screw type continuous treaters have been used for wheat, but these are useless for legumes because the seed coats are too fragile. One type of continuous treater is vertical. Seed poured into the top drops to a cone which spreads it. The seed then falls into an inverted cone which collects it to the center and dumps it onto another cone, etc. This is a more satisfactory type of treater for volatile treatments like certain organic mercuries than for protective treatments like cuprous oxide or chloranil.

Measurement of Coverage: — Coverage of multiple surfaces by fungicides has been measured even less frequently than coverage of single surfaces. In the literature repose many data on deposits of fungicides and insecticides as determined chemically. Most of these are not useful in studying coverage because the samplers have seldom given consideration to the location of the leaf on the plant. Usually, the samples are said to have been taken "at random". This means that the analyses show average deposit, not distribution of deposit. A. L. WEBER *et al.* (1937) analyzed apple leaves from the tops and from the bottoms of trees for lead arsenate, however, to show that careful spraying will eliminate the usual difficulty of poor coverage in the top.

No records have been found of pictorial studies of coverage of leaves in various parts of the foliage crown. The pictorial studies seem to have been limited to single surfaces.

A few studies, a precious few bioassays, have been made of coverage. Sometimes even these were not made for the purpose of studying coverage. Some studies labelled, "coverage", have really dealt with deposition, not distribution of deposits.

Complicated as the problem of bioassaying coverage in the laboratory is, it is complicated many times over in the field. In the field, one is confronted with all the problems that he meets in the laboratory and many more besides. We were not sure that density of deposit and uniformity of coverage were wholly unconfounded in the laboratory where a single surface was being used. Certainly we cannot be sure in the field.

In the laboratory the surface is fixed immobile in front of the nozzle. In the field it sways around. We would like to hit the leaves in the rear ranks but they are screened by those in front.

Still the essence of the problem seems similar. One must distinguish the probability of hitting a spore on any leaf from the probability of killing it with what hits it.

We noted in that last chapter that slope of the dosage-response curve can be used as a measure of uniformity of coverage. Presumably also slope should be equally useful in the field for measuring uniformity of coverage.

Field and Laboratory Slopes: — It is obvious to anyone that coverage of multiple surfaces in the field should be less uniform than coverage of a single surface in the laboratory. If so, the slope of the dosage-response curve of any given fungicide should be flatter in the field than in the laboratory. It has been so with compounds tested thus far. The fact may be illustrated (Fig. 5) by data on yellow cuprous oxide in the laboratory against *Macrosporium sarcinaeforme* and in the field against *Alternaria solani* on tomatoes.

Interrelations between Concentration and Volume: — For a single surface it has been shown that concentration of toxicant and volume of spray fluid are closely related. If run-off is not permitted, coverage of single surfaces can be improved by reducing the concentration and increasing the volume so that total deposit remains a constant.

Presumably the same relations hold for multiple as for single surfaces. As a sprayer or a duster moves down the field the amount of available time is limited for squirting the material through holes in the outer crown down to inner leaves. Presumably, therefore, increasing

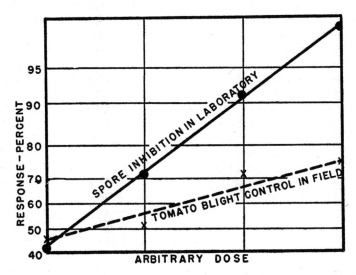

FIGURE 5. — Slope of the dosage-response curve for yellow cuprous oxide (A) in the laboratory against *Macrosporium sarcinaeforme* and (B) in the field against *Alternaria solani*.

the volume per minute should improve the opportunity for covering the bare spots and thus increase the uniformity of coverage over all the leaves to be treated.

Under the theories of coverage so far enunciated, the slope of the dosage-response curve should be steepened as volume of spray is increased. As the story unfolds below it will be seen that sometimes this is true in the field, sometimes not. The whole matter seems still to be very much in flux. Perhaps it is best simply to record the cases that are available leaving the evaluation for further research.

The research so far available may be classified into that showing flat slopes for high gallonage and that showing steep slopes for high gallonage.

Flat Slopes: —Research was started here in 1940 on the bioassay of coverage in the field. In order to control *Alternaria solani,* tomatoes were sprayed with cuprous oxide at 3 gallonages and 4 concentrations to give 12 amounts of copper per acre. Gallonage was increased by increasing both nozzle size and spray time (see HORSFALL and HEUBERGER, 1942). All LD values within the range of control obtained were displaced leftward as the gallonage was increased, but the slope flattened as gallonage increased. Survey of the literature brings to light three other sets of rather meager data that can be calculated in terms of dosage-response curves in the usual way to show flat slopes with increasing gallonage.

W. C. DUTTON (1926) made one of the earliest attempts to distinguish concentration from volume of lime-sulfur and bordeaux on apple trees. He says "assuming that . . . . other conditions have been met, it is evident that there are two factors which have a direct bearing on the degree of control. They are what might be termed *coverage* and *concentration*. By coverage is meant the covering of the surface of the foliage and fruit with a film of the diluted fungicide, and concentration may be defined as the actual amount of the fungicidal material in this covering film." His definitions would have been more precise had he used deposition instead of concentration. DUTTON concluded that "the light applications of strong lime-sulphur and strong bordeaux were both slightly less effective than heavy applications of weak lime-sulfur and weak bordeaux." He obtained his heavy deposits by repeated applications with drying between. Actually he applied more material with his heavy applications of weak material than with light applications of strong material, so that he should have obtained better control with it.

If his data are plotted on log.-probability paper, it will be found that his higher gallonage gave flatter slopes than his lower gallonage, but the LD values are displaced to the right. He has only 2-point curves.

H. W. THURSTON and H. J. MILLER (1938) published data using two sizes of spray guns to apply four concentrations of lime-sulfur for apple scab. Their data also can be plotted on log.-probability paper to give good straight lines with 4-point curves. Their results agree with those of DUTTON.

H. I. MORRIS *et al.* (1941) present a few data for bordeaux on citrus brown-rot that can be recalculated for our purpose. By taking the liberty of assuming that 3.6 gallons per tree for one concentration is equal to 4.0 gallons per tree for another concentration and that 6.0 gallons per tree is equal to 6.7 gallons, then they have two 2-point curves. The curve for 6 gallons per tree is flatter than that for 4 gallons per tree, but there is a cross-over in the middle so that LD 90 is higher for 6 gallons than for 4 gallons but LD 80 is lower for 6 gallons than for 4 gallons. Of course, if slopes are not parallel they must cross. It so happens that the data in the other tests cited were all outside the cross-over point.

Steep Slopes: — In 1941 tomatoes were sprayed again here for *Alternaria solani* in a coverage experiment (see HORSFALL and HEUBERGER, 1942). To avoid confounding nozzle size and spray time as in the previous test, only spray time was varied using as before a single nozzle rod. Four spray times and four concentrations were used. In this test a clear cut steep slope was obtained with high gallonage, whether the data were read as foliage infection or stem lesions. This, of course, agrees with the laboratory results that increasing the volume of spray increases the slope presumably as it increases the probabilities of hitting the spores. It is significant that cross-over occurs in the middle range.

In all the experiments just reported the same concentrations were applied at each gallonage. This makes an experiment orthogonal with regard to concentration but skewed with respect to amount per acre. This means that the treatments are not tested in the same dosage range per tree or in the same range of control. Unless the slope is completely constant, this could bring about discordant results.

E. M. STODDARD and W. D. HENRY (1943) tested coverage in 1943 with wettable sulfur on apples for scab. They measured their trees and regulated spray time accordingly. STODDARD and HENRY used the proper concentrations to make the experiment orthogonal with respect to amount of sulfur per tree. It had to be skewed, then, with respect to concentration. With this design the data come within the same dosage range, however, with smaller chance for error than otherwise.

They obtained a clear cut case of steeper slope for 20 gallons per tree than for 5 gallons per tree, but with a cross-over in the center as HEUBERGER and HORSFALL had had on tomatoes in 1941.

Position of the Dosage-Response Curve: — It will be noted that, in all of the cases of flat slope for high gallons, the curves for high gallons are located to the right of those for low gallons. Even in the two cases of steep slopes, the high gallons curve is displaced to the right below the cross-over. The probable reason for this displacement of the curves to the right on the basis of amount of toxicant applied per tree is that deposition in the field as already noted increases only as the logarithm of gallonage. Hence the amount of toxicant actually on the foliage for the high gallonage is much lower than that indicated by the base line. Unfortunately, no deposition figures are available for the experiments in question, but it seems very probable that if they were available and were used on the "x" axis, the position of the high gallonage curve would be displaced to the left of that for low gallonage—indicating that the performance of material actually applied is increased by increasing gallonage. Of course, the farmer has to purchase the protectant that runs off on the ground, so that so far as he is concerned the indicated position of the curves is the proper one.

The literature holds many data on coverage that cannot be evaluated with certainty. Some are recorded in yield, which is a composite of many factors such as spray injury as well as disease control. Many tests have been done with nozzle size, pressure, double spraying, and concentration, but they do not have any counterparts where the effect of increasing coverage can be separated from the effect of increasing the amount of toxicant. However useful such data may be to the farmer, they are not very usable in studying the dynamics of coverage on multiple surfaces.

Nevertheless, one field experiment is worth citing. BLODGETT and MADER (1934) used such a design in potato spraying. They illustrated distribution of bordeaux over potato foliage. A change in pressure from 200 to 400 pounds per square inch on the spray liquid increased gallonage from 77 to 128 per acre and increased the percentage of area covered on the individual leaves by 38.3 per cent. If they kept the pressure constant at 200 pounds and increased gallonage by larger nozzles from 77 to 128 per acre, they increased the area covered by only 18.4 per cent. Apparently, coverage is increased more efficiently by increasing pressure than by increasing nozzle size.

Dusting: — Very few experiments have been made on altering coverage of multiple surfaces with dusts. It has been shown above that dusts settle on exposed single surfaces at random. There is no reason to assume that they settle on foliage in the field at random, however, because of interference of one leaf by another. Presumably, therefore, improving the randomness of dust application in the field should change the slope of the dosage-response curve.

L. M. SMITH (1938) dusted crickets in a settling tower in the laboratory with barium fluosilicate to determine if ". . . 10 pounds per acre of an 80 per cent poison mixture is exactly as effective as 20 pounds of a 40 per cent mixture of the same poison." The experimental data are variable. Linear plots were made on arithmetic grid for dosage-response curves. The surviving crickets eat those killed by the poison so that dosage must be difficult to know. The author concluded that "the dilute dusts are much more effective per unit of poison than are the concentrated dusts." This conclusion agrees with many of the conclusions already presented on coverage, but SMITH's data are unconvincing of themselves.

TURNER (1945) has just reported some of his studies and a review of recent literature on the coverage factor in the application of insecticidal dusts. He showed that electrostatic charge seemed to be important in the coverage by dusts and that for derris, the less the poundage of dust per acre, the less the rotenone required for equal control of insects. His curves, however, were not straight for all amounts per acre. The curve was concave at 10 pounds per acre, nearly straight at 20 pounds, and progressively convex at 40 and 80 pounds. The convexity or concavity of the curves may be due to an interaction of the third factor, electrostatic charge, rather than to an interaction between concentration and poundage, however.

Canners purchasing dusted pea seed often wonder if it is covered as well as it should be. Coverage of seed protectants presumably can be improved by increasing the time of treatment. In one of our tests the percentage of control of pea seed decay (as probits) increased as the logarithm of mixing time. E. I. ARNOLD and J. G. HORSFALL (1936) report an unusual case of the effect of mixing time on coverage of pea seeds. Treatment of pea seeds with dusts like cuprous oxide increases interfacial friction. Their data show that the friction increases with the logarithm of mixing time "undoubtedly because it increases coverage." They further report that it appeared that "seed mixed 1,000 revolutions had had two or three times as much red copper oxide mixed with it as the seed mixed 100 revolutions."

In this laboratory we have made extensive experiments on the subject of improving coverage of seed protectants by extending low dosages with dust, but the data have been unconvincing. More research needs to be done on the matter of coverage of seed protectants.

An experiment on density of coverage as distinct from randomness of coverage can be made on multiple surfaces as on single surfaces by using a material with different particle sizes. The data of HEUBERGER and HORSFALL (1939) for three sizes of cuprous oxide dusts as pea seed protectants can be plotted on log.-probability paper. The slopes are parallel, but position is displaced leftward by the smaller particles. Clearly the density of coverage has been increased, but the randomness of distribution has been unaltered, just as in laboratory spraying of single surfaces. Likewise unpublished data by the same authors with dusts of red and yellow cuprous oxides on muskmelon foliage in the field against *Macrosporium cucumerinum* give confirmatory results. The slopes of the two particle size fractions are parallel but that for the smaller particle (yellow cuprous oxide) is displaced to the left.

We need much more information on the analogies and homologies between dusting and spraying in the matter of coverage. On first thought one tends to assume that the diluent in a dust is equivalent to water in a spray. It probably is not. It seems more probable that the air discharged by the fan is more nearly analogous to liquid in a sprayer. The diluent aids in metering the toxicant into the air stream, not in distributing it over the foliage. New research needs doing on applying dust toxicants pure. If machinery could be devised for that purpose it would save present difficulties of fractionation and reactions between toxicant and diluent.

Redistribution: — RICAUD and PAULIN (acc. LARGE, 1940) who were two of MILLARDET'S competitors for the honor of discovering bordeaux mixture claimed that they had shown that grapes growing on strings and poles treated with copper sulfate showed less downy mildew than their neighbors. Whatever be the merits of the claim as priority on bordeaux mixture, it is at any rate the first recorded case of redistribution of a protectant. Undoubtedly, the copper had been soaked out of the string or out of the wood and had been reprecipitated on the grape foliage.

R. O. MAGIE (1942) rediscovered this phenomenon in the case of downy mildew of hops in New York. Apparently, E. S. SALMON and W. M. WARE (1931) were the first to suggest that protectants were redistributed by rainfall.

Redistribution of fungicides is coming in for considerable attention just now. A thorough consideration of the matter may clarify many factors in the dynamics of protectant action.

In apple tree spraying, pest control in the tops of trees is often less than in the bottoms. Usually, this has been ascribed to poorer coverage of the tops than the bottoms because the tops are difficult to reach with material. In recent years this has been ascribed to redistribution of protectant by rainfall — the rain washes it and splashes it from the upper tissue and redeposits it on the lower tissue. WEBER et al. (1937) give data showing that with careful spraying, the top of an apple tree is almost as well covered with lead arsenate as the bottom leaves, but that after weathering the top leaves retain less arsenic than the bottom leaves. This was referred to as redistribution.

Another explanation, however, is possible. The top of a tree is much more heavily exposed to rainfall and sunshine than the bottom and hence it is much more likely to lose its protection than the bottom leaves are. The top leaves in effect are exposed to heavy splashing rains, the bottom to slow leaching rains. In fact, WEBER *et al.* (1937) remark that "one rain of 2.20 inches (obviously heavy) will remove, by washing, more residue than nine small rains totalling 2.49 inches."

STODDARD and HEUBERGER (1943) looked into this matter by using unsprayed tissue on the same trees. If redistribution were a factor, material should be washed to the new tissue and the material of least tenacity should wash off the most readily and be redistributed best. It was not so. They conclude that redistribution cannot be a factor in their tests.

Redistribution implies differential run-off of the toxicant-bearing rainwater. Rainwater carries copper from bordeaux-sprayed foliage as C. S. CRANDALL (1909) showed. No doubt it carries other toxicants as well from foliage sprayed with them. HAMILTON *et al.* (1943) have reported that from 50 to 80 percent of an initial deposit of ferric dimethyldithiocarbamate or sulfur is removed by 0.1 inch of rain, but about 10 percent of this may be transferred to unsprayed foliage. The problem to settle is, how is the toxicant extracted by the lower leaves and redeposited. Limited data as already presented in Chapter VI on deposition show that run-off water carries its load of suspensoid with it. If the toxicant to be redistributed is a suspensoid in the rainwater, presumably it would run off with the drop.

The fact that it does seem to be redeposited in some cases suggests that it is not carried as a suspensoid.

If redistribution really occurs as it seems to, it may account for many anomalies in results from spraying. For example, the "Long Island potato boom" is an arrangement in which no attempt is made to hit the lower, inner foliage where *Phytophthora* is most likely to strike. The nozzles spraying downward are carried along above the foliage. It could be that redistribution saves the inner foliage.

Chapter IX

TENACITY

Since the majority of fungous pests of plants attack during rainy periods, protectants must be capable of hanging on to a surface during wind, sun and storms. This quality of a protectant has been called "tenacity" by FAJANS and MARTIN (1937). Deposit defines the amount of protectant applied initially. Residue is the amount of protectant left at any given time after weathering begins.

During the past decade many new protectants have been introduced. Few have succeeded. Low tenacity has been the chief obstacle to success. Unless the material possesses an inherent ability to cling to a surface during weathering processes, it is almost doomed to failure. A sticker may save it, but its chances are low. Bordeaux mixture above all else has tenacity. Were bordeaux mixture less tenacious, it would long since have been replaced as an agricultural protective fungicide.

In discussing coverage we took pains to distinguish the coverage of single and multiple surfaces. Tenacity is a matter that concerns single surfaces and the material applied to them. Tenacity is concerned with the likes and dislikes of surfaces and protectants for each other when they are exposed together under the stress of sun, wind and rain.

Tenacity, like deposition, cannot be discussed and evaluated without due consideration at all steps to both the material and the surface. Compounds obviously differ in their resistance to weathering, but surfaces likewise give up materials to rainfall to different degrees. We will consider that tenacity is a quality of the material. The quality of the surface that determines its ability to hold materials in opposition to the forces of weathering has not been named, but it should be named. No name, however, suggests itself at present.

Effect of the Surface: — FAJANS and MARTIN (1937) learned that surfaces, which are difficult to wet, lose material to rainfall less easily than those easy to wet. HAMILTON (1935) obtained experimental evidence that rough apple skins hold sulfur and lead arsenate about twice as well as smooth apple skins. It is common experience that it is easier to wash smooth hands than rough hands to the same degree of cleanness.

Effect of Wind: — In general wind is not important in resistance to weathering of spray deposits except insofar as it may increase the drive of rains. In the special case of dusts, however, wind often does remove much of the deposit.

POTTS and BARNES (1931) report that 40 per cent of arsenical dusts may be removed by wind. This is, of course, one of the many reasons why dusts should be applied to damp foliage. In our dusting tests we find that for equal control of *Alternaria solani* on tomatoes twice as much copper in a dust mixture is required for application to dry foliage as to wet foliage. This agrees well with the 40 per cent loss as reported by POTTS and BARNES.

Effect of Foliage Brushing: — Leaves continually rustle in the breeze and they definitely scrape each other when the wind rises. GREEN and GOLDSWORTHY (1937) held that leaf brushing is responsible for much loss of material, although they admit that outer apple foliage loses spray residue more rapidly than inner foliage, despite the fact that brushing is probably least there.

Effect of Growth: — As plant tissue grows it automatically thins a spray residue. The dynamics of this are not understood. It seems likely that growth might cause a residue to flake off as well as stretch it. Experiments using a stretchable rubber surface might be enlightening.

Effects of Rain: — Rain is a prime corroder of protective layers. Water erosion is so important in agriculture that a huge organization exists in the United States to study and combat its effects on top soil. A knowledge of the dynamics of water corrosion is likewise important in understanding the preservation of deposits of protective fungicides.

Mechanical Removal and Leaching by Rain: — Rain probably removes deposits by simple mechanical erosion and by leaching. Mechanical erosion can often be observed under a microscope when fairly heavy deposits are flooded with water. Complex deposits are known to leach differentially. WILCOXON and McCALLAN (1938) have clearly demostrated and E. E. WILSON (1942) has confirmed that calcium sulfate leaches preferentially from bordeaux deposits so that they actually become relatively richer in copper than when they were laid down. Undoubtedly, arsenate of lead deposits leach differentially under some conditions (D. E. H. FREAR and H. H. WORTHLEY, 1940) so that the arsenic is lost more rapidly than the lead.

Mineral oil affects the preferential leaching of bordeaux deposits according to E. E. WILSON (1942). Copper seems to dissolve in the oil and leach out with the oil more rapidly than if no oil were present.

Calcium and sulfate ions leach less rapidly from oiled than from unoiled deposits. Hence, as weathering proceeds, oiled deposits become leaner in copper and richer in calcium sulfate than unoiled deposits.

The type of rainfall is important. The hard driving force of a June thundershower in the United States would seem to be more important in removing a protective layer than the slow misty rains of England. In fact WEBER *et al.* (1937) showed that a single heavy rain removed much more arsenate of lead from apples than nine small rains of equal volume. This agrees with common knowledge that one heavy rain will erode a field much more heavily than an equal amount of water in light rains.

J. M. HAMILTON's (1932) opposite conclusion that "five rains with a total of 0.85 inches washed off more sulfur than one rain of 1.35 inches" did not take account of the fact that the 0.85 inches of rain fell on an original deposit when it was big and easy to wash, whereas the 1.35 inches fell on a residue already badly eroded by the 0.85 inches.

Rate of Wash-off: — Any 12-year-old who must wash the family car knows that the first flush with the hose removes a major share of the mud from any given fender. He also knows that his succeeding efforts pay him less and less as he goes along. This indicates that removal of mud from a car proceeds according to the law of diminishing returns, *i.e.* logarithmically.

Analysis of the laboratory data of H. J. MILLER (1943) on wash-off of copper materials shows that residue is washed from glass in proportion to the logarithm of the amount of water applied. Unpublished data supplied by Dr. J. W. HEUBERGER show that in bioassay of tenacity, the probit of percentage kill of spores decreases according to the logarithm of the number of rinsing strokes used in washing a copper deposit.

The literature yields few useful data on rate of wash-off of field deposits. With few exceptions all data so far found were obtained during and perhaps following serial applications of the materials. The deposits analyzed have been piled on top of weathered residues left from previous applications. However useful such data may be to practical farmers, it is useful only with much reservation in a study of the dynamics of deposit corrosion.

R. O. MAGIE and J. G. HORSFALL (1936) applied some fixed copper materials in midsummer to previously non-sprayed apple and cherry foliage. Further analysis of their data (Fig. 6) shows that the materials weathered off approximately according to the logarithm of the amount of rainfall.

Apparently, R. W. THATCHER and L. R. STREETER (1925) applied lime-sulfur sprays and sulfur dust to untreated foliage. During a fairly cool part of the season the rate of wash-off seemed to be a function of the logarithm of amount of rainfall. The rate of loss from the second application during a hot dry part of the season was much more rapid than logarithmic. They suggest that rainfall may be a minor factor in loss of deposits of sulfur. Loss by sublimation undoubtedly played a part in the hot weather.

Data have been similarly plotted for other deposits applied serially.

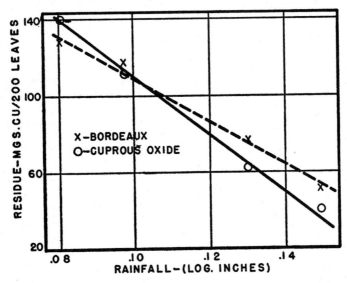

FIGURE 6. — Weathering curve of red cuprous oxide and bordeaux mixture on apple leaves in the field.

The logarithm of the rainfall overcorrects for HAMILTON'S (1932) data on sulfur and undercorrects for MILLER'S (1943) data on copper materials. It seems significant that the logarithm of time gives an approximate straight line in both cases. This is further evidence for the point made by THATCHER and STREETER that rainfall may be a minor factor in the weathering of spray deposits in the field.

Effect of Size and Coarseness of Deposit: — The lad who washes his mother's car by hosing recognizes two characteristics of the muddy deposit that he must remove — coarseness and depth. He knows that coarse deposits made of splattered pieces of mud wash off easily. E. E. WILSON (1942) showed that coarse deposits of bordeaux mixture obtained by mixing concentrated ingredients lost 65 per cent of their copper during 2.96 inches of rainfall whereas fine even deposits lost only 18.1 per cent of their copper during the same rains. WILSON reports some inconclusive data which suggest that bordeaux prepared with CaO resists rainfall better than bordeaux prepared with $Ca(OH)_2$. This could well be a matter of coarseness of deposit because Ca $(OH)_2$ particles tend to be coarser than CaO particles converted to $Ca(OH)_2$ in the spray tank.

Large deposits can also be produced by applying equally fine materials to deeper depths. Unpublished laboratory data here show that the slope of the logarithmic wash-off curve is steeper for such dense deposits than for lighter ones. H. C. YOUNG and L. E. TISDALE (1929) hold that large sulfur deposits weather more rapidly than smaller ones. The data of THATCHER and STREETER (1925) show also that large sulfur deposits wash more rapidly than small deposits. MADER and BLODGETT (1935) give illustrative data on 4-4-100, 8-8-100 and 16-16-100 bordeaux mixture on potatoes. When 100 gallons of these concentrations were applied per acre the amount washed off in a given time was 52.8, 51.5 and 47.2 per cent respectively. When applied in 154 gallons per acre the amount washed off was 57.9, 43.2 and 46.5 per cent, respectively. Thus in five cases out of six the tenacity coefficients decreased as the size of the deposit increased.

Deposit, of course, builds up with serial application during the season. It seems probable that a large deposit so built up might weather differently from one newly applied, because in the former case, the easily washed portions of the deposit would have weathered away leaving only the more resistant portions. Moreover, serial applications would tend to give a more uniform coverage to the foliage than fewer applications. HOPPERSTEAD et al. (1943) have published useful data on this point. Bordeaux was applied to apples for bitter rot. All spraying ended August 25. In one case seven sprays were applied up to that time beginning June 7, in another case six sprays were applied beginning June 27, then five sprays beginning July 3, and finally four sprays beginning July 15. The tenacity coefficients for the period between the cessation of spraying on August 25 and September 8 were as follows: 7 sprays — 85.5; 6 sprays — 85.1; 5 sprays — 60.0; and 4 sprays — 58.1. Clearly a big deposit made up of many applications weathers more slowly than a small deposit made up of fewer applications.

Effect of Particle Size: — It seems reasonable to deduce that small particles of protectant should resist the forces of weathering more strongly than large ones. If tenacity is a surface adsorption phenomenon, small particles should adhere better than large ones because they expose more surface per gram of material and hence they should cling more tightly. In fact WILCOXON and McCALLAN (1931) showed that such is the case with sulfur dust in the laboratory but in this laboratory we have not been able to show that yellow copper oxide resists weathering any more strongly than red copper oxide and yet the particles are only about ½ to ⅓ as large in diameter as red copper oxide.

THATCHER and STREETER (1925) showed that small particles of sulfur resist weathering better than large particles when applied in the field.

Effect of Detergents: — The extensive research on soaps, natural and synthetic, in protectants is interesting and significant in considering tenacity. As we have already discussed under coverage, detergents are added under the theory of "spreading" over a surface, so that it is more completely covered. If no rain were to descend on the treated surface this would be a practical and useful procedure, as for eradicants in controlling such diseases as powdery mildews.

Soap and water are well-known agents for removing deposits from surfaces — commonly called washing off the dirt. The inclusion of a soap in a deposit even under the euphonious name of detergent is to encourage its wash-off. Therefore despite volumes of published material on spreaders, they are seldom used in practice in applying plant protectants. Apparently, the deleterious effects on tenacity offset the beneficial effects on coverage.

Effect of Stickers: — A material added to a protectant to improve tenacity is called a sticker. A sticker should not be confused with a deposit builder which is designed to aid preferential deposition from sprays as discussed under deposition. A sticker may or may not possess deposit building properties.

The term sticker has a connotation of gluing that is not especially happy because it may becloud a true understanding of the dynamics of the action of stickers. At present stickers may be visualized as operating by four more or less distinct mechanisms, cementing, gluing, oiling and then some unknown process by which basic materials increase tenacity.

Cementing seems to be the basis of the sticking properties of many materials. Bordeaux mixture seems to depend in part upon the plaster of Paris cement that is formed by the calcium sulfate that is occluded in the dried residue. This is the same mechanism by which Portland cement sets and hardens. Too much lime makes a Portland cement which crumbles and weathers poorly. Likewise W. KELHOFER (1907) first showed that excess lime in bordeaux reduces its tenacity. This fact has been confirmed by O. BUTLER and T. O. SMITH (1919) and by many others.

The cement idea has been developed in many directions. Iron sulfate, magnesium sulfate, barium sulfate, aluminum sulfate have been proposed as stickers for bordeaux mixture. None of these probably adds much to the performance of the plaster of Paris cement normally formed in bordeaux.

These metallic sulfate-lime complexes probably do help to stick other materials. J. W. HEUBERGER and J. F. ADAMS (1936) proposed that sulfur be cemented to the foliage with zinc sulfate-lime complex. Recently HEUBERGER and T. F. MANNS (1943) suggested that the same cement be used for organic materials, as, for example, disodium ethylene bisdithiocarbamate.

The gluing of protectants to surfaces with animal glue was proposed early in the history of bordeaux mixture. This started a rash of proposals for organic colloids to use as glues. LODEMAN mentioned milk (casein) as early as 1896. L. DEGRULLY (1898) proposed egg white and dried blood and dried blood is still being investigated for the purpose by slaughter houses.

These proteinaceous colloids do improve tenacity of particulate compounds especially if lime is present to form an insoluble complex. The use of lime with casein, for example, was proposed specifically by V. VERMOREL and E. DANTONY (1913). This mixture enjoyed a wide popularity in the twenties under the trade name of Kayso, but it has largely gone out because no one could demonstrate that it paid its way. Lime and casein form the basis for modern water paints that dry to a reasonably washable surface.

Two factors have operated to kill the success of calcium caseinate and other proteinaceous colloids as stickers. (1) They have interfered with the fungicidal action of the toxicants as discussed below. (2) They are all somewhat surface active. This decreases the time to run off. This in turn causes a low initial deposit which tends to defeat ahead of time their objective of promoting tenacity. A tenacious small deposit may be no better, if as good, as a larger deposit without so much tenacity.

BOURCART (1913) says "The effect of a greater part of these new bouillies is . . . . quite illusory."

Oils, especially glyceride drying oils are excellent stickers, as painters will testify. They constitute the most effective stickers available for protectants. C. E. HOOD (1926) is credited in the entomological literature as first proposing oil (fish oil) as a sticker for arsenate of lead. BOURCART (1913) speaks of oils as stickers for fungicides in 1913. MARTIN and SALMON (1933) proposed vegetable glyceride oils as stickers. FAJANS and MARTIN (1937) compared hydrocarbon oils and glyceride oils as stickers in the laboratory and found the latter superior.

E. E. WILSON (1942) concluded that hydrocarbon oil is superior to cottonseed oil as a sticker, but he used his hydrocarbon oil in a higher concentration than his cottonseed oil. At equal concentrations the cottonseed oil was superior as a sticker to hydrocarbon oil, but since the statistical odds were not high enough for significance, WILSON drew the conclusion that it was no better.

Oils appear to act in two ways as stickers. They penetrate the treated surface either through crevices or by solution in the surface waxes on the plant. Glyceride oils then oxidize and harden somewhat thus occluding the particles of protectant. Secondly, the oils change the treated surface into one difficult to wet by rain and thus the rain runs off "like water off a duck's back" without taking the deposit with it.

Basic materials exert peculiar properties as stickers. J. M. GUILLON and G. GOUIRAND (1898) observed as early as 1898 that basic copper acetate was more tenacious than neutral copper acetate. This was confirmed by O. BUTLER and T. O. SMITH (1919). Metallic oxides seem to be especially tenacious possibly because they hydrolyze in water. Cuprous oxide is the most tenacious of all fixed copper materials. WAMPLER and HOSKINS (1939) report the striking tenacity of mixtures containing hydrous aluminum oxide. H. C. YOUNG and J. R. BECKENBACH (1936) suggested that the magnesium oxide in Wyogel bentonite contributes to its tenacity. S. F. POTTS and D. F. BARNES (1931) show that the tenacity of arsenical dusts is improved by ferric oxide. It seems quite probable that the greater part of the tenacity of bordeaux mixture may be due to the hydrous oxide present since WILCOXON and McCALLAN (1938) show that the plaster of Paris goes out of the residue more rapidly than the copper. Even the paint people use the weather-resisting properties of metallic oxides; witness lead oxide, zinc oxide and titanium oxide.

The mechanism of this action is hazy. It seems worth while to extend the theory of R. F. COHEE and J. L. ST. JOHN (1934) who suggested that lead being basic combines with the fatty acids in the apple cuticle. It seems likely therefore that metallic oxides in general may combine chemically with the cuticle and thus resist loss from weathering. MILLARDET and GAYON (see C. S. CRANDALL, 1909, p. 230) contended that copper from bordeaux is fixed in the cuticle so that it cannot be washed out even with dilute acid.

This theory of the chemical combination of oxides with cuticular fatty acids seems excellent until one recalls that metallic oxides cling better than other metallic salts to glass surfaces and cellulose nitrate as well. The tenacity then seems to reside primarily in the material rather than in the surface.

Relation between Fungicidal Value and Tenacity: — Insoluble protectants as discussed elsewhere are supposed to act by slow solubilization of the active ingredient especially in the presence of the germinating spores. If any of the toxicant becomes soluble, it is then vulnerable to loss by leaching. Other things being equal, then, the most soluble fungicide should be the most toxic and the least tenacious.

During the past five years several thousand organic compounds have been tested as protectants in this laboratory. In general the most toxic compounds have the least resistance to weathering. If the tenacity is improved with stickers, the fungicidal value usually falls.

E. B. HOLLAND et al. (1929) suggest without data that attempts to increase tenacity of bordeaux might impair toxicity. H. MARTIN (1932) makes a similar suggestion especially as regards casein and gelatine with copper materials. Being proteins they might keep any soluble copper precipitated so that it could not attack the proteins of the spore.

A general opinion of practical pathologists is voiced by HOPPERSTEAD et al. (1943). "The spreader stickers used did not aid in the control of bitter rot (of apples) even though the fungicidal deposits were increased in some cases."

Chapter X

ARTIFICIAL IMMUNIZATION AND CHEMOTHERAPY

Up to now we have been dealing exclusively with chemicals applied to the exterior of plants where they act as protectants in one way or another. Before giving consideration to the chemicals themselves that are used as fungicides, it is desirable to consider the action of chemicals when applied to immunize plants against disease or to cure them of disease.

The first process can be labelled as artificial immunization and the second as chemotherapy.

Artificial Immunization: — Some research has been done in the past to establish the chemical basis for resistance of plants to disease. Two typical papers may be cited. WALKER and LINK (1935) have shown the relation of protocatechuic acid to the resistance of onions to smudge. GREATHOUSE and RIGLER (1940b) have made a series of studies of the chemical resistance of plants to *Phymatotrichum omnivorum*.

Since natural resistance in many cases probably does have a chemical basis, then it is logical to assume that resistance can be imparted by introducing chemicals artificially. The problem, of course, is to find suitable chemicals.

ZENTMYER (1942a) has shown that the percentage of infection of *Ceratostomella ulmi* on elms can be reduced by pre-inoculation injection of hydroquinone, benzoic acid, and p-nitrophenol. In other words he artificially immunized some of the trees. And now STODDARD (1944) has shown that p-aminobenzene sulfonamide and hydroquinone have the ability of immunizing peach trees against the virus disease of peach called the X-disease. And DIMOCK (1944) has reported excellent control of the foliar nematode disease of chrysanthemum by a pre-inoculation treatment of the soil with sodium selenate. Entomologists earlier had shown an internal effect of sodium selenate on control of insects and mites on roses.

POLYAKOV (1941) claimed to have increased the resistance of wheat plants to rust by means of a long series of chemicals. He felt that the immunization was connected with the thio, amino, or cyanide groups.

Plant pathologists from time to time have hoped to "vaccinate" plants against disease but without notable results. TEHON (1944) has just reported success in vaccinating elm trees against *Verticillium albo-atrum* by pre-inoculation treatments with staled medium in which the fungus had grown.

Whatever be the best mechanism, we shall certainly hear much more and soon about artificial immunization of plants against disease and insects as well. It may be that the practical success will be limited to plants like elms or peaches where the individual value is high. If, however, a technique can be devised for introducing the chemicals through the roots, then field crops and vegetables may be treated.

Chemotherapy: — Chemotherapy is usually an internal treatment. We have already said that therapy is the principle of curing sick plants. Various therapeutic procedures could be mentioned such as surgery and application of heat or chemicals. The chemical cure of diseased plants can be defined as chemotherapy. This term seems to stem back to EHRLICH and his now famous work on chemical cure for human syphilis. CUNNINGHAM (1935) made use of the word, "therapeutant" in a more general sense of any chemical control such as protection. This hardly seems justified.

The dogma that chemical treatment for plant diseases is largely protective may have to be revised fairly soon, because cases of chemotherapy are multiplying. Protective procedures for disease control seem to professional men to be philosophically sounder than curative procedures, but disease to the man in the street is an occurrence that is expected to pass him by. He normally expects nature to keep him and his animals and plants healthy. To him curative procedure is preferable. As long as that state of mind exists, chemotherapy will be an entrancing possibility — witness the enormous interest in sulfa drugs for human and animal diseases.

Such a basic interest among the laymen in the cure of plant diseases by internal therapy has made the field the happy hunting ground for quacks. They have exploited the field so heavily and have failed so frequently and miserably, that it is difficult now to discuss the subject in respectable scientific circles without encountering a certain amount of eye-brow-lifting.

Of course, chemotherapy is a delicate operation which may require finesse beyond the ability of the amateur. The amateur can slop bordeaux mixture or sulfur dust onto foliage and obtain fairly reasonable disease protection, but he seldom is satisfied with the results of his amateurish attempts to pasteurize cabbage seeds to cure them of infection by *Fusarium* yellows. It will probably be even more difficult for him to apply injection procedures when they will have been perfected.

Chemotherapy seems to divide itself into three sections with divergent objectives: (*a*) cure of nutritional disorders, (*b*) selective fungicidal action, and (*c*) toxin inactivation. The first involves feeding the plant artificially to cure deficiencies. The second involves killing a pathogene that is already established without serious damage to the host. The third involves a new approach in plant pathology, the antidoting of toxins. The second involves interference with parasitism. The third involves interference with pathogenism.

Cure of Nutritional Disorders: — The major success up to now with chemotherapy has been in the field of the control of nutritional disorders. Much of the story has been summarized recently by W. A. Roach (1939). The chlorosis of oak trees due to iron deficiency is easily cured by trunk injection. The same is true of zinc deficiency diseases of some citrus trees. Sprays onto foliage will penetrate sufficiently to cure copper deficiency, boron deficiency and many others.

Selective Fungicidal Action: — Through the years of history, empirical research has developed a fairly large list of pathogenes that can be killed out of tissue without disrupting fatally the operations of the host. The success of this operation usually depends on the fact that the pathogene may "drop its guard" slightly during some segment of its life cycle so that it may be a trifle more susceptible than the host. This may be because the pathogene is essentially external, because the host is dormant, or simply because the host protoplasm may be more tolerant than that of the pathogene.

Pathogene External: — The pathogenes of the powdery mildew diseases prefer to grow on the outside of the plant, sending down haustoria through the cuticle into the cells beneath for sustenance. The powdery mildew fungi thus become sitting ducks for a selective curative fungicide. Since the cell walls of the fungi are uncuticularized, they are more exposed to the toxicant than the cells of the leaf which sit behind a barrier of cuticle. The fungus is not wholly defenseless, however. The mycelium is very difficult to wet with spray materials and hence it is not as easily knocked off as at first apparent. Detergents must be added if the mycelium is to be wetted and killed. In fact, one of the first detergents in a spray on record is Robertson's use of soap with a sulfur spray to control powdery mildew of peach back in 1824. To avoid the difficulties in wetting the mycelium, sulfur dust is almost universally used nowadays against powdery mildews.

Another well-known case of chemical cure of an external parasite is the control of *Rhizoctonia* and to some degree of *Actinomyces* scab of potato by dipping or soaking the tubers in fungicides. H. L.

BOLLEY (1891) opened this field by dipping the diseased tubers in mercuric chloride and J. C. ARTHUR (1897) extended the field by suggesting formaldehyde.

Host Protoplasm Dormant: — In many cases the pathogene overwinters in the resting organs of the host such as roots, tubers, and seeds, or it may overwinter in the bark. Curing of the infection in such material has long intrigued the plant pathologist, because the host protoplasm is relatively inert in a resting body, and it should be relatively resistant, therefore, to the action of poisons. Such no doubt is the case, but the fungous protoplasm is usually taking a rest too, and it also seems to be more resistant than usual to toxic action. Nevertheless, several cases of success in this area of activity bear witness to the fact that the resting protoplasm of the host may be more tolerant to treatment than the resting protoplasm of the pathogene.

The best known case of chemotherapy of diseased resting organs is the treatment of cereal seeds for such diseases as loose smut, and those caused by *Helminthosporium, Gibberella,* and the like. The first successful therapeutic agent was formaldehyde as suggested by GEUTHER (1895). L. HILTNER (1915) pointed out, apparently for the first time, that mercuric chloride possesses therapeutic powers against mycelium inside the seed of rye infected with *Fusarium.* Later it was found that the organic mercuries which had been introduced by E. RIEHM (1913) are also effective agents for curing internal infection in seeds.

HILTNER's concept of the therapeutic action of mercuric chloride probably was fathered by EHRLICH's work on chemotherapy of human syphilis with arsenical compounds. It was natural, too, to take over EHRLICH's concept of "dosis curativa" and "dosis tolerata". These terms have been used freely in the German literature of plant pathology. The terms have the sound of scientific precision. The concepts are valid, but the establishment of the curative and toxic dose with precision is extraordinarily difficult as discussed in Chapter IV on data assessment. In brief, this is because "experimental flutter" is very important at the ceiling or at the floor of response.

The treatment of diseased bark of perennial plants in the dormant stage seems to have been started by L. H. DAY (1928) with his zinc chloride treatment of cankers on pear caused by *Erwinia amylovora.* J. A. McCLINTOCK (1931) claimed that the zinc chloride penetrated the tissues and actually killed out the bacteria. Zinc chloride is certainly damaging to normal host tissue. Apparently the host recovers from chemical damage, however. Recently, O. H. ELMER (1942) has shown that dormant raspberry canes infected with *Elsinoe veneta* can be cured by applications of lime-sulfur.

Host Protoplasm Tolerant: — The new internal treatment with paradichlorobenzene of tobacco infected with *Peronospora tabacina* is an interesting case of apparent therapy. This startling new treatment was first reported by H. R. ANGELL *et al.* (1935) in Australia. It involves fumigating diseased seedlings with benzene or paradichlorobenzene. Here the growing host protoplasm is just as close to the toxicant as the fungus protoplasm. It is not protected by a cuticle nor is it in the resting stage. In fact, the protoplasm in a seedling is probably in its most vigorous stage. Whether the chemical kills the fungus without affecting the host protoplasm is a moot point. F. A. WOLF *et al.* (1940) think that the fungus is not killed.

There is other evidence that paradichlorobenzene is not especially toxic to host protoplasm because it penetrates borer holes in peach stems without serious damage. Paradichlorobenzene, however, does not appear to be very toxic to the protoplasm of many fungi, either, because it is common mycological procedure (CROWELL, 1941) to kill mites in fungous cultures by dropping a crystal into each culture tube. Tests in this laboratory have indicated no toxicity to *Macrosporium sarcinaeforme* and *Sclerotinia fructicola*. It may be that the toxicity is limited to *Phycomycetes*. ANDERSON (1940) reported that Pythium damping-off is reduced by fumigation with paradichlorobenzene. This leads one to hope that techniques may be devised for using paradichlorobenzene on other downy mildew diseases like that of potato late blight.

Bordeaux mixture is not of much value as a spray for downy mildew of tobacco and it often leaves much to be desired as a spray for late blight of potatoes. Perhaps paradichlorobenzene could be substituted. Perhaps it could be dissolved in cottonseed oil, emulsified in water and used as a spray for curing infected potato plants.

On the other hand, as suggested in a previous chapter, the control of downy mildew of tobacco may not be a case of therapy in the sense of curing the plants. Some evidence suggests that it may be protective in the sense of preventing sporulation.

The possibility of killing pests, with selective pesticides applied internally to plants by injection has intrigued layman and scientist alike for generations. According to W. A. ROACH (1939) an anonymous paper written in 1602 suggested that ". . . wormes, which grow into the tree can be killed by boring downward into the pith and filling it with pepper, laurell, and incense". Possibly this was not as fantastic as it sounds because modern research in entomology has shown the insecticidal properties of some of the constituents of pepper and laurel.

BOLLEY (1906) injected trees with copper sulfate, formaldehyde, and ferrous sulfate. He thought he reduced the severity of *Exoascus*. The epiphytotic of *Endothia parasitica* on chestnuts called up a rash of attempts to control the disease with selective fungicides — none of which seemed to succeed. C. RUMBOLD (1920) summarized the work. She made one significant remark that, "Toxins may be made harmless" by injected chemicals, but apparently she made no experiments in this field, which lay fallow until HOWARD's work 20 years later.

M. A. BROOKS and H. H. STOREY (1923) after several years of work in selective fungicides for tree injection to control silver leaf concluded that ". . . . at present there seems to be little hope of discovering a substance which can be easily injected into a silvered fruit tree, ... which while harmless to the host, is toxic to *Stereum purpureum."*

Not daunted, C. M. SCHERER (1927) and H. L. JACOBS (1929) reported slight success with thymol injections for selective action on *Erwinia amylovora* and *Verticillium albo-atrum,* respectively. L. R. TEHON and H. L. JACOBS (1939) followed up the work on thymol, but the practical results do not seem startling.

In the year 1945, the possibilities still appear to be discouraging for finding a selective internal fungicide to use on actively growing host tissue although the door has been opened a crack by some interesting new work.

F. C. STRONG and D. CATION (1940) were able to cure cedar trees diseased with rust galls by spraying them with sodium dinitro-*o*-cresylate and ARK (1941) confirmed the general significance of the result by using the same chemical and some others to cure plants affected with crown gall. Within the year BROWN and BOYLE (1944) have shown that crown gall can be cured also by painting crude penicillin over the surface.

Specifications for a Selective Fungicide: — A study of the successful selective fungicides suggests that the effect should be transient. This specification, of course, is not critically necessary in the case of an externally borne pest like powdery mildew. Next to sulfur for powdery mildew, the first therapeutic agent was heat as developed by J. L. JENSEN (1888) in Denmark for loose smut of wheat, a disease that is borne internally in wheat seed. Heat is used also to cure internal diseases of cabbage and tomato.

Since heat is not a chemical, the dynamics of its fungicidal action will not be discussed further here. It is cited to show that curative action should be transient.

Volatility assures transiency in chemicals. Most chemicals used for curative purposes are volatile.

Formaldehyde, of course, is notoriously volatile as most freshman zoologists will testify from their investigation of the anatomy of pickled dogfish. Up to R. J. HASKELL's (1917) time, cereal seeds were soaked in formaldehyde solution and then aired. HASKELL improved the volatility of the formalin, reduced the injury and increased performance by piling the cereal seed, spraying a fairly concentrated solution on, covering the seed overnight, and airing it in the morning.

J. D. SAYRE and R. C. THOMAS (1927) eliminated the water entirely and depended strictly on fumigation by adsorbing the formaldehyde gas on a dry filler and using the material as a dust seed treatment.

Formaldehyde has now been almost completely replaced as a seed disinfectant by the less injurious organic mercuries. They also are slowly volatile.

We have already spoken about the volatility of paradichlorobenzene in the treatment of tobacco foliage. Even sulfur, which is so widely used for curing plants affected with powdery mildew, is volatile. In fact, powdery mildew of plants in greenhouses is often combated by painting the steam pipes with sulfur. The heat sublimes the sulfur and it collects on the leaves.

Of course, reinfection may vitiate all the results of curative action. The curing of potatoes infected with *Rhizoctonia* sclerotia may be worthless if the clean tubers are planted in contaminated soil. This difficulty with chemotherapy is parallel to that with eradicants if the pathogene has several generations per year.

Antidoting Toxins: — A new development to the credit of F. L. HOWARD (1941) is on the horizon of plant pathology. It aims to control plant diseases by antidoting the toxins with which many pathogenes do their dirty work.

The older theory of direct fungicidal action stems back to PASTEUR's theories. PASTEUR was a salesman without peer. He advertised the germ theory of disease so vigorously that the mass of workers in animal and plant pathology all began feverishly to look for microorganisms and later for viruses as the etiological agents in disease.

PASTEUR's theory of the causation of disease bred the correlative theory that disease control involved treating the parasite. Almost the whole structure of fungicides was reared on this foundation. The plants were treated with materials to kill the fungus.

The new approach constitutes a basic change in thinking (HORS-FALL and ZENTMYER, 1941, 1942). It recognizes the significant distinction between pathogenicity and parasitism, that parasitism can occur without pathogenicity and that pathogenicity can occur without parasitism. The older approach aimed at killing the fungus so that it could be neither parasitic nor pathogenic. The new approach proposes to abolish pathogenic effects which in many, many cases are due to toxic by-products of the growth of the associated microorganism.

Antidoting toxins seems to have been demonstrated so far for both vascular diseases and root-rots. It seems convenient to discuss here also the very new research on internal chemotherapy for virus diseases since they act in effect like foreign poisons.

Vascular Diseases: — C. M. HUTCHINSON (1913) first demonstrated the fact that the symptoms of wilt diseases of plants are caused by toxins that the pathogene secretes into the tissue.

HOWARD (1941) having learned that the bleeding canker of maples is toxin-induced, found that the fungous toxin could be antidoted in the laboratory and in the tree by treatment with diamino azobenzene dihydrochloride (Orange Helione). Of course, it is difficult to obtain complete distribution of the chemical through the tree and hence the commercial adaptation of the new method may hit many snags. The possibility has been demonstrated, however, that chemicals can be introduced into a living plant, antidote foreign poisons, and make the plant feel better. Eventually the practical difficulties will be surmounted.

At this point, ZENTMYER (1942b) took up the Dutch elm disease and showed that it is toxin-induced. He extracted a toxin from *Ceratostomella ulmi* and produced all the typical vascular symptoms of Dutch elm disease. The leaves wilted, then curled and died. The vascular system became discolored and plugged. Clearly he produced the pathogenic effects of Dutch elm disease without permitting the fungus to get near the trees.

HORSFALL and ZENTMYER (1941) found that Howard's diamino azobenzene dihydrochloride was capable of antidoting the toxin of the Dutch elm disease and that 8-hydroxyquinoline sulfate and malachite green would also antidote the toxin.

When these three chemicals were considered, it seemed that basic nitrogen might be the source of the antidoting action. This suggested urea as a common source of basic nitrogen, and urea also showed promise (see HORSFALL and ZENTMYER, 1942).

It now seems probable that FRON'S (1936) success with curing "tracheomycoses" of elms and carnations with 8-hydroxyquinoline sulfate may have been a matter of antidoting toxins rather than of selective fungicidal action. BROOKS and STOREY (1923) seem to have tested the material without success on silver leaf of plums, a toxin-induced disease, although ROACH (1939) is more hopeful about it for the same disease.

Meanwhile, in research on small trees ZENTMYER (1942a) found other new chemicals that appear promising. These are hydroquinone, 8-hydroxyquinoline benzoate, benzoic acid and p-nitrophenol. Eggplants were found to serve well as "guinea pigs" because they are easy to grow and because the amount of wilting can be measured accurately.

The discovery of hydroquinone suggested that the reducing properties of the earlier compounds rather than their content of basic nitrogen might have been responsible in part for the antidoting action. For this reason ascorbic acid (vitamin C) was tried. It has strong reducing properties. When traces of ascorbic acid were injected into eggplants sick with *Verticillium albo-atrum,* they recovered markedly (see ZENTMYER and HORSFALL, 1943). They wilted less than checks in the middle of the day. In fact the leaf temperature, "fever," fell as a more nearly normal level of water loss returned.

Even though the toxin of Dutch elm disease could be antidoted by several types of compounds, the practical control of the disease in large trees may not be easily attained, apparently because of two practical difficulties in application.

First, by the time the trees show toxic symptoms, the xylem vessels may be so plugged with gums and tyloses that the tree may be beyond recovery. This suggests that the gums should be dissolved. Research on that point is under way.

Second, Dutch elm disease often attacks the giant old elms. These trees have a small proportion of translocation tissue. Lateral movement, then, is slow and hence the antidote seldom or never penetrates to all the requisite infection pockets. Toxin continues to be released and the tree continues sickly.

Small trees respond much better to treatment, so that it appears only a matter of time and experience before a technique may be devised for treatment of the larger ones.

The problems of internal therapy by antidoting are now largely matters of the physics and chemistry of distribution throughout the affected plants.

C. MAY (1941) has summarized our knowledge of injection gadgets — including simple and fancy bore holes for liquid injection, pressure injection, distributive injection, and the use of gelatin capsules for dry injection. He overlooked the possibility of root injection and the treatment of foliage. Mineral deficiencies are frequently corrected by spraying the missing element onto the foliage. Possibly antidotes also can be introduced in sufficient quantities through the roots as FRON (1936) suggests or through the foliage as HORSFALL and ZENTMYER (1941) suggest.

If L. C. CURTIS' (1944a) new theory of "sucked in" guttation water is as sound as it now appears, it seems possible to apply antidotes to foliage as dusts to be dissolved in the guttation water. As the plant changes from positive internal pressure and guttation to negative pressure and transpiration, the guttation drops seem to be sucked back in, thus carrying the antidote deep into the leaf and stem.

Root-Rots: — Internal vascular diseases are not the only toxin-induced diseases. DORAN (1928b) has shown that tobacco brown root is due to a toxin liberated into the soil by decaying timothy, and has shown similarly that black root of strawberry is due primarily to toxins liberated as "sewage" products in organic matter decomposition. GRIES (1943b) has found that the toxins are associated with a specific microorganism.

Many, many root-rots are ascribed to parasites so weak that they would not be considered if the disease were on the foliage.

It appears that the organisms listed as pathogenes are frequently members of the normal soil flora. These organisms such as *Fusarium, Rhizoctonia, Pythium* are sometimes called facultative parasites. Possibly they could better be considered as pathogenes without parasitic capability.

It seems probable that they produce their pathogenic effects by the excretory products that they give off. If a root happens to be near, it is killed by the excretion. As the root dies it becomes pabulum just as much as other dead organic matter in the soil.

A long list of such diseases from *Rhizoctonia* on wheat and grass, Texas root rot of cotton, *Thielavia* on tobacco can be alleviated in large measure by treatment with ammonia — a basic nitrogen compound. The correlation with the antidotes for Dutch elm disease toxins is too good to be accidental. It suggested to HORSFALL and ZENTMYER (1942) that the diseases concerned are toxin-induced and that the effect on control is one of antidoting. In fact L. M. BLANK and P. J. TALLEY (1941) showed that ammonia is non-toxic to the cotton root rot fungus.

Virus Diseases: — STODDARD (1942) appears to have opened an entirely new field to chemotherapy with his researches on the inactivation *in vivo* of the virus of the X-disease of peach. He soaked infected budsticks in solutions or suspensions and then budded them to healthy peaches. The virus seemed to have been killed out or heavily reduced by urea, calcium 8-hydroxyquinolinate, magnesium 8-hydroxy-quinolinate, *o*-nitrophenol, and sodium thiosulfate. STODDARD was probably fortunate in the virus he chose, because it is so unstable that it cannot be transmitted mechanically except by budding. It might well prove to be more difficult to cure plants affected with a stable virus like tobacco mosaic virus.

Of course, considerable research has been done by JAMES JOHN-SON (1941) and others on the inactivation of viruses in the laboratory, but he did not continue his studies on living plants.

STODDARD and ZENTMYER (1943) subsequently showed the striking similarity in the list of chemicals that inhibited the toxin of the Dutch elm disease and inactivated the virus of X-disease.

Specifications for an Antidote: — So far as knowledge goes at present, the prime quality of a toxin antidote or a virus inactivator is that it be an oxidizer or a reducer. This suggests, of course, that the mechanism of action is one either of oxidizing or reducing the toxin to an innocuous level. Presumably, the innocuous level is the oxidation-reduction level at which the host protoplasm operates.

Chapter XI

ACTION OF COPPER

Chemical control of plant diseases has depended much on heavy metals for its success. The toxicity of heavy metals was probably first observed in mercury. This was suggested for wheat bunt almost two hundred years ago by AUCANTE (see WOOLMAN and HUMPHREY, 1924). It was proposed for wood preservation in 1705 by HOMBERG according to HUNT and GARRATT (1938). The toxicity of copper to spores was discovered shortly thereafter by SCHULTHESS.

Of course, interest in heavy metals bloomed in the honeymoon period of bordeaux mixture. E. WÜTHRICH (1892) demonstrated the superior fungicidal properties of mercury over copper, and the inferior fungicidal properties of ferrous sulfate and zinc chloride. WÜTHRICH concluded that no metal was likely to drive copper out of the field and after 50 years we can observe that no metal has.

During the 50-year interval VERMOREL and DANTONY (1910) suggested silver. The shortage of copper during the last war in Germany brought out the fungicidal properties of cerium as proposed by O. APPEL (1917). A. WÖBER (1920) reported on various metals in relation to the periodic table. A similar and more extensive study was made by McCALLAN and WILCOXON (1934) who put silver as the most toxic metal, followed by osmium, mercury, cadmium, cerium, thallium. They think that copper may occupy the Biblical seventh place. Recently W. SEIFRIZ and M. URAGUCHI (1941) list the metals in the following order of toxicity to a slime mold. $Ag>Hg>Cd>Tl>Cu>Pb>Zn>Y>Sr>La>Rb$.

The action of copper will be discussed in some detail. It is probable that other heavy metals will act somewhat similarly.

Copper is a most peculiar metal. Much of its existence is spent in humdrum combinations such as copper sulfate and other simple salts, but it may combine also in fantastic double salts or form extracurricular linkages so complex that they can hardly even be hinted at in elementary texts on chemistry. Sulfur, the great competitor of copper in the fungicide field, is able also to engage in clandestine activities not shared by the majority of elements.

Copper and sulfur may be expected to act unexpectedly.

Types of Copper Fungicides: — Copper may be used as simple salts, as basic salts, or as organic complexes.

In the United States cuprous oxide was perhaps the first of the normal salts to be used alone in tonnage. W. P. RALEIGH (1933) suggested a molasses mixture which had cuprous oxide as its active ingredient, but the practical use of the material seems to have stemmed from its use as a seed protectant by HORSFALL (1932b). At present it is sold as Yellow Cuprocide in America or as Perrenox in the British Empire.

Copper silicate (as Coposil) was introduced by A. C. SESSIONS (1936). Copper Zeolite (as ZO) was introduced by A. A. NIKITIN (1937), Copper phosphate, another normal salt, was introduced by GOLDSWORTHY and GREEN (1933). None of these has reached heavy levels of consumption, probably because of low tenacity.

Copper sulfate was used for years on wheat seeds until DREISCH (1873) discovered the salubrious effects of lime in reducing its phytotoxicity. Lime converts copper sulfate to a basic salt; and now copper is used mostly in basic salts, the precise nature of which is still calculated to touch off a battle between chemists in the field.

Nobody studied DREISCH's (1873) mixture of basic copper salts but when MILLARDET shouted the merits of it and it got a trade name, bordeaux mixture, it came in for a large share of chemical attention. MILLARDET and his chemical colleague GAYON made a simple chemical equation to illustrate the reaction between copper sulfate and lime as follows:

$$CuSO_4 + Ca(OH)_2 \rightleftharpoons Cu(OH)_2 + CaSO_4$$

This proposal began a series of researches which came full circle nearly 50 years later when MARTIN (1932) suggested that bordeaux was $Cu(OH)_2$ stabilized by calcium sulfate. In the interim L. SOSTEGNI (1890) started investigators baying down the trail of the basic sulfates.

S. U. PICKERING (1907) has done much work on the basic sulfates first suggesting that tribasic sulfate may be the active ingredient. Much intermediate work could be cited in support of various theories of the nature of the basic salts formed. E. POSNJAK and G. TUNELL (1929) made phase rule studies of the reaction and deduced that $4CuO \cdot SO_3 \cdot 3H_2O$ is formed. This salt is called tribasic copper sulfate.

When MARTIN (1932) returned to MILLARDET and GAYON's theory of $Cu(OH)_2$ he recognized PICKERING's criticism that $Cu(OH)_2$ is not stable alone, that it dehydrates to CuO. He held, however, that this is prevented by the calcium sulfate.

The famous controversy over whether MILLARDET or someone else should get the credit for bordeaux mixture had not even cooled when others crashed the field with their competitive materials. A. AUDOY-NAUD (1885) substituted ammonium hydroxide for calcium hydroxide and "Eau Celeste" (the skyblue water) was born. E. MASSON (1887) suggested sodium carbonate instead of lime and burgundy mixture was underway.

S. W. JOHNSON (1891) offered ammonium carbonate as the alkali. Later JOHNSON's mixture was rediscovered and named Cheshunt mixture by BEWLEY (1921).

None of these basic mixtures has ever enjoyed the popularity of bordeaux mixture, chiefly because bordeaux mixture is the least injurious and most tenacious mixture of them all.

Bordeaux mixture has probably contributed more to the world's food supply than any other single pesticide. Its success has justified the existence of many a plant pathologist and they have reciprocated by filling libraries with articles on it.

Bordeaux mixture as a composition of matter seems to have been put together in 1800 by J. L. PROUST. It was used prior to 1842 by the French peasants (see BUTLER, 1914) who wanted a horrendous- and poisonous-looking mess to daub on to ripening grapes to prevent pilfering. It was so satisfactory for the purpose that it continued in use. It was still being plastered on roadside grapes when the disastrous outbreak of downy mildew threatened the French grape industry in 1878. ALEXIS MILLARDET, hiking along the highway in 1882 observed that the anti-thief plaster was also an anti-mildew plaster.

The drama of discovering a remedy for an epiphytotic while it was still "epiphyting" blew bordeaux mixture all over the world in record time. The impetus was so strong that it continues to impel the use of bordeaux mixture for controlling diseases on hosts where modern methods are capable of producing more food.

Because of the phytotoxicity of the copper component, bordeaux mixture lost out on rosaceous plants shortly after the turn of the century when sulfur had a resurgence of popularity. The severe droughts in the United States in the thirties uncovered the phytotoxicity of lime, a material formerly considered as inert (see J. G. HORSFALL and R. F. SUIT, 1938).

As a result of this there has been a great surge of effort to replace bordeaux mixture by factory-made basic and normal copper salts (see summary by MARSH, 1937). The normal salts have already been mentioned. The basic salts without lime that are currently being sold are basic chlorides such as Cuprenox, Kupfer paster Bosna, and Caffaro in Europe and Copper A in America.

Of course, the original factory-made basic copper fungicide was basic copper acetate as used early in France and discussed in some detail by O. BUTLER and T. O. SMITH (1922).

Quite recently, with the trend to organic fungicides as discussed in Chapters XII, XIII and XIV, some effort has been made to combine the toxicity of copper with that of certain organic radicals. Our experience in this laboratory is that results in general are disappointing. Often the combined toxicity is lower than that of either component. Salicylaldoxime, for example, is toxic but the copper salt of salicylaldoxime is essentially non-toxic as we have found and as MARTIN *et al.* (1942) also reported.

The most complete study so far on the toxicity of organic copper compounds is to be found in the report of MARTIN *et al.* (1942).

Availability: — As already discussed in Chapter V on the principles of chemical protection, the action of any protectant rests on its availability and inherent toxicity. Availability covers the factors involved in the liberation of the toxicant from the protectant and its adsorption or absorption by the fungus. Inherent toxicity is the ability of the available toxicant to kill or inhibit the fungus.

The study of copper as a fungicide has probably yielded more data on availability than studies of any other fungicide. Pathologists are intrigued by the fact that copper in bordeaux mixture can kill spores when it is so highly insoluble in water, that it will resist rain action for weeks.

Although there are exceptions as discussed below, the great majority of opinion holds that the copper must become slowly soluble in water if it is to kill fungi. For example, spores of *Alternaria solani* in the presence of copper deposits are killed if water is present. DORAN (1923) has shown the significant fact, however, that the spores can germinate right on copper deposits if no free water is present— only enough air humidity to promote germination. It is no wonder that copper sprays will not protect tomato against the *Alternaria* disease.

The amount of available copper formed in an infection court before the spore can germinate or before the fungus can penetrate is influenced (1) by the chemical and physical qualities of the compounds concerned and (2) by the substances existing in the fluids in the infection court.

Effect of the Qualities of the Protectant: — Copper protectants vary in the speed with which they liberate available copper and hence in their ability to protect. The most obvious difference between materials is the specific surface of the particles, that is, the surface exposed to chemical reaction. In fact, it is most difficult to be sure that this is not the only factor that differs between materials.

The specific surface varies inversely with particle size and it varies with the nature of the particle surface. HEUBERGER and HORSFALL (1939) and R. A. HYRE (1942) have investigated particle size of copper protectants. The LD 50 drops sharply as the particles are comminuted. Slope apparently does not change, indicating that the only factor that changes is availability, not inherent toxicity.

Assuming that basic copper sulfate is the active ingredient in bordeaux mixture, it is some 10 to 20 fold more fungicidal than factory-made basic copper sulfate according to data of HORSFALL and HEUBERGER (1942). This is probably a matter of particle size because the drying necessary for the production of a commercial powder causes the particles to grow enormously in size and hence to lose specific surface.

The nature of the particle surface is important in availability. An angular particle exposes more surface than a spherical particle of equal weight. Further study of our data on particle size of cuprous oxides has given evidence for this. Cuprous oxide was air-pulverized, i.e., micronized. The air pulverizer reduces particle size by rubbing particles together. This knocks off the edges and makes them more nearly spherical than before treatment. The evidence so far available shows that the particles, though, optically smaller, have less specific surface and less potency than expected.

HORSFALL, MARSH, and MARTIN (1937) have shown that copper oxides prepared by a heating process are less fungicidal than an equal number of particles of the same apparent size prepared by precipitation methods. They suggested that the thermal oxides probably exist with a fused, smoother, and denser surface than those prepared electrolytically. In fact, those prepared electrolytically could well be porous.

Effect of Fluids in the Infection Court: — Four possibilities exist for an influence of the solubilization medium in the infection court. Pure water might dissolve enough copper to kill the spores. It might contain substances from the air, or soil in the case of buried materials, such as O_2, CO_2, or NH_3. It might contain host excretions or excretions from the germinating spores or growing mycelia.

Insofar as solubility in pure water is concerned, the results as usual depend upon the experimental design. Often the dried protectant is soaked in water for some days and then filtered. The filtrate is not toxic. A pessimist would deduce that insufficient copper will be dissolved in pure water to kill spores.

NÄGELI (1893) observed the death of *Spirogyra* filaments in water held in a copper container, but he was unable with his indicators to demonstrate soluble copper. He therefore set up an "oligodynamic" theory of action — literally action by a few.   He postulated that copper entered solution, but was absorbed by the algal threads as rapidly as it dissolved until they had accumulated a toxic dose. McCALLAN (1930b) and GOLDSWORTHY and GREEN (1938) perfused the spores with a slow stream of water containing a sub-lethal concentration of copper.   The spores accumulated enough copper to be killed, thus confirming NÄGELI.

The opponents of the oligodynamic theory point out that spores in a normal infection court are not perfused — that the only movement is that of diffusion.   Its proponents answer that the reservoir of copper in the protectant replenishes the copper as it is absorbed by the spores and that this is equivalent to perfusion.

A point of view long and extensively supported in the literature is that spores in nature germinate in rainwater which is sometimes mysteriously called "meteoric water".   Meteoric water is said to solubilize copper protectants.   MILLARDET and GAYON (see CRANDALL, 1909) originated the theory by pointing out the existence in rainwater of CO_2 and ammonia, both of which are capable of dissolving copper.   This has been amply confirmed.

The unstated assumption, of course, is, that if copper is brought into solution by meteoric water, it is toxic, but few experts seem to have investigated the toxicity to spores of copper that has been solubilized by CO_2.   K. F. KELLERMAN and T. D. BECKWITH (1906) have shown that CO_2 reduces rather than increases the toxicity of copper materials to colon and typhoid bacilli.   B. T. P. BARKER and C. T. GIMINGHAM (1914b) claimed that injuriousness of copper to foliage is reduced in the presense of CO_2. In our laboratory CO_2 in the spore drop reduces the potency of cuprous oxide to spores of *M. sarcinaeforme*. Hence CO_2 in the spore drop almost certainly is not a factor in availability of copper in protectants. Ammonia, however, does increase the toxicity of cuprous oxide.

Proponents of other theories of solubilization like McCALLAN (1930b) point out very significantly that no action of meteoric water is needed to explain the fungicidal value of copper protectants because the property is displayed in distilled water.

Another favorite theory of toxic action is that the hosts may excrete substances into the spore drops that may dissolve copper.   This was first proposed by SWINGLE (1896) and independently by BARTH (1894) without much supporting data, and it has been kept alive by those interested in host injury from copper.   S. M. BAIN (1902) held that "something" escaped from the peach leaf to dissolve copper.   R. SCHANDER (1904) supported BAIN.   It seems strange that no one gave consideration to guttation fluid which leaves excrete.   This is an obvious source of solubilizing agents. BAIN (1902) took the gums secreted at the margins of peach leaves but, of course, he found no effect on solubilization of copper. CURTIS (1944a) showed that, among other things, guttation water contains ammonia which dissolves copper from yellow cuprous oxide and from bordeaux mixture. Such dissolved copper is more toxic to spores than untreated deposits of the protectants.

Here again the obvious criticism as McCALLAN (1930b) pointed out is that spores are killed by copper deposits on glass slides where host excretions are excluded. In fact MARSH (1936) goes so far as to show that protectants sprayed onto host leaves are less active than when sprayed onto glass slides. There are other reasons for this, but nevertheless the toxicity was not increased in his tests.

The theory that is the darling of many experimenters is the suicide theory — the theory that spores excrete substances which dissolve copper from the protectant and that this copper attacks the spores and kills them. This theory, first suggested by SWINGLE (1896), has grown and blossomed under the careful cultivation of workers like BARKER and GIMINGHAM (1911, 1914a) and of McCALLAN (1930b). It was severely pruned, almost chopped down by PICKERING (1912) and BUTLER (1914) but it seems to have recovered so that it looks better now than before.

The theory does seem to have much to support it. McCALLAN (1930b) germinated spores of Sclerotinia fructicola in water and filtered them off. The filtrate dissolved enough copper from a deposit of bordeaux to kill a second crop of conidia whereas "The filtrate from suspensions of germinating spores was nontoxic". Perhaps the expression "not as toxic" would be preferable in the light of McCALLAN'S warnings elsewhere in his other papers (1930a) that staling products from spore germination are toxic.

W. F. HANNA et al. (1932) showed that the odor given off by spores of Tilletia foetens is due to trimethyl amine. PETIT (1930) found that the fungicidal value of various copper compounds to the bunt fungus is correlated with their solubility in monomethyl amine. McCALLAN and WILCOXON (1936) suggested that amines are present in the excretions of spores of Neurospora sitophila and HORSFALL, MARSH and MARTIN (1937) found a partial correlation of the fungicidal value of copper oxides and their rate of solubility in the simple amino acid, glycine.

Glutamine (CURTIS, 1944b) is known to be excreted at times in guttation fluid. Possibly this amide also could be related to fungicidal value of copper. The action of amines may be similar to that of ammonia.

One heavy bit of evidence that could be cited against the suicide theory and in support of the oligodynamic theory is that as the spore density in a drop increases, the percentage of kill falls off. If each spore produces its own poison, it should be killed regardless of the number present. But if killing is caused by the slow liberation of copper from a reservoir in the deposit, then competition among the spores for this copper should reduce the amount for each one and hence reduce the kill. McCallan (1930a) has many data showing that the amount of copper necessary to kill each spore is a constant.

Probably the best deduction to be made is that no one theory can ever completely explain the solubilization or availability of the copper. Nature is probably not as simple as that.

Inherent Toxicity: — Having explored the possibilities whereby the copper becomes available for killing the spores, the next step is how does it kill them. The explanations are almost as varied as the investigators in the field.

Effect of Type of Compound: — Until the dosage-response curve for testing fungicidal action appeared, about all that we knew about compounds was that they were good, bad, or indifferent. Now one can get an idea as to whether the mechanism of action differs. Horsfall, Marsh and Martin (1937) suggested that cuprous oxide killed spores by a different mechanism from that of cupric oxide. In general their data show that the slope of the former is steeper than that of the latter. Martin et al. (1942) also gave data showing that cuprous oxide has a steeper slope than that of cupric oxide.

Parker-Rhodes (1941) set up an intriguing hypothesis that a compound probably passes through several steps before it reaches the stage where it is capable of permeating and killing the spore. He suggested that the larger the number of intervening steps, the flatter the slope of the dosage-response curve. The reason for this is unclear. Since the thiourea complex of copper has a very steep slope, he deduced that it or a related substance may represent the permeative compound.

Martin et. al (1942) tested a large number of copper compounds and found that many such as cupric chloride "appear to have a greater inherent toxicity than cupric sulfate".

The site of action is not even understood. Many investigators have glibly assumed that the action occurs inside the spore, but A. J. Clark (1933) suggests that most drugs probably act both at the surface of cells as well as inside the cell. There is evidence for action at both foci in the case of copper.

Effect of Copper on Oxidation-Reduction Systems of the Spore: — As will be discussed later, some organic materials may be fungicidal because they dislocate the oxidation-reduction system of the spore. Copper is known to be a strong pro-oxidant. Rubber factories must exercise care to prevent copper contamination in rubber to avoid oxidation.

G. and Mme. VILLEDIEU (1923), a French couple, wrote a series of papers beginning in 1920 to show that copper fungicides kill spores not by direct poisoning, but rather by catalytic oxidation. R. DuBois (1923) upon the publication of the theory by the VILLEDIEUS claimed that he had advanced the idea in 1890. The theory was supported by H. D. HOOKER (1924) and by E. CHAINE (1929). The direct experimental proof of the argument has been vague and so unconvincing that it has been brushed aside by most researchers. One fair argument is that the basic oxides such as MARTIN says occur in bordeaux mixture are good catalysts. The VILLEDIEUS have but a weak explanation for the fact that many basic oxides are not active, suggesting that they become coated with carbonate. One argument that flustered them is that copper sulfate is toxic. This is no basic oxide. They countered with the proposal (1924) that the toxic dose is in the concentration range where hydrolysis converts the sulfate to hydroxide.

The possible effect on the oxidation-reduction system may occur on the cell surface because J. H. QUASTEL (see CLARK, 1933) has shown that oxidation carried out by bacteria occurs at the cell surface. PRÉVOST (1807) showed that copper can be removed from spores of the wheat bunt fungus by soaking them in hydrochloric acid. J. BODNAR and A. TERENYI (1930) were able also to remove copper from spores by treatment with calcium nitrate. LIN (1940) confirmed this. BODNAR and TERENYI suggested that the copper must have been external in order to be leached out.

Permeation of the Cell Wall: — BODNAR and TERENYI were not able to leach out the copper when it went in as an ammonia complex. This meant to them that the copper had permeated the spore wall into the interior where it was not accessible to the acid or to calcium nitrate. WÜTHRICH (1892) demonstrated copper inside the spore with potassium ferrocyanide and NÄGELI (1893) showed that the protoplast of copper-treated *Spirogyra* crumbled presumably because the copper entered the cell.

Some cell walls are definitely not permeable to copper. Tomato seeds can be soaked overnight in a saturated solution of copper sulfate without injury and yet the tomato protoplasm is injured by copper if copper gets in. R. L. STARKEY and S. A. WAKSMAN (1943) found a fungus that would grow in very concentrated copper solutions presumably because the cell wall is impermeable to copper.

The mechanism of permeability is not certainly understood. L. KAHLENBERG and R. H. TRUE (1896) held that copper can penetrate only in an ionized state. MARSH (1938) found a soluble copper salt, the phthalocyanine, that is not toxic. Possibly this is because the salt does not ionize. MARTIN et al. (1942) suggested that cupric sebacate and cupric phthalate probably penetrate as the undissociated molecule.

Once the copper is inside, how does it kill? The most commonly accepted theory is that the heavy metal coagulates and immobilizes the protoplasm so that it can no longer function. Thin-walled cells like zoospores are known to burst in copper solutions, presumably because the protoplast swells as it coagulates. H. ARMET (1930) has recently covered the subject of coagulation from copper.

In 1905, EWERT suggested that copper has a deleterious effect inside a leaf by poisoning the diastase that is active in the starch-sugar system. This suggests that the copper might poison still other enzyme systems.

Chapter XII

ACTION OF SULFUR

Apparently sulfur is a "natural" as a pesticide. HOMER, the Greek poet, spoke of the "pest-averting" sulfur. Sulfur ointments are widely used in home-remedies and by medical men for skin afflictions. Sulfur at present fills a big gap in plant disease control practices, not because it is such an all-powerful protectant but because it has proved less phytotoxic on many plants than heavy metals such as copper. Sulfur has caught the public-eye lately because it occurs in the sulfa "wonder-drugs". Startling as the organic sulfur compounds are in animal pathology some of them seem to be coming into as much relative prominence in the field of plant pathology also. Farmers are flooding the market with calls for the new "thio" fungicides.

Sulfur is close to selenium and tellurium in the periodic table, but neither of these is particularly good as a fungicide. Selenium seems to be more toxic to animal than to plant protoplasm. It makes a fair insecticide or acaricide for a few usages.

Types of Sulfur Fungicides: — Flowers of sulfur have probably been used longer than any other form of sulfur. No doubt, HOMER had flowers of sulfur in mind. It is formed when raw sulfur is purified by sublimation. When sulfur is pulverized mechanically, it forms sulfur flour—or sulfur dust.

Early in the last century, KENRICK boiled sulfur and lime together to form an orange liquid. A French gardener, GRISON, rediscovered this mixture in 1852 and it became known as "Eau Grison" but now known as lime-sulfur. Lime-sulfur is probably the most powerful of the sulfur fungicides but also the most phytotoxic.

CORDLEY (1909) is usually credited with the modern introduction of lime-sulfur as a foliage protectant on the basis of its earlier use as an insecticide. CORDLEY, of course, was almost 75 years later than KENRICK. Earlier the material had been used exclusively as an eradicant for powdery mildew or peach leaf curl.

The first modification of modern lime-sulfur was self-boiled lime-sulfur, made with the heat of the slaking of CaO. It is lower in phytotoxicity than lime-sulfur. This is a deception in effect because its lower phytotoxicity is simply due to the fact that it is not as completely reacted as ordinary lime-sulfur. Self-boiled lime-sulfur is no longer used. Dried lime-sulfur was introduced about 1918 but it also is seldom used now. It was largely replaced by wettable sulfur.

FARLEY (1923) usually is credited with introducing the idea of wettable sulfur, but BOURCART (1913) refers to a wettable sulfur made with rosin. Wettable sulfur, in turn, is now being replaced by flotation sulfur.

In 1913 BOURCART mentioned sulfur from gas-manufacture, referring especially to the advantage of small particles that it possesses. This sulfur did not gain much acceptance until M. A. SMITH (1930) introduced it to America in 1930 as flotation sulfur. The material is made by passing coal-gas through suspensions of ferric oxide, and then washing out impurities. Fruit growers have now swung heavily to flotation sulfur because of its superior effectiveness. Flotation sulfur bids fair to drive off the market other forms of sulfur for protective spraying, but it will probably be driven out in turn by organic sulfur compounds.

Mode of Action of Sulfur Fungicides: — The action of sulfur as a fungicide presents the same type of problems as that of any protectant such as bordeaux mixture. Does an insoluble substance like sulfur penetrate a spore wall? And, if so, how does it kill after it has penetrated? That is, how does it become available and what is the nature of its inherent toxicity?

Availability: — It is interesting that the study of availability of sulfur has not followed the same path as the availability of bordeaux mixture. Seldom do we read of the action of meteoric water, of host and spore excretions.

Possibly the reason is that sulfur is known to "act at a distance" without the necessity for a solubilizer. ROBERTSON in 1824 said that sulfur "emits a powerful effluvia", and BERGMAN (1852) controlled powdery mildew in greenhouses by painting the steam pipes with sulfur. This suggests that the sulfur is gaseous.

BARKER (1926) stopped the aerial migration of sulfur with a dry paper filter and concluded that the sulfur migrates as minute particles.

Of course, temperature should be a factor in the "action at a distance" because rising temperatures increase the vapor pressure of sulfur. In 1869 H. H. MARES suggested that sulfur is fungicidal to powdery mildew only when the temperature is above 20° C. DORAN (1922) made much of temperature as a critical factor in the control of apple scab, even suggesting that the cool climate of New Hampshire might prevent the sulfur from being effective. HORSFALL (1930) chose a fungus, *Heterosporium phlei*, capable of germinating at low temperatures. The percentage of spores killed when they were placed on sulfur deposits, was the same whether the temperature was

3° or 30° C. Doubtless, a rise in temperature increases the speed of sulfur killing, but it also increases the speed of spore germination. Since the total effect is not altered by temperature, it follows that the temperature coefficient of the two processes is probably somewhere near equal.

We deduced that water solubility was desirable in the availability of copper protectants. Presumably it should be a factor in availability of sulfur protectants. Water-soluble lime-sulfur is certainly more potent than insoluble elemental sulfur, but on the other hand, it has different chemical properties as well. To confound the matter further, the sulfur in sodium sulfate is water-soluble but non-toxic.

Little is known of the permeation of sulfur through the spore wall. Data of McCallan and Wilcoxon (1931) indicate that sulfur can penetrate a collodion membrane because spores were killed by sulfur when they were separated from the sulfur by such a membrane. Doran (1922) was able to kill dry spores with sulfur more easily than wet spores. This finding should be linked, perhaps, with the fact that dry seeds are more easily injured by toxic salts or heat than wet seeds as Braun (1920) has shown. One wonders what presoaking would do to spores treated with other toxicants than sulfur.

Barker et al. (1920) and later Parker-Rhodes (1942) suggested the possibility that excretions from spores themselves might assist in making toxic sulfur available.

Inherent Toxicity: — As with copper protectants the inherent toxicity of sulfur may be exerted at two foci, inside the fungus and on the surface. As with copper no good techniques have been devised to separate the two. One of the significant areas for study is the strong similarity between the action of sulfur as a fungicide and its action in the vulcanization of rubber. Neither process is well understood but a comparative study of them should be worthwhile.

Similarity of Sulfur in Fungicidal Action and Rubber Vulcanization: — Marsh (1938) was the first to record a comparative study of sulfur in rubber and sulfur as a fungicide. Dimond and Horsfall (1943) pursued it further.

The action of sulfur in both processes is accelerated by metallic oxides as noted by Dimond and Horsfall (1944). It has been known for some time, of course, that lime is beneficial to the fungicidal action of sulfur. Martin and Salmon (1932) showed that many alkalis would improve the action of sulfur. Blodgett (1913) thought that lime would reduce activity of sulfur, but he neglected to allow for the dilution effect of the lime. Vulcanization is accelerated by several organic sulfur compounds such as tetramethylthiuramdisulfide (Tuads or TMTD) and mercaptobenzothiazole (Captax). These also accelerate fungicidal action of sulfur as DIMOND and HORSFALL (1943 and 1944) have shown. In fact, these organic sulfurs are fungicidal in their own right as MARSH (1938) has shown.

Metallic oxides such as zinc oxide seem to add their effect independently of the organic accelerators in rubber vulcanization but apparently they do not in the case of fungicidal action. Zinc oxide will synergise tetramethylthiuramdisulfide, however, as a fungicide (DIMOND and HORSFALL, 1943), and calcium hydroxide will accelerate the action of ferric dimethyldithiocarbamate in the field.

The vulcanization of rubber by sulfur is aided by several organic amines such as diphenyl guanidine. Research in this laboratory shows a hint of such improvement in the fungicidal action of sulfur, but the effect is not prominent, if indeed, it occurs at all.

Effect of Oxidized Sulfur: — It seems very significant in view of the discussion of oxidation and reduction in Chapter XIV on organic fungicides that the toxic action of sulfur has been claimed to be due to oxidized substances on one hand and to reduced substances on the other. Both explanations are almost certainly true in some instances because no one will doubt, for example, that SO_2, an oxidized form of sulfur, and H_2S, a reduced form of sulfur are both toxic. It would be obstructionist in outlook to hold that one or the other is responsible alone.

Little attention has been given to differentiating the oxidizing effect on the spore, if it produces a reduced sulfur, from the reducing effect on the spore when it is treated with a reduced sulfur, and *vice versa*. In the case of H_2S or SO_2, the effect will probably be different if the substance is introduced from outside the spore drop than if it is produced inside the spore drop.

To take oxidation first, E. MACH and K. PORTELE (1884) suggested that SO_2 was the active agent, formed by oxidation of the sulfur in the air. In water, of course, this forms sulfurous acid. N. MARCILLE (1911) would have SO_3 the active agent, which makes sulfuric acid in water.

H. C. YOUNG (1922) opened a controversy with the theory that pentathionic acid is responsible for sulfur toxicity, basing part of his argument on the thought that this acid is volatile, but so is SO_2 and SO_3. As a build-up for their theory that H_2S is responsible, WILCOXON and McCALLAN (1930) did very extensive research on pentathionic acid, holding that it is no more toxic than could be accounted for by the hydrogen ions that it contains. In fact, McCAL-

LAN and WILCOXON were preceded in this conclusion by W. A. ROACH and M. D. GLYNNE (1928) who showed that H-ion concentration probably accounted for the toxicity of sulfurous, sulfuric, dithionic, trithionic, tetrathionic, and pentathionic acids to *Synchytrium endobioticum*. They reported that neutral salts of these acids are non-toxic. We have found here that sodium tetrathionate is non-toxic. PARKER-RHODES (1942) reports that sodium dithionate is non-toxic.

On the assumption that sulfur action is due to oxidized sulfur, H. A. LEE and J. P. MARTIN (1927) added an oxidizer $KMnO_4$ and obtained improved control of *Helminthosporium* eye spot disease of sugar cane in the field. H. C. YOUNG and R. WILLIAMS (1928) similarly improved the control of apple scab. HAMILTON (1931) attempted to negate the theory on the bases (1) that $KMnO_4$ does not increase the volatility of the sulfur and (2) that $KMnO_4$ itself is toxic to *Venturia inaequalis* and does not improve the performance of the sulfur in a spore drop. The first point is not necessarily apropos and the second needs further work in the light of modern methods of untangling the effect of mixed poisons as discussed in Chapter XV. Moreover, to add $KMnO_4$ in a protective deposit gives it time to oxidize the sulfur before the spore arrives. Adding $KMnO_4$ to the spore drop would oxidize both sulfur and spore. The effects might be different.

Although some sulfur action is probably due to acids formed by oxidation, the action in some cases must be explained otherwise, as for example when alkalis seem to encourage rather than to discourage action as they would if acids were wholly responsible.

Effect of Reduced Sulfur: — E. POLLACCI in 1875 proposed that hydrogen sulfide is the active agent in fungicidal action of sulfur. This theory has gained many adherents particularly since the modern work by MARSH (1929) and McCALLAN and WILCOXON (1931). PARKER-RHODES (1942) has shown the fungicidal action of other reduced forms of sulfur.

The work on H_2S has failed to distinguish between the significance of H_2S production and H_2S toxicity although McCALLAN and WILCOXON (1931) must have glimpsed a difference when they showed that some spores produce more H_2S than they can use and that others produce less than is necessary to kill them.

A tiny spore of *Glomerella cingulata* liberates into the air enough H_2S to kill two much larger spores of *Sclerotinia fructicola*, to say nothing of the H_2S retained by the *Glomerella* spore itself. Nevertheless, it would have to produce 50 times as much as it does to kill itself. On the other hand one *Sclerotinia* spore can produce enough H_2S to kill three of its kind. Apparently, the ability to produce H_2S has little to do with susceptibility to it. MARSH (1929) showed that susceptibility of fungi to H_2S is not necessarily associated with susceptibility to sulfur.

It would appear that *Glomerella* protoplasm has a set of enzymes of such a nature that it can function even in the presence of a strong reducing substance like H_2S. In fact it is so reduced that it can reduce sulfur to H_2S.

Macrosporium sarcinaeforme is not killed on sulfur deposits, whereas *Sclerotinia fructicola* is. McCALLAN and WILCOXON (1931) would explain this on the grounds that *M. sarcinaeforme* produces only ⅓ enough H_2S to kill itself, whereas *S. fructicola* produces three times as much as required. This suggested to us that if spores of both organisms were germinated in the same spore drop on a sulfur deposit, the extra H_2S from *Sclerotinia* should kill *Macrosporium*. It did. This is the only experiment in which *Macrosporium* has died on a sulfur deposit.

McCALLAN and WILCOXON (1931) have shown that the H_2S is formed on or in the spore, not on the sulfur. They suggest that -SH compounds such as glutathione, a tripeptide of glycine, glutamic acid, and cysteine, are responsible for reducing the sulfur to H_2S. One wonders if the glutathione is oxidized in the process of making H_2S. Apparently it is not, because McCALLAN and WILCOXON say that much more H_2S is formed than could be accounted for by any possible content of preformed -SH compound.

Presumably this implies an enzymatic catalysis of H_2S production. This is evidenced by the fact that heating to 55° C. will inactivate the H_2S producing system. Moreover, *Sclerotinia* will continue to produce H_2S apparently after the spore is dead from H_2S poisoning.

Effect of Polysulfide: — H_2S is not the whole story. J. V. EYRE and E. S. SALMON (1916) were unable to kill conidia of *Sphaerotheca humuli* with H_2S and F. W. FOREMAN (1910) reported that *Botrytis cinerea* is able to germinate in a saturated solution of H_2S. MARTIN and SALMON (1932) found that *Sphaerotheca humuli* could not be killed by any of the following reduced forms of sulfur: sulfite, hydrosulfite, sulfoxylate, or thiosulfate. Presumably the redox system in the spore is in such a reduced state that these compounds will not reduce it further.

W. A. KELLERMAN and W. T. SWINGLE (1890) first used potassium sulfide (probably polysulfide) as a fungicide for oat smut. Carbon disulfide is not a very good fungicide. BOURCART (1913) reported zinc sulfide indifferently effective and copper sulfide ineffective as fungicides. In our laboratory tests cupric sulfide is not effective against *M. sarcinaeforme.*

MARTIN and SALMON (1932) having found that *Sphaerotheca humuli* is not sensitive to reduced forms of sulfur, showed that it is sensitive to polysulfides. In view of the similarity of *Botrytis* to the powdery mildew as regards sensitivity to H_2S as just discussed, it should follow that *Botrytis* like powdery mildew should also be sensitive to polysulfides. FOREMAN says that *Botrytis* is. Of course, this correlation may not be significant because apparently polysulfides are toxic to most spores. In fact, DORAN (1922) showed that one of the most sulfur-sensitive organisms, *Venturia inaequalis,* is more sensitive to calcium polysulfide than to elemental sulfur. *M. sarcinaeforme,* which germinates among elemental sulfur particles, is killed easily by metallic polysulfides.

HAMILTON (1935) found that calcium monosulfide is less fungicidal to *Venturia inaequalis* than calcium polysulfide.

Organic Sulfur Fungicides: — The story of organic sulfur compounds is being unfolded so rapidly that any discussion of them can hope only for a "stop-action" snap-shot, not anything even approximating a portrait. In the field of fungicides the most significant group comprises the derivatives and relatives of dithiocarbamic acid which are usually made by reacting an aliphatic amine such as dimethyl- or diethylamine with carbon disulfide and an alkali.

Thiocarbamates: — The discussion might start with the beautifully symmetrical compound tetramethylthiuramdisulfide, a compound first described by W. H. TISDALE and I. WILLIAMS (1934).

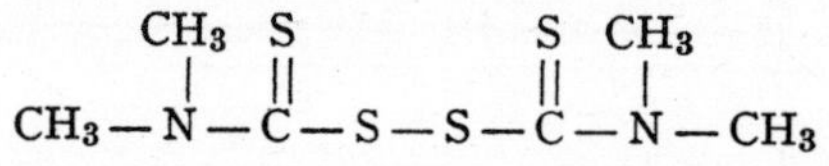

$$CH_3 - N \begin{matrix} CH_3 \\ | \end{matrix} \begin{matrix} S \\ || \\ C \end{matrix} - S - S - \begin{matrix} S \\ || \\ C \end{matrix} \begin{matrix} CH_3 \\ | \\ N \end{matrix} - CH_3$$

FIGURE 7. — Structure of Tetramethylthiuramdisulfide.

The compound will now be called TMTD for short. Its fungicidal properties have been discussed by MARSH (1938). Much was said about it in 1944 by many, many people under the names of the Thiosan and Arasan in America and Sulsol in England. It has been mentioned previously in this chapter under rubber vulcanization as Tuads.

Often metallic salts are formed by inserting the metal between the central sulfurs. A bivalent metal like zinc maintains the symmetry, but the ferric salt, which is the best known, must have three thiocarbamate groupings because the iron is trivalent.

Tetramethylthiuramdisulfide has a most extraordinary curve of toxicity as DIMOND et al. (1941) reported. The curve as shown in Fig. 8 has two peaks with two distinct log-probit curves in it. The toxicity of the material in the upper levels of concentration is presumably due to the action of molecular TMTD. With dilution this toxicity falls in the expected fashion. Ionization probably occurs with dilution so that the peak of toxicity in the lower ranges may be due to the two dithiocarbamate ions. With further dilution the toxicity falls again.

Inspection of the structural formula indicates that several explanations might cover the toxicity of TMTD. Research has been done here

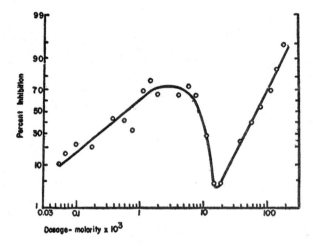

FIGURE 8. — The unusual double maximum curve of toxicity of tetramethylthiuramdisulfide. After DIMOND et al. (1941).

on the nature of its toxicity. It contains two dimethyl amines, an — S — S — linkage and a C = S group. Dimethyl amine has little toxicity as DIMOND and HORSFALL (1944) have shown. It may be that the — S — S — or polysulfide linkage is the toxic ingredient, because metallic polysulfides are toxic. The significance of the — S — S — linkage was tested in two organic polysulfides, diphenyl disulfide ϕ — S — S — ϕ, and p — p' — dinitro diphenyl disulfide. Neither of these was toxic to *Macrosporium sarcinaeforme* nor to *Sclerotinia fructicola*.

It seems strange that calcium polysulfide, $Ca = S = S_x$, is so strongly fungicidal while ϕ — S — S — ϕ is not. Possibly this is due to the fact that the sulfur chain is open in the case of calcium polysulfide and closed in the case of diphenyl disulfide. It is possible also that the difference is due to the double bonds in calcium polysulfide.

The effect of the — S — S — grouping in TMTD was tested in another way by using a similar compound containing amines and C = S groups, but not — S — S —. Such a compound has just recently been made available. It is disodium ethylene bisdithiocarbamate

$$Na-S-\underset{\underset{S}{\|}}{C}-\underset{\underset{H}{|}}{N}-CH_2CH_2-\underset{\underset{H}{|}}{N}-\underset{\underset{S}{\|}}{C}-S-Na$$

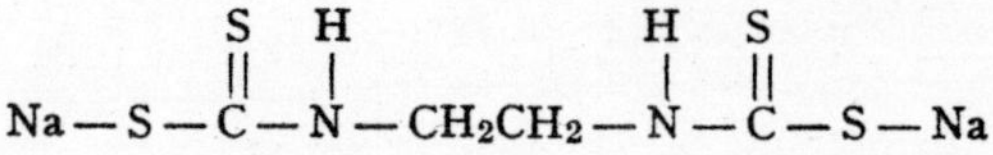

FIGURE 9. — Structure of disodium ethylene bisdithiocarbamate.

This compound was reported quite fungicidal by DIMOND et al. (1943).

From the evidence available it follows that probably the — S — S — linkage does not account for the toxicity of TMTD. If so, only the C = S group is left to account for the effect.

TMTD has two of the C = S linkages. Several organic fungicides with this grouping were tested. The following compounds showed toxicity to *Sclerotinia fructicola*:

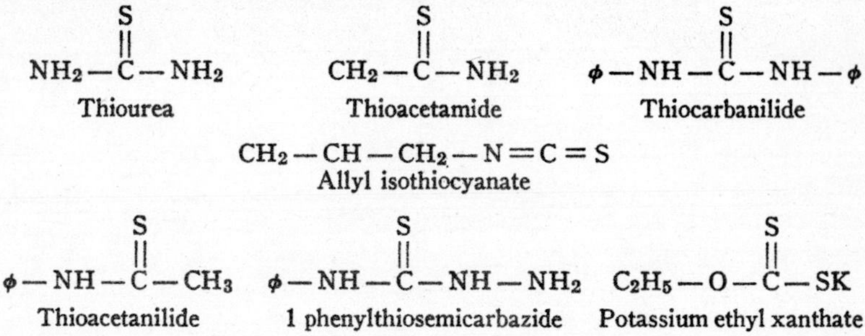

$$NH_2-\underset{\overset{\|}{S}}{C}-NH_2 \qquad CH_2-\underset{\overset{\|}{S}}{C}-NH_2 \qquad \phi-NH-\underset{\overset{\|}{S}}{C}-NH-\phi$$

Thiourea   Thioacetamide   Thiocarbanilide

$$CH_2-CH-CH_2-N=C=S$$

Allyl isothiocyanate

$$\phi-NH-\underset{\overset{\|}{S}}{C}-CH_3 \qquad \phi-NH-\underset{\overset{\|}{S}}{C}-NH-NH_2 \qquad C_2H_5-O-\underset{\overset{\|}{S}}{C}-SK$$

Thioacetanilide   1 phenylthiosemicarbazide   Potassium ethyl xanthate

FIGURE 10. — Structure of sulfur compounds based on C = S.

Thioacetamide, thioacetanilide, and thiocarbanilide were not toxic to *Macrosporium sarcinaeforme*. WALKER et al. (1937) have shown that allyl isothiocyanate and some of its relatives are fungistatic. The fungistatic properties of potassium ethyl xanthate were reported by BOURCART (1913) and by GOLDSWORTHY et al. (1942).

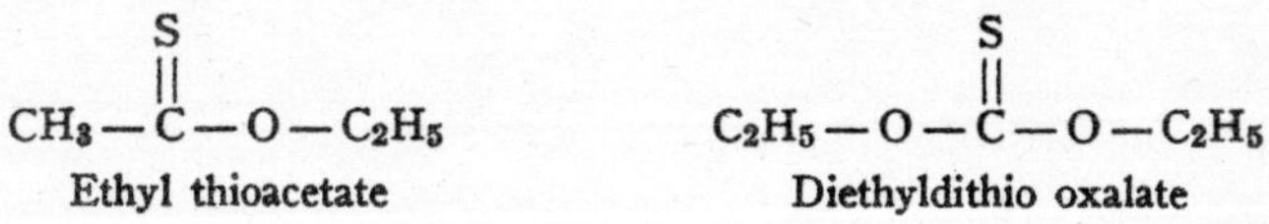

$$CH_3-\underset{\overset{\|}{S}}{C}-O-C_2H_5 \qquad\qquad C_2H_5-O-\underset{\overset{\|}{S}}{C}-O-C_2H_5$$

Ethyl thioacetate   Diethyldithio oxalate

FIGURE 11. — Structure of two sulfur compounds with O next to C = S.

The only two compounds with the $C = S$ grouping that were not toxic to either organism are ethyl thioacetate and diethyldithio oxalate. These compounds are very similar. It seems significant that both of these compounds have oxygen attached to the same carbon atom as the double-bond sulfur. It is true that one of the active compounds, potassium ethyl xanthate, has oxygen attached to the same carbon atom as the double-bond sulfur, but the toxicity of this one could be explained on the basis of the — SK radical as discussed below. A comparison of it and the other materials with the dose-response technique should bring out any differences.

From these studies, it follows that the toxicity of TMTD is probably due to the $C = S$ rather than to the — S — S group.

Sulfur often occurs in the sulfhydryl group — SH, sometimes called the mercaptan group. The simplest compound is H — S — H, hydrogen sulfide, which has been discussed above. We have tried only four other compounds in this group. Three were toxic: thioglycollic acid ($HSCH_2COOH$), 2 amino-4-chlorothiophenol hydrochloride (Fig. 12), and mercaptobenzothiazole (Fig. 12). MARSH (1938) has shown the fungistatic properties of the last. One — SH compound, *p*-thiocresol (Fig. 12), was not toxic in the tests.

Sulfa Drugs: — Most of the sulfa drugs, so useful in animal pathology, are not strikingly fungicidal or fungistatic, at least to *Sclerotinia* and *Macrosporium*. It might be worth while to investigate their genestatic properties. The first of the sulfa drugs to catch the public eye was *p*-aminobenzene sulfonamide (Fig. 12). Neither this compound nor its relatives, sulfathiazole and sulfapyridine, was toxic to *Macrosporium* and only slightly so to *Sclerotinia*.

The sulfur atom in these compounds is 6 valent in the SO_2 group, which is called the sulfone nucleus. The sulfone nucleus was found to be non-toxic in several organic compounds. It can be made fungistatic by substituting chlorines for the two amine hydrogens of *p*-aminobenzene sulfonamide to give dichloramine T. Another toxic sulfone compound is *p*-toluene sulfone chloride (Fig. 12) but the toxicity here is probably due to the chlorine and not to the sulfone nucleus.

If oxygen is attached to a tetravalent sulfur, the sulfoxide $S = O$ is formed. Of course, if the two free bonds are taken up by oxygen, $O = S = O$, or SO_2, is formed and this is toxic. If the two bonds are filled otherwise as in diphenyl sulfoxide (Fig. 12) or in phenothiazine sulfoxide, the toxicity is lost. GOLDSWORTHY and GREEN (1939) also have reported that phenothiazine sulfoxide is not fungicidal.

Phenothiazine: — Another sulfur grouping that has received some attention lately is phenothiazine or thiodiphenyl amine (Fig. 13). Occasionally it may be listed as fungicidal, but present evidence suggests that the toxicity is due to an impurity, probably the oxidized form, phenothiazone. (Fig. 13). Pure phenothiazine is a white crystalline substance. Phenothiazone is red or pink. Phenothiazone

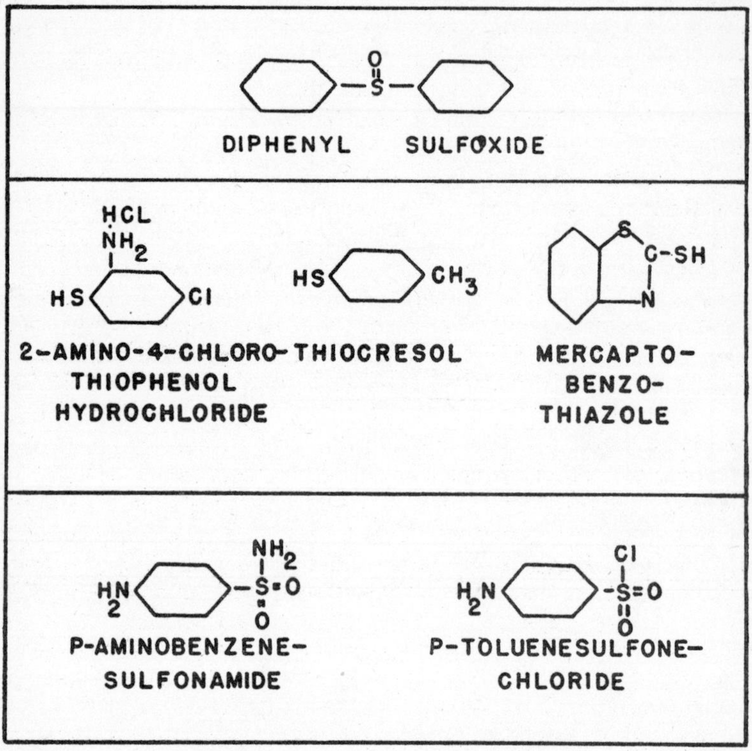

FIGURE 12. — Structural formulae of various organic sulfur compounds.

is bactericidal as well as fungicidal (see GOLDSWORTHY and GREEN, 1939). It finds a fair amount of use nowadays in human and animal medicine as a urinary disinfectant.

It will be noted that phenothiazone has a quinoid structure which is common to several other new organic fungicides as discussed later in Chapter XIV. This suggests that its toxicity may be due to its quinoid character. If so, quinoid relatives should be toxic and non-quinoid relatives should be non-toxic. One of the commonest quinoid relatives is methylene blue, which is known to be fungistatic. The

p-quinoid structure for methylene blue is shown in Fig. 13. Lauth's violet or thionine is also fungistatic. It is quite similar in structure to methylene blue.

One exception to the quinoid theory seems to occur. Thionol is just like phenothiazone in structure except that — OH is added in the seventh position. Thionol was non-toxic in our tests and GOLDSWORTHY and GREEN (1939) also report it non-fungicidal. No explanation is available as to why this quinoid structure is non-toxic. Possibly more chemical work is needed to indicate whether it is really quinoid or not.

Eleven non-quinoid structures, related to phenothiazone have been tested. None of these was fungicidal unless the toxicity were due to

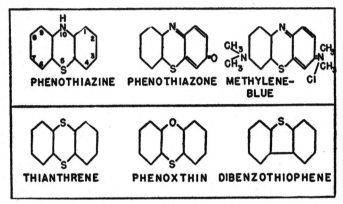

FIGURE 13. — Structural formulae of phenothiazine derivatives.

some substituent itself. The structures of three of the significant compounds are illustrated in Fig. 13. In thianthrene, sulfur replaces the nitrogen in the tenth position. In phenoxthin, oxygen replaces the nitrogen, and in dibenzothiophene, the nitrogen is gone altogether. Carbazole (see Fig. 15 in next chapter) is a compound spacially similar to dibenzothiophene except that the nitrogen is present and the sulfur is gone.

Six compounds with substitutions on the phenothiazine nucleus were tried. The substitution of a lauramide grouping on the nitrogen has no effect on the toxicity. If — OH is placed in the third position, where the oxygen of phenothiazone is, no toxicity is produced. If methyl is added in the first position or ethoxy to the eighth position of 3 hydroxy phenothiazone, a little toxicity seems to be added. If aniline is added in the third position instead of — OH, toxicity is definitely improved. If p-ethoxy aniline is placed in the third position, toxicity is definitely improved. This is equivalent to adding a p-ethoxy group to aniline, however, which as shown later in Chapter XIII improves toxicity of aniline. Hence the improvement seems to be due to that and not due to the actual improvement of phenothiazine. We have already said that the addition of oxygen on the sulfur of phenothiazine adds no toxicity.

THE ACTION OF ORGANIC NITROGEN COMPOUNDS

An astonishing number of organic compounds that are fungicidal contain nitrogen. Even the "thiocarbamate" fungicides discussed in the chapter on sulfur contain nitrogen as well as sulfur.

We here have made an extensive preliminary search of toxicity of nitrogen and other compounds to *Macrosporium sarcinaeforme* and *Sclerotinia fructicola* (see DIMOND and HORSFALL, 1942). The data will be used extensively in this and in the next chapter. Toxicity is often a matter of the dosage level and conditions of testing. A negative statement on toxicity, therefore, must be rated with care. Another investigator working under other conditions might conceivably rank the material as toxic.

Nitrogen occurs primarily in the trivalent form. Except under special conditions, it is non-toxic in the trivalent form. Sometimes it acts as if it were pentavalent, but chemists battle about the extra valences. Nevertheless, the nitrogen seems to impart toxicity to those compounds in which it is tied to other elements or radicals through these extra linkages. The two unusual types are represented by quaternary ammoniums and NO_2 compounds.

Amines: — The commonest type of trivalent nitrogen occurs in the amines. Few amines without other toxic groups can be described as greatly fungicidal or fungistatic.

In our tests the following amines were not fungicidal. The non-toxic primary amines were: monomethyl amine, *n*-mono butyl amine, aniline, cyclohexyl amine, xylidine, *m*-xylidine, *o*-anisidine. The non-toxic secondary amines were: dimethyl amine, dibutyl amine, diamyl amine, ditolyl amine, dicyclohexyl amine, phenyl beta naphthylamine, ethylidine aniline. The non-toxic tertiary amines were: trimethyl amine, butyl diethanol amine, tributyl amine, dimethyl aniline, ethyl benzyl aniline, diethyl aniline.

Aniline (phenyl amine) has been studied rather extensively here. It was not toxic in our screening test. Four methyl derivatives on the ring were not toxic: *o*-methyl (*o*-toluidine), *p*-methyl (*p*-toluidine), 2-4 methyl (xylidine), 3-5 methyl (*m*-xylidine).

If a reactive hydrogen is added in the alcohol group, OH, to form *o*-amino phenol (Fig. 14), high toxicity is produced. If, however, the H of the OH is replaced by methyl as in *o*-anisidine (Fig. 14), the toxicity is lost, probably because the reactive H has been replaced by a non-reactive group.

The addition of a carboxyl group, — COOH, produces toxicity, of course, as in the case of *p*-amino benzoic acid. The substitution of a sulfonic group in the ring also adds toxicity as in sulfanilic acid (Fig. 14). Just as in the case of the hydroxyl compound, if the H in the carboxyl group is replaced, the toxicity falls. If ammonia replaces the H in sulfanilic acid, the new compound is *p*-amino benzene sulfon-

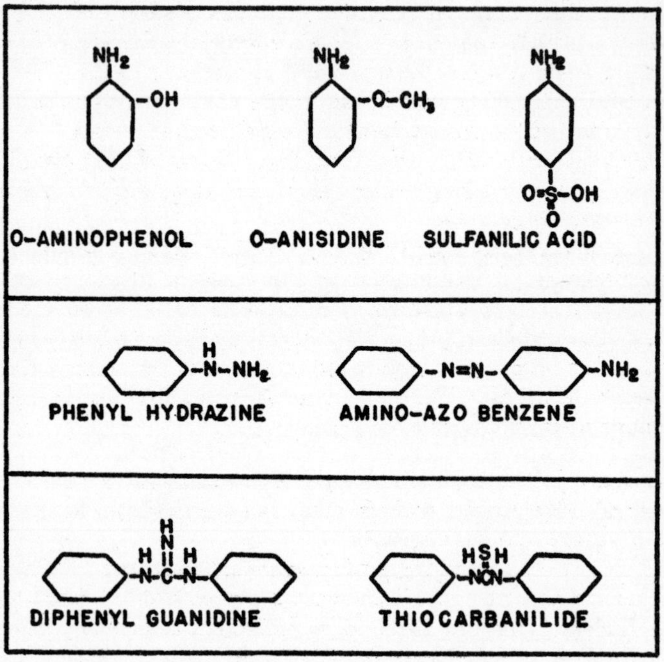

FIGURE 14. — Structural formulae of several aniline derivatives.

amide, a sulfa drug, the fungistatic properties of which, as already discussed, are not remarkable.

One of the interesting properties of aniline is that an extra amine group adds toxicity. An extra NH_2 can be added in juxtaposition to the one already present as in phenyl hydrazine (Fig. 14). This juxtaposition of two nitrogens looks significant. It may be responsible in part for the toxicity of 1-phenyl thiosemicarbazide (see Fig. 10), although this compound has the toxic C = S grouping as discussed in the previous chapter on sulfur. Two juxtaposed nitrogens occur also in the azo compounds such as amino-azo benzene (Fig. 14), many of which are fungicidal or fungistatic.

If the harmonious relation between the twin nitrogens is split by another group, however, the toxicity is reduced or eliminated. The two nitrogens of amino azo benzene are separated in effect by a substituted methyl group in diphenyl guanidine (Fig. 14), and the potency drops. MARSH (1938) has shown that triphenyl guanidine and diortho tolyl guanidine are only mildly toxic. Diphenyl guanidine phthalate in our tests proved non-toxic.

Similarly, the two nitrogens are separated by a C = S group in thiocarbanilide (Fig. 14). The toxicity is seriously reduced. What is left may justifiably be ascribed to the toxic C = S group.

Two nitrogens can be separated by a benzene ring as in p-phenylene diamine $NH_2 — \phi — NH_2$ and the toxicity is reduced.

Oximes: — A fairly common group with trivalent nitrogen is the oxime, NOH. Many oximes have been tested here, but only three toxic ones have been found: salicylaldoxime, p- and o-quinone dioximes. o-Quinone dioxime is somewhat more fungicidal than p-quinone dioxime (see Fig. 19 in next chapter). They are somewhat unstable in the field and may not ever arrive at commercial development. Another interesting development is o-benzoquinone dionium peroxide, which makes an excellent seed protectant. It was developed at the Geneva, New York, Experiment Station parallel to Spergon. It has been tested as Spergonex.

Cyanide Derivatives: — Many fungicides are also insecticidal. Cyanides are nitrogen compounds that discourage insects seriously without affecting fungi greatly. $H — C \equiv N$ is the simplest form. This nitrogen even though tied three ways to carbon is not fungicidal. Hydrocyanic acid may also be called formonitrile. Entomologists have found other nitriles like phthalonitrile to be useful, but it also is not fungicidal. Neither is acetonitrile, propionitrile, succinonitrile, benzonitrile. Alpha and beta naphthonitrile are mildly fungistatic, however, presumably because of the naphthol nucleus, or because the number of carbon atoms approaches 12 as discussed later.

The addition of sulfur to cyanide forms thiocyanate $— S — C \equiv N$, which has shown much promise in organic combinations as an insecticide. The three bonds between carbon and nitrogen are maintained. Dozens of these have been tested here as fungicides, but few have shown any real promise. Not even the sulfur imparts toxicity, presumably because it is $— S —$. The isomeric compound, isothiocyanate, $— N = C = S$, proves to be toxic to fungi, however. The toxicity is probably due not to the nitrogen, but to the sulfur, which occurs in the toxic combination C = S, already discussed in the previous chapter on sulfur. The isothiocyanates are both insecticidal and fungicidal.

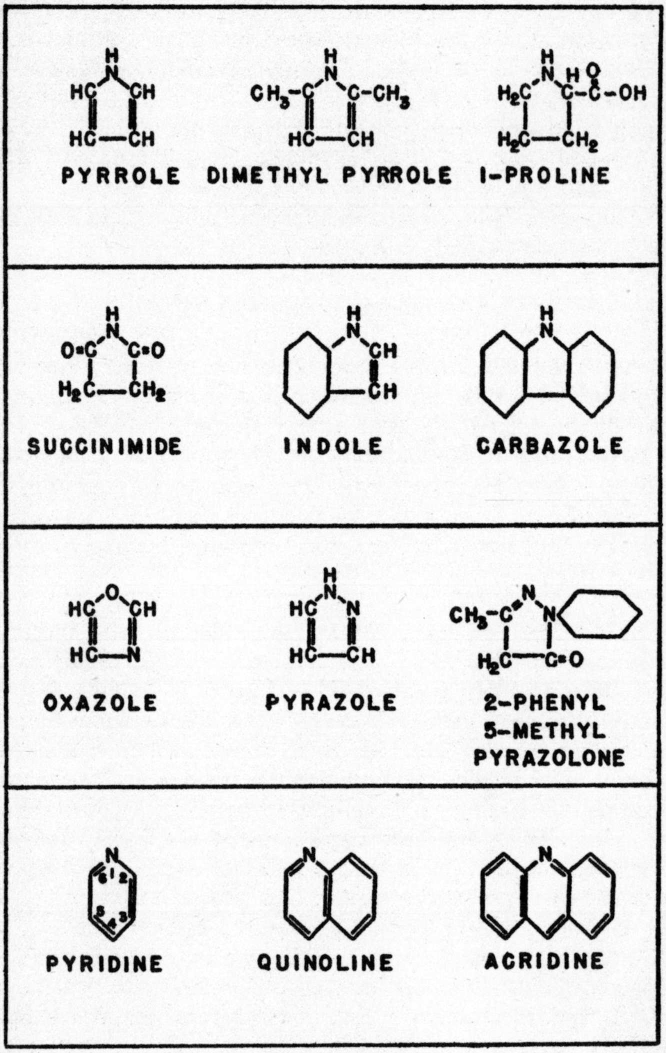

FIGURE 15. — Structural formulae of several heterocyclic nitrogen compounds.

Heterocyclic Nitrogen Compounds: — Heterocyclic trivalent nitrogen compounds occur commonly in nature. An extensive study of the fungistatic properties of these has been made here. The five-membered ring is pyrrole (Fig. 15). It is a mild fungistat. 2,5-Dimethyl pyrrole and dimethyl pyrrole ethane also are fungistatic. Hydrogenation apparently reduces potency. Pyrrolidine alpha carboxylic acid or 1-proline (Fig. 15) is not toxic despite the carboxyl group. Likewise succinimide (Fig. 15) is not toxic despite the carbonyl groups. Moreover, neither indole (benzopyrrole) nor carbazole (Fig. 15) is toxic.

Oxazole has both nitrogen and oxygen in the heterocycle (Fig. 15). Two of its derivatives, 2, 3, 4 trimethyl oxazoline and 2, 3, 4, triethyl oxazoline were tried. Neither was toxic. Pyrazole has two nitrogens in the ring (Fig. 15). One derivative, antipyrene or 2-phenyl-5-methyl pyrazolone (Fig. 15) was tried but was not toxic.

Thiazole contains sulfur and nitrogen in the ring, but as discussed already under sulfur, thiazole imparts little toxicity.

It will be noted that only those compounds with opposite double bonds as in quinone possess any measurable toxicity to our fungi and even these are only mildly toxic.

Pyridine (Fig. 15) can be considered as the nucleus for the six atom heterocycles containing nitrogen. It has fair insecticidal properties as TATTERSFIELD and GIMINGHAM (1927a) have reported. It is one of the constituents of nicotine. It has only the mildest of fungicidal properties. It is sometimes used in fungus cultures to kill mites without excessive damage to the fungus. Pyridine may be considered as the starting point for the alkaloids. G. A. GREATHOUSE and N. E. RIGLER (1940b) suggested that the alkaloids in some plants may impart resistance to disease.

Pyridine can be methylated in the second position to give alpha picoline, in the third position to give beta picoline, and in the second and sixth position to give 2, 6 lutadine. None of these was fungicidal in our screening tests. If pyridine is hydrogenated, it forms piperidine, the nucleus of the alkaloid in black pepper. This was not fungicidal. An amine group added in the second position was also non-fungicidal.

A benzene ring can be added to pyridine to give quinoline (Fig. 15) but the toxicity is not exciting. RIGLER and GREATHOUSE (1941) have tested the fungistatic properties of quinoline derivatives in dosage series against *Phymatotrichum omnivorum* in culture. The slopes for the various derivatives are not parallel. This fact suggests that they act differently.

The addition of — OH to quinoline in the eighth position raises the fungistatic value enormously, presumably because the — OH provides a replaceable hydrogen as in phenol. The situation is in sharp contrast, however, to that in phenothiazone, where, as already discussed, the addition of — OH in the seventh position knocks out the toxicity. According to the tests of RIGLER and GREATHOUSE (1941), the addition of — OH to quinoline in the two position is much less valuable, however. In fact, it is hardly fungistatic at all. Our tests confirm this result.

Of course, 8-hydroxyquinoline has been used for many years as a bacteriostatic substance. HILTNER (1914) used it as a treatment for wheat seed 30 years ago. Recently, it has shown promise, as mentioned in Chapter X, as a chemotherapeutic agent for vascular diseases of plants.

Acridine is pyridine with a benzene ring on either side (Fig. 15). This compound has fungistatic properties. This may seem strange since pyridine and quinoline are so weak. Possibly the answer lies in the fact that the ring on the right bears an ortho-quinoid relation to the pyridine nucleus. Quinoline has no quinoid structure. The quinoid structure will be discussed in more detail in the next chapter.

Quaternary Ammonium Compounds: — Nitrogen may assume four valences with even a fifth so-called electrovalence in the quaternary ammonium type of nitrogen compound. Toxicity is the rule among compounds in this interesting and significant group, possibly because the nitrogen is not acting its usual 3-valent conservative role. Research in this group has just begun to roll at present.

A. L. RAWLINS et al. (1942) say that the germicidal properties of the quaternary ammonium salts were neglected until G. DOMAGK's (1935) report on long-chain quaternary ammonium compounds. DOMAGK is the father of sulfa drugs. DOMAGK was late on quaternary ammonium salts, however. C. H. RICHARDSON and C. R. SMITH (1923) twelve years earlier had given an account of their aphicidal power showing that on a molar basis the tetramethyl ammonium chloride (Fig. 16) is seven times as toxic as the tetraethyl compound. TATTERSFIELD and GIMINGHAM (1927a) tested many derivatives against aphids. They gave dosage-response data which show that the slopes are parallel for tetramethyl ammonium chloride and tetraethyl ammonium chloride. This suggests that the inherent toxicity is equal but that availability differs. The LD 50 values were 0.00135 and 0.0060 M per liter of spray, respectively. Thus we note that the methyl derivative is about $4\frac{1}{2}$ times as toxic as the ethyl.

DOMAGK's quaternary ammonium compounds are surface-active, *i.e.*, they are soap-like. They have been used for some years in the textile industry as wetting agents.

DOMAGK (1935) proposed Zephiran to disinfest human skin. This may be called alkyl dimethyl benzyl ammonium chloride. Others in this group of compounds that are on the market are Triton K12 (lauryl dimethyl benzyl ammonium chloride), Triton K60 (alkyl dimethyl benzyl ammonium chloride), Hydrocide (alkyl hydroxy benzyl dimethyl ammonium phosphate), Retarder LA (stearyl trimethyl ammonium bromide). B. F. MILLER and Z. BAKER (1940) reported on the bactericidal properties of these. All have been found to be fungistatic in our laboratory.

Sometimes two of the four valences are tied up in a heterocycle. Perhaps the earliest known of this type is an acridinium derivative. It is acriflavine hydrochloride (Fig. 16). According to

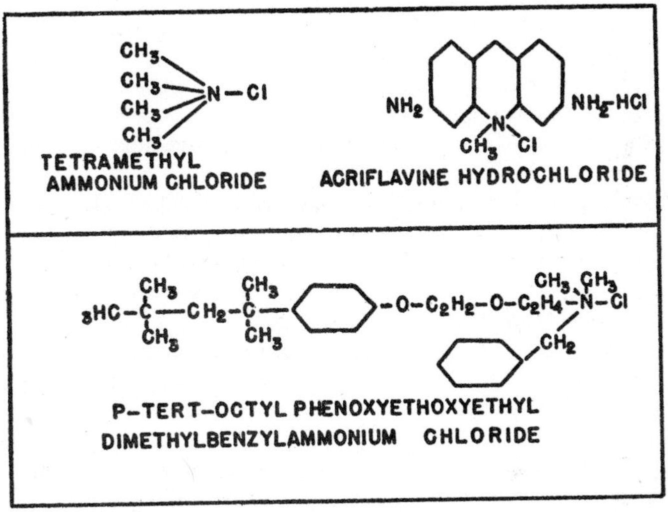

FIGURE 16. — Structural formulae of three quaternary ammonium compounds.

G. L. JENKINS and W. H. HARTUNG (1943), it was used as a wound antiseptic during World War I. This of course, was ahead of C. H. RICHARDSON and C. R. SMITH (1923). Another one of these heterocyclic quaternary nitrogen compounds that has bactericidal properties is cetyl pyridinium chloride. The bactericidal properties of this material have been reported by SHELTON (Abs. 99th meeting Amer. Chem. Soc., 1940).

A characteristic of all these compounds will be noted. They have an acidic radical, like chloride, or other anion. The major part of the molecule occurs in the positive ion or cation. Hence they are called cationic compounds or cationic detergents. They are, therefore, basic and presumably combine tightly with negative materials, such as fungous hyphae and textiles.

F. L. HOWARD and H. L. KEIL (1943) were the first plant pathologists to have published on the materials. They note that the compounds possess steep dosage-response curves. This seems to be characteristic of them, because all we have tested show very steep curves. Apparently, the curves are all parallel, indicating that the substituents have no influence on the mode of action. If they have an influence, it is probably concerned with availability, not inherent toxicity. The curves plotted from data of TATTERSFIELD and GIMINGHAM (1927a) on aphicidal action are also very steep.

BATEMAN (1933) says that cationic poisons show steeper dosage-response curves than anionic poisons. The quaternary ammonium salts are cationic. From this evidence, it may be deduced that the characteristic steepness of the curves for cationic quaternary ammonium compounds is due to the fact that the toxicant is in the positive ion. The compounds are surface active too. It has been shown in Chapter VII on coverage that surface active compounds may steepen dosage-response curves by improving coverage.

A large number of fungistatic dyes like malachite green, auramine O, acridine yellow, crystal violet are also quaternary ammonium derivatives. Part of the fungistatic properties of methylene blue, discussed in the previous chapter on sulfur, may be due to the fact that it is a quaternary ammonium compound.

RAWLINS et al. (1942) have studied intensively the complex quaternary ammonium salts as bactericides and to some extent as fungicides. They have concluded that the cation should contain one long chain, one short aralkyl group, and two lower alkyl groups (methyl is good here). Closed ring substituents on the aromatic nucleus are definitely inferior to alkyl groups in enhancing germicidal activity. Halogen substitution in the aryl groups does not enhance germicidal efficiency, but may decrease it. The anion may be derived from any simple mineral or organic acid.

They were most enthusiastic about one compound, *p-tert*-octyl phenoxyethoxyethyl dimethylbenzylammonium chloride (Fig. 16). This compound is called Phemerol. It is acquiring a place in the drug field as an antiseptic.

F. L. HOWARD and M. B. SORRELL (1943) have shown that phenyl mercuric derivatives of quaternary ammonium compounds such as phenyl mercuric triethanol amine lactate (Puratized N5-X) exert excellent chemotherapeutic and protective powers when used in the field for control of *Venturia inaequalis*. The compound also finds use as a mildew-proofing agent for textiles.

Most of the quaternary ammonium compounds appear to be too soluble in water to be of use as protectants, but they will probably find a place in phytopathology as eradicants or therapeutic agents. They appear to be useful also as eradicants for certain insects. In the field of medical fungicides, they offer promise as eradicants for dermatophytes because of their soapy properties. They will clean as well as disinfect.

Another group of chemical compounds whose structural formulae superficially resemble quaternary ammonium compounds are the amine hydrochlorides. The chemical difference is that the split occurs between the chloride (or other acid radical) and the rest of the molecule in the case of the quaternary ammoniums, but it occurs between the HC1 and the rest of the compound in the case of the hydrochlorides.

Nevertheless, out of some 20 or more of these tested, none was without more or less potency to our fungous spores. This is in marked contrast to the low potency of the amines in general. Those tested include hydroxylamine hydrochloride, amino-azo-benzene hydrochloride, benzidine hydrochloride, 2-amino-4-chloro thiophenol hydrochloride (see Fig. 12 in the previous chapter for formula), cinchonine hydrochloride, quinidine hydrochloride, 1, 4-diamino butane dihydrochloride, and several hydrochloride dyes. Wherever compared, the hydrochloride was more toxic than the original material. It is also more soluble. Hence the extra toxicity may be due to greater solubility and therefore to better permeation of the hydrochloride than of the original material.

Nitrated Organic Compounds: — Nitrogen steps out of its normal 3-valent role in the nitro group and in so doing it often assumes a fungicidal role. Often the nitro group is written (see Fig. 17) as

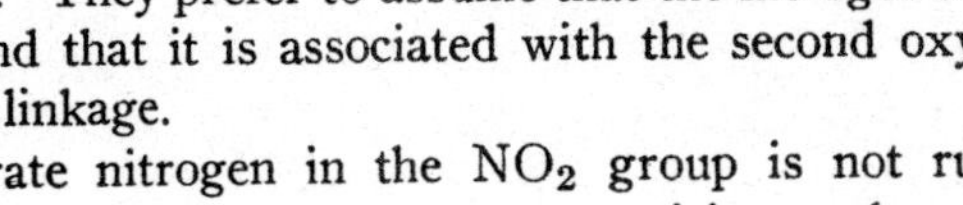

$$-\overset{\overset{\textstyle O}{\|}}{N}=O \qquad\qquad -\overset{\overset{\textstyle O}{\|}}{N}\rightarrow O$$

FIGURE 17. — Alternative structures for the nitro group.

if it were pentavalent, but some chemists dispute that character for the structure. They prefer to assume that the nitrogen has its normal 3 valences and that it is associated with the second oxygen through a coordinate linkage.

At any rate nitrogen in the NO_2 group is not run-of-the-mill nitrogen, and hence it usually imparts toxicity to the compounds in which it occurs.

Through a new process, nitro paraffins have been placed on the market in some quantity. Eleven have been tried here against spores of *Macrosporium sarcinaeforme* and *Sclerotinia fructicola*. None was toxic. This would appear to discourage the use of nitration to produce fungicides.

The same result does not apply to the aromatic nitro compounds, however. A very great number of toxicants are to be found there and the literature is growing, especially the insecticidal literature.

It is difficult to decide who first used nitrated aromatic compounds as pesticides. According to GIMINGHAM *et al.* (1926) the K salt of 3, 5 dinitro-*o*-cresylate was used in Germany in the nineties as an insecticide. It never succeeded as a foliage treatment, however, because it is too phytotoxic.

From literature on wood preservation it appears that MALENKOVIC used a mixture of dinitro phenol, aniline and a fluoride in 1909 under the name of Basilite. Then dinitro-*o*-cresol as a sodium salt reappeared in 1912 as a wood preservative in Germany under the name of antinnonin.

Dinitro-*o*-cresol is a yellow dye called Victoria yellow. In its most recent upsurge in plant pathology dinitro-*o*-cresol is reincarnated as Elgetol, but it is still antinnonin with a new trade mark, this time from France instead of from Germany. KEITT (1939) suggested it for eradicating *Venturia inaequalis* from old apple leaves on the ground.

F. C. STRONG and D. CATION (1940) used it as a therapeutic agent to cure cedars infected with cedar rust galls and P. A. ARK (1941) has used it as a therapeutic agent to cure plants diseased with crown gall.

The strong phytotoxicity of the compound is being used today in Sinox, a selective weed killer. P. P. PIRONE (1942) has shown that Sinox is a reasonably good fungicide for the control of turf diseases.

The nitro compounds have had a long run as insecticides. Much of our knowledge of structure in relation to toxicity has been learned by the entomologists.

TATTERSFIELD (1927) reported that the introduction of one nitro group into phenol increases its toxicity somewhat, with the *para* substitution being more potent than the *ortho*. On the basis of its toxicity and solubility, TATTERSFIELD suggested that *o*-nitrophenol might react differently from *p*-nitrophenol. BATEMAN (1933) showed that the slope of the dosage-response curve for the *ortho* compound is flatter than that for the *para* compound against fungi. This is an interesting confirmation of the usefulness of the dosage-response curve as a measure of differences between materials. I. H. BLANK (1933) reported that *o*-nitrophenol has superior fungistatic properties for leather preservation against *Aspergillus niger* than *p*-nitrophenol. The fungicidal properties are reversed. The *para* form is superior to the *ortho* form. From these various studies we must deduce that the spacial relationships of the nitrophenol molecule are important, not only for inherent toxicity, but also for availability. It points up very clearly the fact that studies merely on some given LD value such as the hypothetical "killing point" or LD 100 are incomplete. They give little information on whether two materials act qualitatively as well as quantitatively different.

Continuing his studies on the nitrophenols TATTERSFIELD reported that "further nitration of the phenols and cresols to the dinitro bodies has a profound effect upon insecticidal values, the 2:4-dinitrophenol

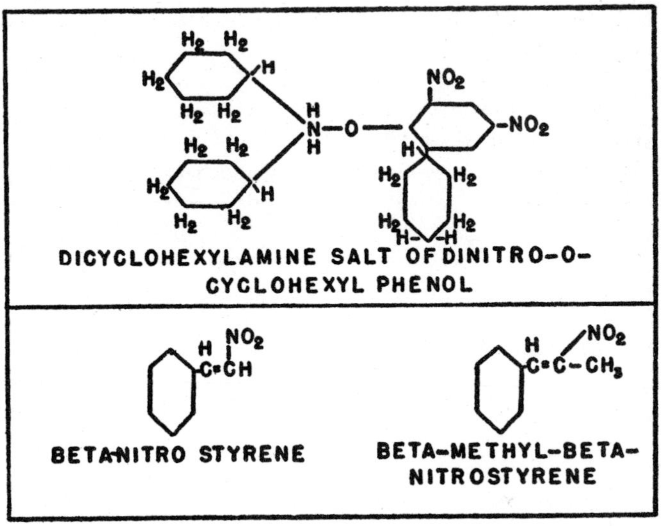

DICYCLOHEXYLAMINE SALT OF DINITRO-O-CYCLOHEXYL PHENOL

BETA NITRO STYRENE

BETA-METHYL-BETA-NITROSTYRENE

FIGURE 18. — Structural formulae of several nitro compounds.

and 3:5-dinitro-*o*-cresol being highly toxic substances". Further nitration reduces toxicity. Our experience with fungous spores is parallel to this and WILCOXON and McCALLAN (1935) showed that *o*-nitrophenol is less fungistatic to *Sclerotinia fructicola* than 2:4-dinitrophenol.

E. BATEMAN and R. BAECHLER (1937) reported that nitrobeta naphthol is more fungistatic than beta naphthol itself to a wood-rotting fungus.

Recent research in entomology has developed a nitrophenol derivative that seems to retain most of its insecticidal properties while losing most of its phytotoxicity. This is dicyclohexylamine salt of dinitro-*o*-cyclohexyl phenol (Fig. 18) (see J. F. KAGY and G. L. McCALL, 1941). Tests here show that the compound has striking fungicidal powers. It has also shown unusual tenacity for an organic protectant and therefore it has shown good protective powers in the field against *Venturia inaequalis*. One wishes that it were even less phytotoxic, however.

Two new nitro compounds that we have tested are betanitrostyrene and betamethyl-betanitro-styrene (Fig. 18). These compounds have excellent fungicidal and reasonably good protective powers on foliage. They have been patented recently in Canada (Canadian patent 417,197).

One of the best known nitrated compounds in the field of fungicides is chloropicrin, CCl_3NO_2, the story of which has been reviewed by R. C. ROARK (1934). It finds its most widespread use as a soil fumigant.

W. BROWN (1935) has introduced pentachloronitrobenzene as a treatment for control of *Botrytis* on lettuce. One wonders if the effect is not the prevention of sporulation. If so, paradichlorobenzene might be just as effective.

Chapter XIV

ACTION OF OTHER ORGANIC COMPOUNDS

Organic materials based on sulfur and nitrogen have already been discussed in Chapters XII and XIII. Here we will consider miscellaneous organic materials and we will discuss what is known of inherent toxicity.

Hydrocarbons: — In general hydrocarbons possess a very low order of potency in preventing spore germination or growth. We, here, cannot measure the toxicity to *Macrosporium sarcinaeforme* or *Sclerotinia fructicola* spores of such compounds as benzene, naphthalene or anthracene and yet F. WEISS and E. L. EVINGER (1932) showed that naphthalene is toxic to *Sclerotium rolfsii* in culture.

B. D. HALSTED and J. A. KELSEY (1903) showed many years ago that aliphatic hydrocarbon or mineral oils have fungicidal properties. McWHORTER (1927) reported that mineral oil is toxic to *Sphaerotheca pannosa*. E. BATEMAN and C. HENNINGSEN (1923) reported that many aromatic oils like anthracene, which occur in creosote, are fungistatic to cultures.

Nevertheless, the fungitoxicity of hydrocarbons cannot be considered as high.

The Hydroxyl Group: — Perhaps one of the simplest modifications of hydrocarbons is the hydroxyl derivative. This characterizes the alcohols whether they occur in open (aliphatic chains) or in closed (aromatic) chains. The OH usually adds toxicity wherever it occurs.

The fact that — OH usually adds toxicity wherever it occurs, recalls that — SH also usually adds toxicity where it occurs. This is to be expected from the fact of elementary chemistry that oxygen and sulfur have many similar reactions.

B. N. UPPAL (1926) has studied in culture the fungistatic properties of open chain alcohols. They are more toxic than the hydrocarbons from which they are derived. According to R. H. BAECHLER (1939) the potency increases with the length of the chain up to 11 carbon atoms. The commonest closed-chain alcohol is phenol which is more toxic than the ring compound, benzene, from which it is derived. Also, it is more toxic than an open chain alcohol with the same number of carbon atoms.

Phenol or carbolic acid is undoubtedly more widely known than any other disinfectant, having been used first by Lord LISTER in

1865 in his pioneer work on antiseptic surgery. Since then an enormous literature has grown up to cover the bactericidal and fungicidal properties of phenol and its relatives. No real attempt to review this literature will be made here. Good recent papers are those by GREATHOUSE and RIGLER (1940a) on fungi and C. M. SUTER (1941) and JENKINS and HARTUNG (1943) on bacteria.

Adding an — OH to a double ring compound, naphthalene, to form α-naphthol, markedly increases its toxicity also to fungi. BATEMAN (1922) found that it was the most fungistatic phenol he used.

Although between them BATEMAN (1922) and BATEMAN and HENNINGSEN (1923) tested anthracene, phenanthrene and their hydroxyl derivatives, one cannot be sure that — OH added toxicity because they used saturated solutions of each. None was fungistatic at that concentration, but neither would bordeaux mixture have been.

It follows that — OH will probably add toxicity to almost any organic compound. Presumably the reason is that the hydrogen is so reactive that it enables the toxicant to combine with the constituents of the living tissues; so that the tissues lose some or all of their ability to function.

It is commonly assumed that if a little will do good, a lot will do more good. What then do additional — OH groups do?

According to GREATHOUSE and RIGLER (1940a) and to FARGHER et al. (1930), when a second — OH is added to phenol to form dihydroxybenzene, the toxicity is reduced. If a third — OH is added, the toxicity is still further reduced. J. C. WALKER and K. P. LINK (1935) found that the extra — OH does not affect the fungistatic value of phenol unless it is placed in the *meta* position in which case it definitely lowers potency. In our tests if a second — OH is added to alpha naphthol to form 1,5 dihydroxy naphthalene, the potency is reduced.

$$\begin{array}{c} H_2 \\ | \end{array}$$

If a second — OH is added to ethyl alcohol, CH_3COH, it becomes

$$\begin{array}{cc} H_2 & H_2 \\ | & | \end{array}$$

ethylene glycol $HOC — COH$. UPPAL (1926) has found that the toxicity is not changed by the extra — OH.

BATEMAN (1922) expected that he could improve the fungistatic properties of phenol by doubling it to biphenol, or improve the fungistatic properties of alpha naphthol by doubling it to alpha binaphthol. Neither of these is toxic at all in saturated solutions whereas phenol and alpha naphthol are. Of course, this finding also may be vitiated somewhat by the fact that he was confounding water solubility with toxicity.

T. B. JOHNSON and F. W. LANE (1921) opened a significant phase of the study of phenols by showing that alkylation increases potency and that potency increases up to about six carbon atoms in the side chain.

The Carbonyl Group: — Frequently, the carbonyl group $C = O$ shows up in chemical compounds. The best known and simplest case of a fungicidal carbonyl group occurs in formaldehyde $H_2C = O$. It has found wide usage in plant pathology as an eradicant treatment of soil and seeds. It was discovered by TRILLAT and introduced to plant pathology by BOLLEY. Despite its popularity in plant and animal pathology, WILCOXON and McCALLAN (1935) pointed out that it is relatively weak among organic fungistats.

UPPAL (1926) showed that the toxicity of straight chain aldehydes to *Phytophthora colocasiae* in culture decreased with length of chain or size of molecule. He tested the possibility also of adding an extra carbonyl group. Glyoxal is $O = CH \cdot HC = O$. It differs from acetaldehyde, $CH_3 \cdot HC = O$, simply in having an extra $HC = O$ group. It is ten times as toxic as acetaldehyde. Apparently an extra aldehyde does not act the same as an extra — OH. The difference in the effect of chain length and of extra toxic "radicals," suggests that the mode of toxic action of aldehydes and hydroxyls is not identical. This should be tested in terms of the slope of the dosage-response curves.

Here again we have a striking similarity between the toxicity of sulfur and oxygen groupings. The $C = S$ group was shown in Chapter XII to be fungicidal and here it appears that $C = O$ is likewise potent.

A relatively new carbonyl type of compound in the fungicide field is the quinone. Beginning early in 1938 at the Geneva, N. Y., Agricultural Station we have been much interested in the group. Tetrachloro-*p*-benzoquinone, under code number 120, was first published as a fungicide from that Station by H. S. CUNNINGHAM and E. G. SHARVELLE (1940). The material is now known to the trade as Spergon. The paper by CUNNINGHAM and SHARVELLE opened a new era in plant pathology. It made organic fungicides fashionable.

A few quinones have been discussed already in Chapter XII on sulfur and Chapter XIII on nitrogen compounds.

The normal benzene ring has alternate double bonds. To become quinoid the ring attaches an oxygen or other bivalent element at opposite corners. This forces an internal rearrangement of valencies so that the double bonds line up on opposite sides of the ring. Ortho quinones can also be formed.

Perhaps the simplest quinone is benzoquinone (Fig. 19). Benzoquinone has slight toxicity, but the reduced form, hydroquinone, has less toxicity. Tetrachloroquinone (Fig. 19) is much more toxic than either. The quinoid structure is maintained and toxicity is maintained by substituting one or both oxygens with nitrogen to form the monooxime or the dioxime (Fig. 19). These have been discussed in Chapter XIII, since they contain nitrogen.

There are many benzoquinoid dyes with known toxicity. Malachite green (Fig. 19) is the most toxic. As more methyl groups are added in brilliant green and crystal violet, the toxicity diminishes, presumably because the molecule is larger. Probably a correction for molarity would correct for the difference in toxicity. This toxicity is fungistatic rather than fungicidal.

1,4 Naphthoquinone (Fig. 19) also is toxic. Strangely enough 1,2 naphthoquinone seems more toxic than 1,4 naphthoquinone. 2,3 Dichlor 1,4 naphthoquinone (Fig. 19) is more toxic than 1,4 naphthoquinone. The addition of — OH as in 5-hydroxy-1,4-naphthoquinone (Fig. 19) adds toxicity to the original naphthoquinone just as it does to hydrocarbons like benzene. 5-Hydroxy-1,4-naphthoquinone is the basis of the yellow brown dye obtained by the colonials from walnut husks. It is said that the colonials rubbed fresh walnut husks onto ring worms to cure them. The compound is called juglone (see GRIES, 1943a and 1944).

Vitamin K is a naphthoquinone. Vitamin K responses are obtained with 2-methyl-1,4 naphthoquinone. This is fungicidal also. It seems weaker in toxicity than 5-hydroxy-1,4-naphthoquinone, but stronger than 1,4-napthoquinone itself. A sample of 2-methyl-1,4-hydronaphthoquinone diacetate and of 2-methyl-1,4-hydronaphthoquinone diphosphate (sodium salt) were obtained from Doctor FEISER of Harvard. Neither was toxic presumably because the quinoid structure is destroyed. Phenanthrene quinone (Fig. 19) was reported by STEINBERG (1940) to be fungicidal. Anthraquinone (Fig. 19) is fungicidal, but less so than naphthoquinone. 1-Methyl anthraquinone is not fungicidal. Acridine (see Fig. 15 in the last chapter) is a three ring structure, but it is greatly more toxic than anthraquinone, possibly because the orthoquinoid structure is based on nitrogen rather than on oxygen. The quinoid structure nevertheless, is significant in acridine because quinoline which has no quinoid structure, has no toxicity.

Xanthone (Fig. 19) has a partial quinoid structure based also on oxygen. It was of interest to compare acridine where orthoquinoid structure is based on nitrogen as a part of the system, with xanthone where a partial quinoid structure is based on oxygen.

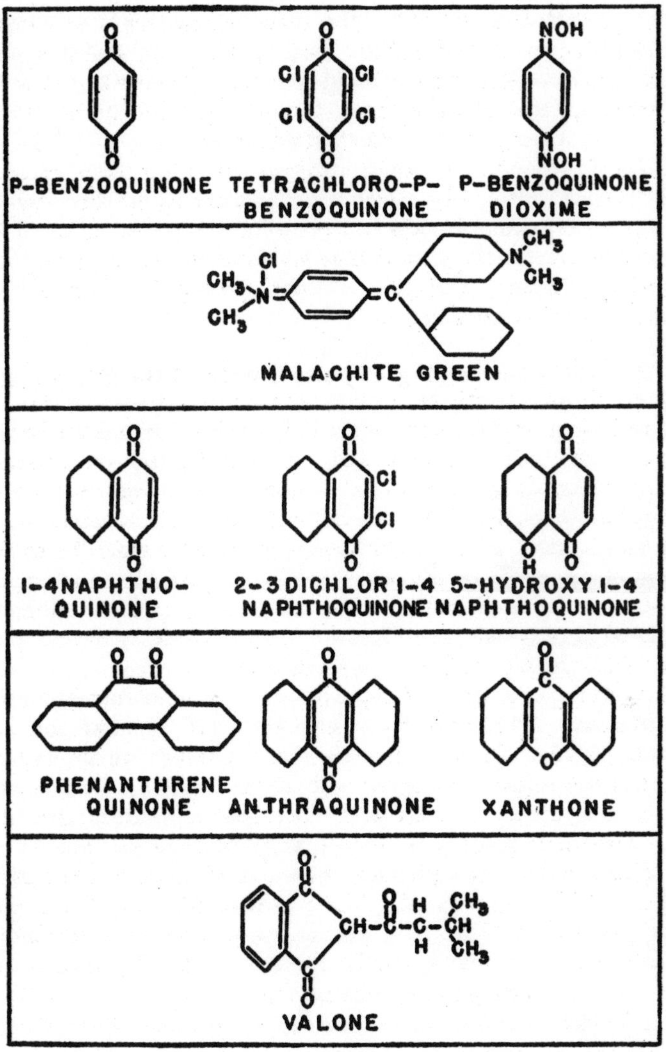

FIGURE 19. — Structural formulae of several quinones.

Acridine has a median lethal dose in arbitrary units of 8.0 whereas xanthone has a median lethal dose of 220. Hence acridine is some 25 times as toxic as xanthone. Moreover, xanthone has a much flatter dosage-response curve than acridine, indicating that the mode of action is different.

The quinoid structure of the phenothiazone materials has been discussed in Chapter XII on sulfur. Briefly it may be said that phenothiazine is non-toxic, but the quinoid structure, phenothiazone, is toxic. Two other quinoid thiazine dyes, thionine and methylene blue are toxic. The former is more toxic than the latter.

A faintly quinoid structure appears in a diketone compound called "Valone" (Fig. 19). This is not as toxic as acridine, but more toxic than xanthone. It will be recalled that certain of the 5 atom heterocycles possess opposite double bonds as in pyrrole (see Fig. 15 in previous chapter) and this is toxic, presumably because it resembles a quinoid structure.

The Carboxyl Group: — The hydroxyl and the carbonyl group are often combined in the same molecule as carboxyl, — COOH. This group makes an organic acid, which is fungicidal. Since the carboxyl group contains both a carbonyl and a hydroxyl group, one would expect it to be more toxic than an alcohol or an aldehyde. UPPAL's (1926) data show that it is. In both aliphatic and aromatic groups, the alcohol is least toxic, the aldehyde is intermediate and the carboxyl is the most toxic. It would be worth knowing whether the improvement due to the combination of — OH and $C = O$ is additive or potentiated synergism (see Chapter XV). UPPAL gave no curves that would be helpful in determining the point.

The potency of a series of aliphatic acids has been studied for fungi by A. KIESEL (1913), and for insects by E. H. SIEGLER and C. H. POPENOE (1925). Many others also have investigated the materials. In general the researchers agree with KIESEL (1913) that, as in the alcohols, the potency of fatty acids increases with the length of the chain. Maximum potency is reached at 10 to 12 carbon atoms. The same relation holds true with soaps according to SIEGLER and POPENOE (1925). C. HOFFMAN et al. (1939) criticized KIESEL for not controlling pH, so they controlled pH, but came up with essentially the same answer. S. M. PECK and H. ROSENFELD (1938) seem to stand almost alone in refuting this generalization.

The replaceable H in the carboxyl group presumably is partly responsible for its toxicity as it seems to be in the — OH group. If therefore it is replaced, the potency should fall. It does. If the H is replaced by sodium, a soap is formed. A soap is less potent than the parent fatty acid as TATTERSFIELD and GIMINGHAM (1927b) found for insects and HOFFMAN et al. (1939) found for fungi. TATTERSFIELD and GIMINGHAM (1927b) further learned that the substitution of the H with NH_2 or CH_3 reduces the potency to insects and RIGLER and GREATHOUSE (1940) noted that the amide of pelargonic acid was only ⅓ as potent against a fungus as the parent acid.

Side chains reduce the potency of fatty acids as HOFFMAN et al. (1939) and RIGLER and GREATHOUSE (1940) showed, and the nearer to the carboxyl the side chain is attached, the more it reduces the potency.

We have noted that the addition of an extra — OH to alcohols reduces potency. K. KITAJIMA and J. KAWAMURA (1931) have shown that an extra carboxyl group likewise reduces the potency of a fatty acid. This looks like a case of antagonism. One wonders whether it is subtractive or potentiated antagonism (see Chapter XV). There are no dosage-response curves to help find out. Apparently the fatty acid acts more like an alcohol in this respect than like an aldehyde. Slopes might be useful to indicate an effect of the carbonyl group in the acid.

Among the practical uses of fatty acids could be listed acetic acid for soil treatment as proposed by DORAN (1928a). Acetic acid in the juice from fermenting tomato seeds helps to combat bacterial canker. Sodium propionate is used as a fungistat for dermatophytosis and calcium propionate is used to protect bread against molds. Recently a new material (REF) made by reacting a mixture of rare earths with formic acid has appeared. It has striking fungicidal and protective powers in our tests.

The fatty acids form animal and vegetable oils and fats when they are combined with glycerol to form glycerides. The structure of the glyceride in cottonseed oil is given in Fig. 20. Glycerides have fungicidal properties according to MARTIN and SALMON (1931, 1933).

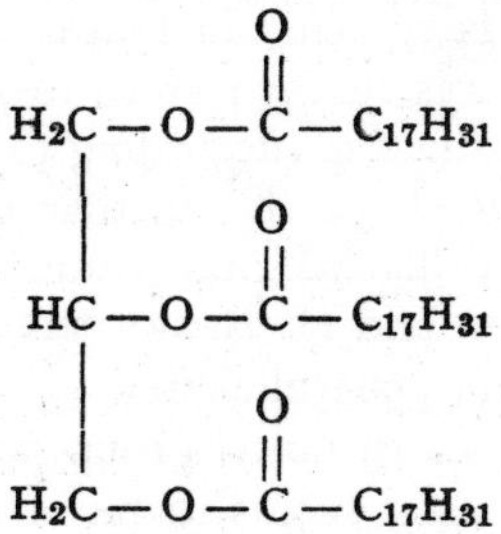

$$
\begin{array}{l}
\quad\quad\quad\quad\ \ O \\
\quad\quad\quad\quad\ \ || \\
H_2C - O - C - C_{17}H_{31} \\
| \\
\quad\quad\quad\quad\ \ O \\
\quad\quad\quad\quad\ \ || \\
HC - O - C - C_{17}H_{31} \\
| \\
\quad\quad\quad\quad\ \ O \\
\quad\quad\quad\quad\ \ || \\
H_2C - O - C - C_{17}H_{31}
\end{array}
$$

FIGURE 20. — The glyceride occurring in cottonseed oil.

The Phenyl Group: — One of the strange phenomena of organic fungicides is that the benzene ring alone is essentially not toxic or certainly very low in toxicity. Yet if it is added to some other compound, it seems to add toxicity that is not inherent in itself. To make a simple case, alpha naphthol is more toxic than phenol. The only difference is the extra ring. Aniline, as already mentioned, has a very low fungistatic quality. If a benzene ring is added *ortho* or *para,* the toxicity is increased. In other cases, however, the reverse seems to be true. Although the data are not clear cut, it seems probable that anthranol with three rings is less toxic than alpha naphthol with two. This situation is reminiscent of the situation in the alcohols and fatty acids where potency increases up to about 12 carbon atoms (naphthol here) and decreases again (anthranol here). If, therefore, the extra ring brings the total number of carbon atoms closer to 12, toxicity is increased, but if it takes the number of carbon atoms much above 12, toxicity decreases.

A study of the diphenyl methanes is interesting. We have already given some consideration to the diphenyl amines. Diphenyl itself $\phi - \phi$ has some small amount of fungicidal quality as reported by BATEMAN (1933). It is used somewhat in wraps for fruits. It was not toxic in our tests to *Macrosporium* or *Sclerotinia*. If it is converted to diphenyl methane $\phi - CH_2 - \phi$, no extra toxicity is added.

A low order of toxicity is added if amines are added as opposite ends of the two rings as in *p-p'* diamino diphenyl methane, $NH_2 - \phi - CH_2 - \phi - NH_2$. Additional toxicity is obtained in the dye, Auramine, which differs from the *p-p'* diamino diphenyl methane in that the amine groups are methylated and the central methane carbon is tied with two valences to a quaternary ammonium nucleus. Presumably the extra toxicity of the Auramine comes from the quaternary ammonium group. Potency is stepped up even more if Auramine O is used. It differs from Auramine chiefly in that one of the rings is converted to quinoid. Presumably the extra toxicity comes from the quinoid structure.

Malachite green already discussed is related to Auramine O. It differs only in that the amine group on the methane carbon is replaced by a third benzene ring to form a triphenyl methane derivative.

Recently CADE (1944) has introduced chlorinated hydroxy diphenyl methanes as disinfectants and as mildew-proofers. We have tested two of these, 2,2'-dihydroxy-5,5'-dichloro diphenyl methane (G4) and 2,2'-dihydroxy-3,5,6-3', 5',6'-hexachloro diphenyl methane (G11). The latter seems to be more fungistatic than the former. Neither gave us good results as a pea seed protectant, possibly more because of phytotoxicity, than lack of protective value.

The new "wonder" insecticide, DDT, is a diphenyl ethane derivative. It is dichlorodiphenyltrichlorethane. The two samples that we tried had no fungicidal properties to *Macrosporium* and *Sclerotinia*.

Effect of Chlorination: — 'A popular example of a.chlorine fungicide is bleaching powder or sodium hypochlorite used in plant pathology laboratories. Chlorination is a common treatment for organic compounds. Examination of chlorinated compounds suggests that chlorine enhances the fungicidal properties of compounds that already possess it but that chlorine is unlikely to impart toxicity to compounds that are not fungicidal to some degree.

For example benzene is not fungicidal under conditions of our tests. Chlorinated benzene is still not fungicidal. Acetoacetanilide is non-toxic and o-chloracetoacetanilide is still not toxic.

Naphthalene is non-toxic and alpha chlor-, dichlor-, tetrachlor- and hexachloronaphthalene are non-toxic. Aniline is non-toxic. Chlorination in the 2, 3, 4, or 2-4 positions does not add toxicity.

Chlorination multiples several fold the fungicidal property of benzoquinone, hydroquinone, and naphthoquinone, however. These are fungicidal to begin with. Similarly toluene sulfonamide has a low fungicidal potency but if it is chlorinated to form dichloramine T, the potency increases markedly.

I. HATFIELD (1935) has published an account of the effect of chlorination on the fungistatic quality of several organic compounds to wood destroying fungi. He says that chlorination to produce a fungicide was first used on a tar oil in 1832 by OXFORD and that MALENKOVIC patented chlorinated benzene and phenol derivatives as wood preservers in 1913.

HATFIELD found that several of the aromatic hydrocarbons like naphthalene and benzene are slightly toxic but their toxicity is improved from 10 to 20 times by chlorination. Similarly chlorination of phenols increases the toxicity from 2 to 100 times. The conversion of the chlorinated phenols to sodium phenolates does not reduce potency as it does for fatty acids. HATFIELD found that the 2, 3, 4, 6- tetrachlorophenol and 2, 4, 5 trichlorophenol and their sodium salts were the most toxic of any of the many chemicals he tested. These chemicals also showed up well in the field as wood preservatives. Pentachlorophenol is the most recent development as a practical wood treatment. It was reported by T. S. CARSWELL and I. HATFIELD (1939).

L. P. CURTIN and M. T. BOGERT (1927) working on wood preservatives found that chlorination of high boiling tar acids (*i.e.* alcohols, presumably anthranol, phenanthrol) reduces the toxicity. Likewise chlorination of such hydrocarbons from creosote as naphthalene reduces its toxicity. Chlorination of the smaller molecules of aromatic alcohol derivatives increases the toxicity. When they chlorinated a commercial mixture of cresols (methyl phenols) the toxicity went up 10 to 15 times. When they chlorinated a mixture of xylenols the toxicity improved eight to ten times. Dichloroxylenol is more toxic than the phenols with either greater or smaller molecular weight.

G. J. Woodward *et al.* (1934) found that chlorinating phenols increases toxicity several fold toward dermatophytic fungi. Montgomery and Moore (1938) have found that chlorinating β naphthol in the alpha position increases its toxicity to spores of *Sclerotinia fructicola.*

Hoffman *et al.* (1940) have shown that a chlorine in the carbon atom next to the carboxyl of propionic acid reduces its fungistatic power, just as substituting CH_3 in the same position does. Substitution on the beta (middle) carbon atom has no effect. Since acetic acid has only two carbon atoms, chlorination reduces its potency, because then the chlorine has to be attached to the carbon atom next to the carboxyl.

Chlorinating aliphatic hydrocarbons makes them very fungicidal whether they were fungicidal before or not. Carbon tetrachloride is the best known of these substances. W. N. Ezekiel and J. J. Taubenhaus (1934) have demonstrated the value of trichlor- and tetrachlorethane as volatile soil fungicides. These materials have not gained a foothold, however.

We have said elsewhere that nitroparaffins are not fungicidal. 1-1 Dichloro-1-nitroethane, however, is a very fungicidal material, probably because of the chlorine and not because of the NO_2 group. If it did not escape so slowly from soil it might make a useful competitor for formaldehyde or chloropicrin.

Mechanisms of Action of Organic Fungicides: — There appear to be almost as many proposed mechanisms of fungicidal action of organic fungicides as experimenters in the field. Indubitably, there are many mechanisms and combinations of mechanisms. Although the separation is exceedingly difficult, it is just as imperative in the organics as in sulfur and copper to distinguish availability from inherent toxicity. Failure to do so has misled many investigators. Bateman and Henningsen (1923) were so sure that toxicity of compounds is due to water-solubility that they did not bother to test otherwise. They would have discarded bordeaux mixture with their technique. They confounded inherent toxicity with availability.

Availability: — At the beginning of the century, two Germans, Overton and Meyer (see A. J. Clark, 1937), set up independently and then collectively a theory to account for the narcotic action of drugs. They held, in effect, that the cell membrane is a fatty emulsion and that compounds penetrate in accordance with their partition coefficient, *i.e.,* the ratio of their solubility in oil and water. The theory has worked so well that it has been extended to many systems of action by poisons.

The correlation is often startling. BATEMAN (1922) found an excellent correlation between fungistatic potency of aromatic alcohols and partition coefficient. The correlation is excellent also with fatty acids and their soaps, according to TATTERSFIELD and GIMINGHAM (1927b). Partition coefficient and potency to insects or fungi both increase as the number of carbon atoms in fatty acids increases up to about 12, and then partition coefficient and potency fall.

Such an agreement of fact with theory is calculated to make researchers wax enthusiastic and many have done so. Nevertheless, this is only correlation. No cause and effect relationship to toxicity has been established. Normally, we expect toxicity to fall as the size of the molecule increases. It does with aldehydes and many other groups. Why should it rise for fatty acids?

The best explanation seems to be that permeation rises, not necessarily inherent toxicity. One suspects that, if acetic acid (2 carbon atoms) were as permeative as lauric (12 carbon atoms), it would be found to be more toxic.

It would be very interesting to know whether permeation of aromatic compounds varies with the number of carbon atoms as in the aliphatic compounds because it will be recalled that quinones and aromatic alcohols whether or not chlorinated are most toxic when they contain in the neighborhood of 12 carbon atoms.

Indubitably, permeation is important in the action of some materials, probably not in the action of all. It is not accidental that potency among fungicides is so often associated with polar groups such as OH, COOH, NH_2, NO_2 and SO_3 These are hydrophilic groups. They are usually tied to large hydrophobic groups. One end of the molecule then is soluble in water, the other, non-polar, in oil. The relative importance of the two ends is what produces any given partition coefficient.

Inherent Toxicity: — After the compound has penetrated the cell, or even if it does not penetrate the cell, we must still account for its ability to prevent the cell from functioning. Several mechanisms seem to be possible. Sometimes the proteins seem to be split up. In other cases, they seem to be precipitated. Sometimes the enzyme systems are blocked, either because necessary metals are precipitated or for other reasons. Sometimes the oxidation-reduction systems are inactivated.

Effect of Unsaturation: — An unsaturated compound has molecules with unsatisfied valences as double or triple bonds. Workers on fungicidal properties of fatty acids invariably report that double bonds increase toxicity. This means that the compounds are more reactive. Quinones have double bonds to account for their toxicity. Aldehydes have double bonds to account for their toxicity. Phenol has double bonds and hence is more toxic than the corresponding 6-atom closed chain or open chain. Of course, exceptions can be cited. The nitrogen in thiocyanates has three ties to its neighboring carbons, but it is not fungicidal. It is insecticidal, however.

The hydrogenation of many compounds reduces their potency presumably because it reduces the number of double bonds.

Splitting of Proteins: — J. TRAUBE (1913) has been battling the Overton-Meyer theory of toxicity for some years, on the basis that permeation and toxicity are due to surface tension effects. In the case of the fatty acids, at least, surface tension is depressed as the number of carbon atoms increases up to 10 or 12 and then increases again just as partition coefficient and toxicity do.

Synthetic agents to depress surface tension are also toxic and even they are most toxic at about 12 carbon atoms according to MILLER and BAKER (1940). They provide a loophole in the theory of permeation. R. M. MUIR (1940) and M. L. ANSON (1939) have shown that synthetic detergents grease and loosen the bonds that hold protein particles together. The viscosity of the protoplasm is reduced. Sometimes the loosening goes so far that the proteins cannot be coagulated. Apparently, if the proteins are split up, they are incapable of organized operations which are necessary to life.

This effect then probably ties in a whole series of oily and soapy substances that are toxic to protoplasm; mineral oil, glyceride oils, fatty acids, soaps, synthetic detergents and many others. Their permeation seems to be in accordance with their partition coefficients, but their toxicity may be due in part at least to their surface activity which splits the proteins.

Precipitation of Proteins: — No doubt many fungicides act by precipitating proteins. The general consensus is that phenol and aldehydes act in that manner. It might be most interesting to study possible antagonizing effects of a supposed protein precipitant like phenol and a protein splitter like sodium dodecyl sulfate in the same mixture.

Precipitation of Metals: — One of the most intriguing of the new theories to account for fungicidal or fungistatic action has just been proposed by ZENTMYER (1943 and 1944). Working with 8-hydroxyquinoline, he noted that it is used in quantitative analyses of metals to precipitate them. *Fusarium oxysporum* f. *lycopersici* requires zinc for growth. Growth of the *Fusarium* is inhibited by 8-hydroxy-quinoline but if the medium is enriched with enough zinc to use up the 8-hydroxyquinoline, the fungus will grow again. Quinone dioxime, salicylaldoxime, and dithio carbamates also precipitate metals. Recent research here in collaboration with ZENTMYER suggests that these compounds may act fungicidally by precipitating the necessary metals in the fungus.

Interference with Active Cell Constituents: — Cells contain ingredients other than metals that participate in life processes. Some of these ingredients may be stable products such as aldehyde sugars. Others such as amines or amino acids may participate in intermediary cell metabolism. A study trip was made by HORSFALL and ZENT-MYER (1944) through the reagent catalog. Almost without exception, it was found that reagents listed for metals, aldehydes, sugars, amines or amino acids were also fungistatic at reasonable concentrations.

It may be contended, of course, that such a survey merely shows that reagents are reagents, but the implications are more than that. They mean that the development of new fungicides can be accelerated by looking for reagents for the cell substances mentioned. The results also help to explain the potency of known fungicides.

For example, it has been shown above in Chapter XII on sulfur that *p*-toluene sulfonyl chloride is a fungicidal substance. It may be that it functions in accordance with the Hinsberg reaction to form a salt with a primary or secondary amine as follows:

$$CH_3 - \phi - SO_2 - Cl + H - NH - CH_3$$
$$\downarrow\uparrow$$
$$CH_3 - \phi - SO_2NH - CH_3 + HCl$$

The salt is a close relative of *p*-toluene sulfonamide which might be expected to be toxic in its own right, but actually it is not very fungistatic.

The potency of phenylhydrazine has been mentioned in Chapter

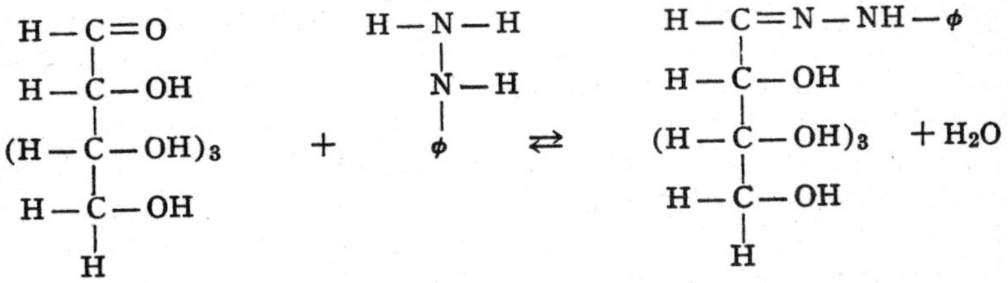

Glucose   + Phenylhydrazine
                 ⇌ Glucose Phenylhydrazone + Water

FIGURE 21. — First stage in the reaction of glucose and phenylhydrazine.

XIII on nitrogen compounds. It seems probable that it may react with the glucose in the cell to form glucose phenylhydrazone as shown in Figure 21.

If a second molecule of phenylhydrazine is added, it oxidizes to carbonyl the — OH group attached to the second carbon atom and is itself reduced to aniline and ammonia. If a third molecule is now added, it reacts with the newly formed carbonyl group in the same way that the first molecule does. The final product shown in Figure 21 is glucosazone.

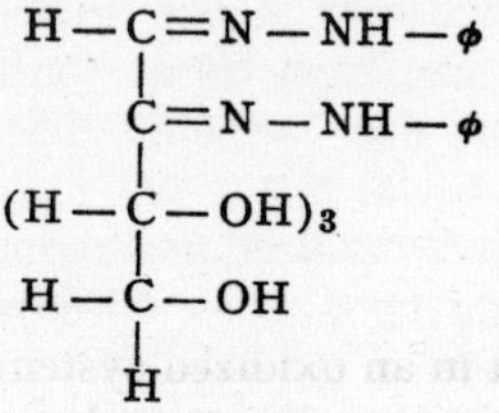

$$
\begin{array}{c}
H - C = N - NH - \phi \\
| \\
C = N - NH - \phi \\
| \\
(H - C - OH)_3 \\
| \\
H - C - OH \\
| \\
H
\end{array}
$$

Glucosazone

FIGURE 22. — Final stage in the reaction between phenylhydrazine and glucose.

It would be most interesting to titrate glucose against phenylhydrazine according to the designs discussed in the next chapter on antagonism and synergism.

Inactivating Vitamins: — Another recently discovered possibility of interference with materials that participate in cell metabolism is that first advanced by WOODS (1940) who suggested that the bactericidal action of p-aminobenzene sulfonamide is to antidote the usefulness of its analog p-aminobenzoic acid in the cell as already discussed in Chapter XII on sulfur.

WOOLLEY (1944) has just extended that theory much further. He has shown or cited cases where analogs for various other vitamins are active against organisms where the specific vitamin is required. He has shown the effect for thiamin, riboflavin, nicotinic acid, pantothenic acid, ascorbic acid, vitamin K and others. WOOLLEY discussed work with animals and with bacteria.

We now need to learn the specific vitamin requirements for any given fungus whose demise is desired and to treat it with the analogs of the critical vitamins and hope that they work. ROBBINS and KAVANAGH (1942) have recently summarized our knowledge of the vitamin requirements of the fungi.

Effect on Enzymes: — Many fungicidal substances are known to be enzyme poisons. Their action therefore could be due to the fact that they prevent enzyme reactions. Much research remains to be done in this field, however.

Oxidation-Reduction Potential: — There is clear evidence that fungicides often act by interfering with the oxidation and reduction mechanisms of the spore. The matter has been discussed in some detail in the chapters on sulfur and copper. This, of course, could be due to an effect on the respiratory or other responses.

Oxidation and reduction are most difficult to discuss because a compound that may be oxidative in one environment may be reducing in another. Until we can have better control over and understanding of such conditions, one can only discuss materials that differ widely.

Many fungicides have oxidized and reduced forms that they oscillate between, depending upon the environment they are in. If the reduced form is placed in an oxidized system, it will tend to reduce it. If the oxidized form is placed in a reduced system, it will tend to oxidize it.

A simple case of such a shifting is to be found in the quinone-hydroquinone system. Quinone may take up hydrogen and form hydroquinone. In the process the double bonds return to the benzene arrangement. This shifting of hydrogen and double bonds looks like the shifting in the vitamin C system, for example, in a plant.

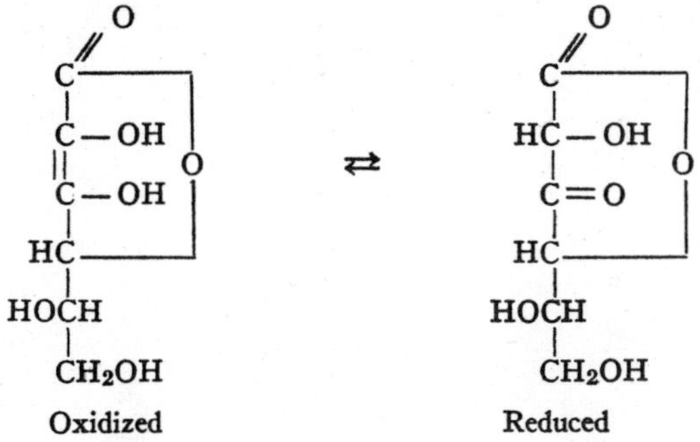

FIGURE 23. — The vitamin C system.

Similar shifts occur in other oxidation-reduction systems in the plant, like those in which cysteine and glutathione function.

An oxidative fungicide is sodium hypochlorite. Tetrachloroquinone (Spergon) is a stronger pro-oxidant than quinone and it is a stronger fungicide.

A reducing fungicide is formaldehyde. The reducing power is due to an active extra hydrogen on the molecule which it loses easily. Although vitamin C is a normal constituent of plant protoplasm, it is strongly fungicidal in an overdose. It is probable that the reduced form of glutathione would also be fungicidal presumably because if used in excess it would overload its own system on the reduced side.

One is tempted to suggest that the striking fungicidal potency of the dinitrophenols may be associated with their strong oxidizing power. People working with them in making explosives during World War I discovered that they were powerful agents to remove fat from the body. Subsequent medical research showed that they helped to oxidize the fatty tissue. In fact the reactions were so powerful that the body temperature would rise.

It may be that the strong phytotoxicity, ovicidal, and fungicidal powers of the dinitro compounds is due in part to their ability to oxidize the fatty covering over the leaf, egg, and spore.

Chapter XV

ANTAGONISM AND SYNERGISM

Today, few pesticides are applied singly. They must be mixed together for various reasons. In 1890 WEED first combined an insecticide with a fungicide when he mixed paris green with bordeaux mixture to control codling moth and apple scab simultaneously. The British call such mixed sprays "combined washes."

Not content just to mix poisons, the pathologists and entomologists add other components of many species and varieties — spreaders, stickers, safeners, deposit builders, etc. Often interactions occur between the various components, sometimes by design, sometimes by accident.

These interactions have fertilized the growth of two concepts, antagonism and synergism. Detailed examination of these concepts suggests that their growth has been more in the nature of witches' brooms than clean-limbed trees, however. Our present knowledge and understanding of antagonism and synergism, therefore, is hazy and incomplete.

Synergism comes from the Greek, syn = with, and ergon = to work. Hence it means to work with — to cooperate. Synergism is limited in the dictionary to the collaboration of spiritual forces. Synergy is used to describe joint action of natural forces. Since synergism is so well established in drug and pesticidal action, however, it will be used here.

Although the basic notion in synergism is to "work with," the term has slowly acquired a connotation of some super type of cooperative action that is greater than the sums of the components. D. I. MACHT (1929) said that one compound must potentiate the other. BLISS (1939) drew a distinction between additive and synergistic action. The two concepts need to be distinguished but they should be considered as species of the generic term, synergism.

It is here proposed that the term supplementary synergism be used to cover what BLISS (1939) called additive joint action. It is here also proposed that potentiated synergism be used to describe those cases where one compound increases the action beyond the sum of the two. Of course, with present techniques, cases will arise that cannot be placed for sure in either of the two classes.

M. T. INMAN (1929) introduced into entomological literature the term, "activator" to denote a supplement which physically improves the performance of a poison. An activator therefore is a material which participates in supplementary synergism. Recently H. L. HAL-

LER *et al.* (1942) used "activate" to describe a relatively inert ingredient which potentiates a toxicant.

Obviously, the term, "activator," cannot apply to both types of synergism. If the term has use, it probably should be reserved for cases of potentiated synergism.

As far as we can appraise present data, supplementary synergism can exist in two types. (1) One component can act to promote more thorough action of another; *i.e.*, increase the effective dose through such action as improved tenacity. (2) Two components can exercise a similar action (see BLISS, 1939) at the same locus.

Potentiated synergism can occur when the components react with each other to produce a different type of toxicant.

Toxicants may act at different foci or on different mechanisms of toxicity. Whether such action is supplemental or potentiating probably differs with circumstances.

Antagonism means "anti-action" or counteraction. Apparently synergism has no precise opposite, such as "anti-ergism" but antagonism is often said to be the opposite (A. J. CLARK, 1933; BLISS, 1939). As far as knowledge goes now, antagonism can be conceived as having two phases cognate with supplementary and potentiated synergism.

One cannot speak of supplementary antagonism, but it would be possible to speak of subtractive antagonism as cognate with supplementary synergism. Potentiated antagonism can be used as cognate with potentiated synergism.

Presumably subtractive antagonism has the same two types as supplementary synergism (1) one component serves to reduce the effective dose of the other, (2) a component of lower toxicity is able to displace another from the locus of toxicity.

Potentiated antagonism can be used to describe those cases in which one component reacts with another to produce a less toxic material.

Antagonism, like synergism, can occur by action at different foci or on different mechanisms of toxicity, but until each case is understood one could not be sure whether it were properly referred to subtractive or potentiated antagonism.

A strong tendency exists for using synergism and antagonism as cloaks for ignorance of the mechanism involved. This is a trend to be deprecated. It would be unfortunate to ruin the concepts of synergism and antagonism by limiting them only to cases where the mechanism is not known.

Sometimes synergism and antagonism tend to be limited to interactions between toxicants. Only one toxicant need be involved. The action of a spreader on a toxicant is just as much in this field as the reaction between arsenate of lead and lime-sulfur.

Assessment of Joint Action: — It is relatively easy to observe whether a response has been lowered, heightened, or not affected. We must know how and how much. To determine how and how much necessitates proper techniques. The single-dose technique will not tell very clearly either how or how much. In general the multiple-dose technique is a superior tool. For reasons already set forth in Chapter IV on data assessment, one cannot measure the effect of interactions in mixtures by adding or subtracting percentage responses from single doses as some have done. KAGY and RICHARDSON (1936) used W. S. ABBOTT's (1929) correction. ABBOTT's correction depends upon addition and subtraction of percentages. It is reasonably satisfactory in the medium levels of mortality, but it undercorrects at the ends of the scale and therefore may be dangerous.

W. GOODWIN *et al.* (1926) found that sub-lethal doses of lime-sulfur and lead arsenate were toxic to spores when mixed. This would appear to be a synergistic system, but nothing can be deduced as to its magnitude.

It seems probable that the air of mystery surrounding synergism and antagonism has arisen from two causes (1) lack of a good method of assay, (2) the frequent refusal to consider an organism as an assemblage of chemical and physical processes, *i.e.,* the prevalence of the vitalistic view. Fortunately, both of these factors are in a decline.

Assuming that an organism does follow physical and chemical laws, then synergism and antagonism can be considered in the same way that chemists are accustomed to treating mixtures of chemicals. As soon as a chemist observes an effect of one chemical on another, he then mixes them in various proportions to investigate the phenomenon. He titrates them.

The titration technique is very useful as we stumble along the trail into the darkness surrounding synergism and antagonism. The simplest design is based on familiar chemical procedure. LIN (1940), for example, took a highly toxic concentration of copper sulfate as a starter in his study of the antagonistic effects of electrolytes. He then varied the concentration of the second ingredient. In general the toxicity of the copper sulfate declined as he increased the amount of electrolyte. ZENTMYER (1944) used essentially the same technique in his study of the interaction between metals and 8-hydroxy-quinoline.

When we come to assay the effect of two poisons acting jointly, we must know the effect of each separately as well as the effect of the mixtures used in the titration experiment. It is best for reasons already described to obtain dosage-response curves for each mixture.

LePelley and Sullivan (1936), and later Dimond and Hors-fall (1944) used an experimental design which differs from the simple titration design just described. Instead of holding one ingredient constant and varying the other, they varied one concomitantly with the other. In effect each is titrated against the other at the same time. The design is essentially that described in Chapter VII on coverage in which concentration goes up as gallonage goes down in order not to alter dose.

The design enables the experimenter to study both synergism and antagonism. He tries to obtain the median lethal dose for each ingredient and for various mixtures of each. In practice, he estimates from previous data the dose of each giving, say, 90 percent response. He then takes 90 percent of one and 10 percent of the other, and then 80 and 20, 60 and 40, 40 and 60, 20 and 80, and then 10 and 90.

The data from such an experiment can best be appraised graphically. The y-axis will represent the LD values and the x-axis the proportions of ingredients — one ingredient at the left, the other ingredient at the right. If the ingredients act alike without synergistic or antagonistic effects, the line connecting all points will be straight. If antagonism has occurred, the line will sway down between the ends like a line full of clothes. If synergism has occurred, it will bulge upward.

The peak of the bulge or the floor of the valley will indicate where the maximum reaction has occurred. If the toxicities of the two ingredients are anywhere near on a molar basis, the combining ratios can be calculated, provided any combination has occurred. This is usually indicated by a change in slope. If so, the slope will reach its maximum steepness or flatness concomitant with the floor of the valley or the peak of the bulge.

The difficulty with all this theory is that seldom is a simple sag or a simple bulge obtained. In our experience, the line has tended to show ridges and valleys as discussed below and as illustrated by Lin (1940). For practical purposes this means that synergism may occur at some relative proportions of the materials and antagonism at other proportions. As yet little in the way of a satisfactory answer has been devised.

Bliss (1939), A. J. Clark (1937), and Finney (1942) have published papers on the statistics of dealing with synergism.

Slope seems to be very useful in appraising the type of joint action. If the synergism or antagonism is due simply to an alteration in effective dose, the slope of the dosage-response curve should not be changed — simply displaced. The reason is that a change in dose does not change the mode of action and hence it should not change the slope.

If synergism or antagonism is potentiated by formation of a new compound, the slope would be expected normally to change. This is because a reaction to form a new chemical should give a different slope. The converse does not follow, however. A different reaction could have the same slope.

The mechanism of joint action will be discussed under the two divisions — subtractive and supplemental action and potentiated action. In order to emphasize the similarities between the two, antagonism and synergism will be discussed together under each topic.

Subtractive and Supplementary Action: — The effective dose is reduced in subtractive antagonism and increased in supplementary synergism. The effective dose of a compound may be altered either by physical or by chemical means. NÄGELI (1893) cites a clear-cut case of subtractive antagonism that is due to a physical cause. He observed that weakly toxic dilutions of metallic poisons on standing decrease in toxicity to *Spirogyra*. Elucidation of the phenomenon showed that the toxicant is adsorbed on the glass walls of the container. The effective dose in the solution is thus reduced. Later work by R. FITCH (1906) showed that materials like pulverized glass adsorb the metal and thus reduce the dose available to spores.

It is conceivable that the reduced fungicidal value of copper in some dust mixtures may be due in part to adsorption of the toxicant onto the surface of the carrier particles. It is interesting, too, and possibly significant in this connection that diseases of low-growing vegetables are often more difficult to control by spraying than those of trees. This may be due in part to adsorption of the toxicant on the particles of soil that may be splashed in some profusion onto the foliage of the low-growing plants.

Another well-known case of subtractive antagonism seems to be that between heavy metals and proteins. This has been known for a long time in bacteriology. NÄGELI (1893) observed that when proteins like gelatine are added to copper solutions, the toxicity to *Spirogyra* is reduced. He concluded that the copper is adsorbed on the surface of the gelatine which exposes enormous surfaces to adsorption on account of its micellar structure.

This phenomenon has a practical bearing. J. B. SKAPTASON and F. M. BLODGETT (1941) showed that derris and pyrethrum powders reduce the effectiveness of copper in controlling *Phytophthora infestans* on potatoes. In studying this phenomenon, HEUBERGER and HORS-

FALL (1942) showed that the protein in the derris and in the pyre-thrum is probably responsible. The slope of the dosage-response curve is not altered by the protein. Hence it can be deduced that there is no change in the mode of toxic action, but rather that the protein simply reduces the copper supply to the spores. It competes with them for copper. This recalls to mind the fact that increasing the number of spores also reduces the effectiveness of copper without changing slope. Apparently, gelatine and spores act alike in their competition for copper.

Sometimes surface active materials act physically to reduce the potency of toxicants when sprayed onto foliage. In these cases the time before run-off is so reduced that the amount of deposit is reduced.

Similarly as discussed in Chapter IX on tenacity, oils may depress the fungicidal action of protectants against spores as J. BRANAS and J. DULAC (1935) suggested. HORSFALL and HAMILTON (1935) have shown that cottonseed oil reduces the toxicity of cuprous oxide to foliage, and E. E. WILSON (1942) has reported that mineral oil depresses the fungicidal value of bordeaux mixture. We have found here in the laboratory that the slope of the dosage-response curves for cuprous oxide and cuprous oxide plus cottonseed oil are parallel. This indicates simply that the oil lowers the availability of the copper. The effect seems to be due to the fact that the particles become coated with an impermeable skin so that the copper cannot escape normally. In short the effective dose is reduced by physical means.

An example of the physical alteration of effective dose upwards, or supplementary synergism, is the use of deposit-builders as discussed under deposition in Chapter VI. If particulate toxicants are wetted by oil, which is then weakly emulsified, the emulsion will break upon arrival on the leaf. The leaf will be wetted by the oil and it will retain the oil plus the oil-wetted protectant while the water phase drips off onto the ground.

The improvement of coverage by extra gallonage of water is another example of an increasing effective dose that is discussed extensively in Chapter VIII. Coverage is an exception in part to the rule that additive effects should show parallel dosage-response curves. Improving randomness of coverage appears to steepen the slope. Therefore, if the slope for a mixture differs from that for a single ingredient, it is imperative to learn whether the effect is a true case of differing action or a hidden effect of coverage.

Two cases of synergism apparently due to action of two components on different links in a chain reaction may be cited.

HEUBERGER (1942b) has described a case in which derris and

cuprous oxide complement each other in the control of *Alternaria solani* on tomatoes. The fungus is carried from plant to plant by flea beetles and it often enters the leaf through flea beetle punctures. Derris reduces the flea beetles and hence it reduces the inoculum potential of the fungus. Then the cuprous oxide in the mixture helps to kill the spores that arrive in the infection court.

CLAYTON (1937) showed a case of cooperative action between cuprous oxide and cotton seed oil in the control of *Peronospora tabacina* on tobacco. As discussed in Chapter V, the cottonseed oil possibly prevents sporulation and thereby reduces the inoculum potential of the fungus. The cuprous oxide probably helps to kill the spores that do form.

Perhaps the most famous type of antagonism among fungicides or bactericides is that between metallic toxicants and other metallic salts. It appears to be a case of subtractive antagonism in which a metal of low toxicity competes with one of high toxicity for the same locus of toxic action. It was first investigated by B. KRÖNIG and T. PAUL (1897) who showed that the toxicity of $HgCl_2$ to bacteria is depressed by NaCl and by other electrolytes. They suggested that the mercury ion was depressed by the action of the chlorine ion which was common to both salts. This conclusion was based, of course, on the assumption that the toxicity is due to the mercury ion.

J. F. CLARK (1901 and 1902) investigated the depression of toxicity of $HgCl_2$ and $CuSO_4$ by electrolytes. He voted against the theory of depressed ionization and held that double salts are formed. Apparently, CLARK was the first to note a bimodal curve in the effect of a pair of salts depending upon concentration. The addition of a small amount of potassium chloride increases the toxicity of $CuCl_2$ to fungous spores. Further addition of KCl then depresses the toxicity. Apparently this is the only part of the curve that was observed by KRÖNIG and PAUL. Clark postulated that first a double salt, Cu = [$CuCl_4$], is formed. Supposedly it is more toxic than $CuCl_2$. Such a salt might conceivably be more toxic than $CuCl_2$ because it has copper in the anion as well as in the cation. As more KCl is added, CLARK thought that the cationic copper is replaced by potassium finally forming $K_2[CuCl_4]$.

One argument favoring CLARK is that mercury and copper form complex double salts freely. One difficulty with his theory is that $CaCl_2$ and KCl depress the effects of each other as any textbook in plant physiology will testify. Calcium is not as adept at forming double salts as copper, but nevertheless, his explanation could still be sound.

If CLARK's theory is correct, the phenomenon is a case of potentiated antagonism and not one of subtraction. Some dosage-response research on the point might help to clarify it.

L. A. HAWKINS (1913) showed that calcium, magnesium, and potassium nitrates depress the toxicity of the nitrates of copper, zinc, and lead. He measured the ions present, and showed fairly conclusively that KRÖNIG and PAUL's hypothesis of ionization depression could not hold. The ionization of the toxicant was depressed as dictated by the theory, but the depression was not large enough to account for the effect. HAWKINS argued vigorously also against CLARK's theory of double salt formation, but he admitted that he was not able to formulate any more satisfactory explanation. HAWKINS made one interesting suggestion that if bordeaux could be made equally as well from KOH as from $Ca(OH)_2$, it should be more toxic, because potassium is less depressive than calcium to copper toxicity.

In connection with the depressive effects of potassium nitrate on copper toxicity as demonstrated by HAWKINS, it seems significant that G. R. TOWNSEND (1942) has just shown that both potassium nitrate and sodium nitrate reduce the protective effect of bordeaux against *Cercospora apii* on celery.

LIN (1940) completed a masterly study of the depressive effects of electrolytes on the toxicity of copper sulfate to *Sclerotinia fructicola*. Using such electrolytes as magnesium and calcium chlorides, nitrates, and sulfates, he found bimodal curves similar to those of CLARK. The toxicity of copper diminished as the concentration of electrolyte increased. After passing through a valley of toxicity, the toxicity of the copper then increased with further increase in concentration of electrolyte. It may not be significant but examination of his graphs suggests that his bimodal curves occur only when the electrolyte carries some other anion than the sulfate, which is common to the anion of copper sulfate. In other words, the depressive effect increases with concentration of any electrolyte, but it subsequently falls away if some other than the common anion, sulfate, is present.

The fact that the depressive effect occurs with other anions than sulfate is further evidence of the inadequacy of the theory of KRÖNIG and PAUL.

LIN (1940) treated spores with copper sulfate and "killed" them for practical purposes. He then resuscitated the spores after several hours by perfusing them with an electrolyte. Shades of Lazarus! Of course, the longer the spores were permitted to stay "dead", the smaller the proportion that could be revived.

The finding was hardly new because as early as 1807 PREVOST had shown that copper-treated spores would be revived by soaking them in dilute acid. V. GEGENBAUER (1921) was able to revive *Staphylococcus aureus* with H_2S even after three days soaking in 1-2,000 $HgCl_2$.

LIN's conclusion, however, was new. He deduced that the copper precipitates the protoplasm and immobilizes it as commonly accepted. When the antagonistic electrolyte enters the cell, it forces the copper out and repeptizes the colloidal system, so that the spore "lives" again. If the spore must remain too long in a state of "suspended" animation before the copper is removed other deteriorative changes presumably occur, so that even removal of the copper will not help the spore to recover.

During the proof reading of this book, the paper by MARSH (1945) appeared. MARSH showed several interesting things (1) that spores of *Sclerotinia fructicola* can absorb copper until it is about 4,000 times as concentrated as in the external medium; (2) that the copper acts to lower the oxygen consumption by the spores; (3) that the antagonistic effect of $MgSO_4$, $CaCl_2$, and KCl is to reduce copper adsorption by the spore and to increase O_2 consumption.

It would be worth knowing if the spores take up the antagonistic electrolyte instead of the copper. The author did not find out.

The depressive effects of electrolytes on the toxic action of soluble salts of copper, calls to mind similar interactions between insoluble salts. It is well known that hydrated lime reduces foliage injury from "insoluble" copper fungicides. For example in one test on copper-sensitive lima bean foliage cuprous oxide injured 50 per cent of the foliage area. The addition of an equal amount of lime [$Ca(OH)_2$] reduced the injury to 38 per cent. The addition of magnesium oxide reduced the injury in proportion to the amount used.

Conversely, cuprous oxide reduces the injury caused by calcium hydroxide and magnesium oxide on lime-sensitive plants like cucurbits according to HORSFALL, HERVEY and SUIT (1939).

Thus it appears that the injurious dose of copper on foliage can be reduced by calcium and magnesium oxides, and that calcium and magnesium oxide injury can be reduced by copper oxide.

An example of what appears, at present, to be a case of subtractive antagonism due to chemical causes has recently come to light in ZENTMYER's (1943) work on the organic fungistat, 8-hydroxyquinoline, as mentioned in the previous chapter. The chemical appears to act by precipitating metals useful to the fungus. *Fusarium oxysporum* f. *lycopersici* requires zinc for proper development. When this fungus is treated with 8-hydroxyquinoline, it fails to grow, but when enough zinc is added to use up the 8-hydroxyquinoline, the fungus grows again.

It seems probable that the effect of the zinc is a simple case of subtractive effect on the 8-hydroxyquinoline. Probably the slope of a dosage-response curve would not be changed.

Potentiated Antagonism: — The interaction of plant extracts on copper fungicides seems to be a case of potentiated antagonism. As early as 1902 J. F. CLARK showed that plant extracts antagonized the action of copper. Conceivably this could be due to the subtractive effects of protein competition but it probably is not, because W. BROWN (1922) showed that the plant decoctions are more advantageous to old spores than to young spores in resisting toxic actions. Then McCALLAN and WILCOXON (1939) sawed out another piece of the puzzle by showing that only exceedingly small quantities of plant extract are required. These quantities are much too small for proteins to have been a factor. This suggests that the response is chiefly one of a vitamin nature rather than of protein antagonism.

LIN (1940) held that the effect is one of energy provided by the nutrient but here again the amount required is too small. DIMOND *et al.* (1941) seemed to clinch the matter by showing that a plant extract (orange juice) not only reduces the toxicity of the copper by pushing the LD 90 to the right, but it also steepens the slope. This suggests that the mode of toxic action has really been altered. On the other hand the result is more likely due to the effect of the growth promoter on the spore population than to an effect on the toxicant. When the growth promoter is added to a population of old spores, they act like young spores which have a steep slope.

Sulfanilamide as D. D. WOODS (1940) has shown is antagonized by para amino benzoic acid. These antagonists resemble each other

p-Amino benzoic acid   *p*-Amino benzene sulfonamide

FIGURE 24. — Similarity in structure of the antagonists, *p*-amino benzoic acid and *p*-aminobenzene sulfonamide.

structurally. Since *p*-amino benzoic acid has vitamin characteristics, it is thought that the bacteria "mistake" the sulfonamide for *p*-amino benzoic acid. F. H. JOHNSON (1942) disputed this explanation.

In the field of insecticides R. H. LePELLEY and W. N. SULLIVAN (1936) investigated the synergism between the toxicity of derris and pyrethrum to house flies. They suggested that the effect is additive and not potentiated. The slopes for the two components and for the mixtures were all parallel. This suggests that the mode of action of all are the same, but it is not conclusive evidence. It could be due to some leveling action on slope like technique, permeation or other physical factor.

To test potentiated synergism the authors used the mixtures not on the basis of equal molar concentrations of each ingredient, but rather on the basis of equitoxic concentrations. They could not distinguish, with their statistics, the performance of a half-and-half mixture from the expected, and hence they concluded that the effect was additive.

The data were re-examined by BLISS (1939) and FINNEY (1942) with new statistics. They were able to demonstrate that the LD 50 values were lower than expected and hence that potentiated synergism occurred. Since this is an argument among statisticians, one wishes that the flies had another chance at the answer. It is worth debating, on the basis of present knowledge, that potentiated synergism can occur without change in slope.

For some years we have been interested here in what seems to be potentiated synergism between cuprous oxide and various other metallic oxides and between cuprous oxide and sulfur as discussed briefly by DIMOND and HORSFALL (1944). Synergism has been observed between cuprous oxide or cupric oxide and other metallic oxides such as zinc, lead, and iron but not between the oxides and other salts or between other copper salts and their counterparts in zinc, lead, or iron. The field seems vast and almost wholly untouched. No explanation is yet available for synergism between cuprous oxide and zinc oxide on spores and antagonism between cuprous oxide and magnesium oxide on toxicity to foliage.

Another striking case of synergism is to be found in the interaction between sulfur and cuprous oxide first hinted at by J. J. TAUBEN-HAUS and P. DECKER (1935). Sulfur has been combined with bordeaux mixture almost ever since bordeaux was first invented. Some have claimed added effects, others not. TOWNSEND (1942) has just printed extensive data on the subject using *Cercospora apii* as the test fungus in the field. Sometimes he obtained significantly more disease control, sometimes not.

In laboratory research here we find that sulfur will invariably synergize cuprous oxide, pushing the LD values leftward. It steepens the slope of the dosage-response curve. It has never synergized any other copper salt except possibly cupric oxide, but it will synergize zinc oxide and probably other oxides. In several years of field testing no clear cut case of synergism between cuprous oxide and sulfur in the field has been obtained except for tip burn on potato. In that test the slope was steepened and LD values were pushed leftward (DIMOND and HORSFALL, 1944). It will be recalled that MARTIN (1932) held that bordeaux contains hydrous cupric oxide, not basic copper sulfate. In this connection, it is conceivable that TOWNSEND's evidence for occasional synergism between sulfur and bordeaux could have been due to an effect on hydrous cupric oxide in bordeaux rather than on basic copper sulfate.

The best explanation so far available of the effect of sulfur on cuprous oxide is that fresh cuprous sulfide is formed, because the slope for the mixture approximates the slope for cuprous sulfide which is steeper than that for cuprous oxide. If this explanation is the correct one, it is another example of substituting sulfur for oxygen in a fungicidally potent combination.

Since the synergism occurs with *Macrosporium* which is not sensitive to elemental sulfur, it follows that the action of the hypothetical cuprous sulfide is probably not due directly to any liberation of sulfur.

The synergism between organisms mentioned in Chapter XII on sulfur is interesting here. *Macrosporium sarcinaeforme* is unable to liberate enough H_2S from elemental sulfur to kill itself. If it is germinated on sulfur deposits in a mixed spore suspension with *Sclerotinia fructicola,* it is killed because *S. fructicola* liberates more H_2S than is required to kill it.

Cuprous oxide and Bancroft, a very acid clay, appear to synergize each other. Cuprous oxide will exaggerate Bancroft clay injury on cucurbits as HORSFALL *et al.* (1939) have illustrated. In the laboratory Bancroft clay displaces LD values of cuprous oxide leftward, but does not seem to change the slope. Presumably this synergism is due to simple solution of copper. HEUBERGER (1942*a*) has shown that Bancroft clay will improve the control of *Alternaria solani* by cuprous oxide.

Another striking case of synergism is that between various thiuramsulfide derivatives and sulfur or metallic oxides. The mechanism of this process is discussed further in Chapter XII under organic sulfur fungicides. Sulfur will change the slope and lower the LD values of tetramethyl thiuramdisulfide and mercaptobenzothiazole (DIMOND and HORSFALL, 1943) but it has no effect (at least in the laboratory here) on the iron or zinc salts of tetramethyl thiuramdisulfide. Neither will sulfur activate disodium ethylene bisdithiocarbamate. It is suggested that sulfur forms polysulfides with tetramethyl thiuramdisulfide. Since the sulfur to sulfur linkage is broken by the metal in the zinc and iron salt and by the ethylene diamine in the case of the disodium ethylene bisdithiocarbamate, polysulfides probably do not form easily, and hence synergism is absent. The strong fungicidal potency of the polysulfides is well known from liquid lime-sulfur.

The explanation of activation by metallic oxides is less well understood. Zinc oxide will definitely synergize tetramethyl thiuramdisulfide presumably by inserting zinc between the two central sulfurs in the same way that sulfur is thought to be inserted. If so, this forms the zinc salt, but preliminary results here suggest that the factory-made zinc salt can also be synergized by zinc oxide. Mercaptobenzothiazole is antagonized, however, by zinc oxide presumably by the formation of the zinc salt which can be shown to be essentially without fungicidal value.

DIMOND and HORSFALL (1943) have suggested a practical application of this fact. Rubberized fabrics are decomposed rapidly in the tropics by bacterial action. They suggest that rubber made with tetramethyl thiuramdisulfide and zinc oxide will probably be much more resistant to decomposition than rubber prepared with mercaptobenzothiazole and zinc oxide.

Zinc oxide will synergize the iron salt and it may also synergize disodium ethylene bisdithiocarbamate. HEUBERGER and MANNS (1943) have shown this also in the field on *Alternaria solani* with a zinc-sulfate lime mixture added to disodium ethylene bisdithiocarbamate.

Calcium oxide will synergize the iron salt in the laboratory and in the field as J. M. HAMILTON, D. H. PALMITER and L. O. WEAVER have shown (1943). Likewise lead arsenate will synergize the iron salt and also disodium ethylene bisdithiocarbamate in the field probably by means of the lead oxide that presumably forms slowly as lead arsenate weathers.

An interesting pair of related cases has come to light recently of synergism in phytotoxicity. For years copper fungicides and nicotine were thought to be compatible. K. J. KADOW *et al.* (1939) ended all that when they showed that fixed nicotine increased copper injury from insoluble copper materials. Since they used no dosage studies it would be difficult to decide whether the effect was supplementary or potentiated synergism.

A case of potentiated synergism in phytotoxicity has come to light recently. CURTIS (1944*a*) showed that plants may excrete fair amounts of ammonia in guttation water. When such guttation water is added to spray deposits of bordeaux mixture and cuprous oxide, the slope of the dosage-response curve is steepened and the LD values are displaced to the left. Artificial guttation water made with ammonia responded similarly.

Presumably the ammonia forms the complex ammonium copper ion which is more toxic than cuprous oxide. This matter will be discussed in more detail in the next chapter.

Chapter XVI

PHYTOTOXICITY

By definition a fungicide is a chemical to kill fungi. A fungus is a plant. Hence a fungicide is a chemical to kill plants. Host plants are no exception. Fungicides can kill or injure host plants.

Phytotoxicity is a term to describe the injuriousness of fungicides to host plants. Formerly the concept was called phytocidal, but since that term implies death, it has been dropped because usually the injury stops short of death.

Basically, of course, the term phytotoxicity covers injuriousness to all plants including fungi, but for our purposes here, it will be limited to toxicity of fungicides to host plants. Phytotoxicity will be discussed from the standpoint of the plant and its reactions as well as from the standpoint of the mechanism of injury.

Symptoms: — Perhaps the most striking, and, therefore, the most commonly observed symptom of phytotoxicity is spotting of treated tissue. Materials that contain heavy metals such as copper produce numerous, rather definite spots on foliage. In the case of copper, these spots are characteristically minute and red or brown colored. Rosaceous plants respond with reddish spots followed by yellowing and abscission of the foliage. L. C. P. KERLING (1928) examined these spots histologically and reported that the main change from normal is that the cells collapse and die. The host does not attempt to wall off the injured area except in the case of peach which walls off almost any injury to the leaf. The tissue inside the wall falls out and a "shot hole" results.

Heavy metals such as copper and zinc produce russeting on fruits especially apples, but also occasionally on tomatoes. H. P. BELL (1941) has studied the histology of russeting by copper on apple fruits. The copper appears to travel down through a trichome into the cell beneath, which then dies. When these cells die, the surrounding tissue walls them off with cork, which in addition to the dead cells themselves, forms the basis for the russet. Sulfur-lead arsenate mixtures also may cause russet.

Leaf scorch and fruit scald are symptoms of high temperature injury from sulfur fungicides. Often fruit scald occurs on fruit in the sun. Likewise copper materials may scorch the edges of cucumber leaves.

Dwarfing is an important symptom. Plants often may show no other symptoms, but the dwarfing may escape casual observation unless untreated plants are immediately adjacent. If the untreated plants happen to be dwarfed also by insects or diseases, the dwarfing of the sprayed plants may still escape detection. The stunting effect of bordeaux mixture on potatoes, as HORSFALL and TURNER (1943) have just shown, escaped notice for 50 years or more in some areas of the northeastern United States because it was matched by equal or more serious stunting from pests.

Cucurbits also are seriously dwarfed by bordeaux mixture as HORSFALL, HERVEY, and SUIT (1939) have shown. In the case of apple, the growth of shoot, leaf, wood, and fruit may be reduced by both lime-sulfur and bordeaux mixture as W. C. DUTTON (1932b) has so well described. D. F. FISHER (1922) has shown that bordeaux mixture dwarfs cherry fruits. Rose growers are often concerned by the fact that sulfur materials reduce growth and especially the "breaking" of new flower buds. Mercury and copper materials as seed treatments dwarf lima bean seedlings. In fact, copper may dwarf many seedlings like cabbage, *Dianthus* and others.

Sometimes the dwarfing effect continues over into the second generation like the Biblical reference to diseases that may be visited on the fathers and on the children. R. BONDE *et al.* (1929) have shown and we have confirmed that potato plants from tubers borne by bordeaux-sprayed vines may be dwarfed. P. H. GREGORY (1940) has found, too, that shoots growing from bulbs sprayed the previous season may be dwarfed. If apple tissue is seriously injured by sulfur one season, blossoming may be reduced the next.

Presumably the growth materials are so immobilized in the tuber or bulb that they cannot move normally to aid in growth.

Bordeaux mixture and lime-sulfur may so injure leaves as to cause them to grow into fantastic shapes. This has been illustrated for cucumbers by HORSFALL, HERVEY, and SUIT (1939) and for apples by DUTTON (1932a). The cause of the deformation is the death of a small segment of the margin of a young leaf. Subsequent growth of the rest of the leaf produces a monstrosity. H. C. YOUNG and R. C. WALTON (1925) called this "gooseneck".

It may well be that new and as yet unheard of symptoms of chemical injury may arise from the organic fungicides now being put on the market. Sodium chlorate as a soil treatment may cause leaves of seedlings to assume a tubular shape. D. D. FORSYTH and M. L. SCHUSTER (1943) have just shown that chloranil, an oxidizer like sodium chlorate, produces a similar monstrosity on leaves of flax if treated seeds are cracked so as to allow penetration.

Sometimes bordeaux-sprayed tomato fruits look like toy balloons tied around from top to bottom with strings. Apparently, the spray prevents growth of the parenchymatous tissue of the core and the locule walls. The locules themselves continue to swell with juice and this puffs them out in bloated form. This phenomenon has been investigated by HORSFALL, MAGIE and SUIT (1938).

Leaves frequently roll upward as a result of heavy metal injury. This has been observed from copper on tomato leaves and it also occurs from zinc injury on apples. The symptom indicates that the palisade tissue expands less rapidly than the mesophyll tissue. In fact, K. D. MENZEL (1935) has given cytological evidence for this.

Leaves may develop a peculiar harshness and stiffness, especially from bordeaux mixture and other copper salts. At times this may become so severe that the leaf will crack when squeezed lightly in the hand. In 1941 a striking example of the hardening effect of copper sprays on muskmelon leaves was observed. These leaves had been sprayed and dusted during the season with various "fixed" copper materials and bordeaux. The treated leaves felt harsh to the hand. A slight hail storm passed through the plots in early August. The hardened leaves on the treated plants stood stiffly up to the hail stones which punctured and shredded them freely, whereas the pliant unsprayed leaves, or leaves sprayed with such organic compounds as chloranil, seemed to have given way before the impact of the hail stones so that they were little damaged.

A sudden August frost hit another field treated similarly the same year. The copper treated leaves were much more severely frosted than the unsprayed leaves in the next row. YOUNG and WALTON (1925) reported that frost was more injurious on sulfured apple leaves than on normal leaves. One wonders if possibly the frost was not more severe on bordeaux sprayed than on normal leaves. H. A. RUNNELS and J. D. WILSON (1933) reported that frost is much more deleterious to bordeaux-sprayed ginseng leaves than to normal leaves. YARWOOD (1943) reports a similar case for potatoes.

Tomato fruits are firmer than normal when they are sprayed with copper materials and they are more resistant to puncture, as HORSFALL and HEUBERGER (1942) have shown. Lima bean seed coats may be so hardened by copper seed treatments, that the plumule cannot break out.

LODEMAN (1895) and F. C. HARRISON (1898) showed that leaves grow thicker than normal when sprayed with bordeaux. B. F. LUTMAN (1916) stated that the extra thickness of sprayed potato leaves is due to the unusual elongation of the palisade tissue. A recent paper by R. W. WATSON (1942) shows that palisade cells elongate as a response to internal drought, and so it is suggested that the excess transpiration often induced by bordeaux mixture may produce enough internal drought to cause this effect.

W. F. PICKETT and C. J. BIRKELAND (1941) have found, on the other hand, that lime-sulfur reduces the length of the palisade cells of the apple leaf. The spaces between parenchyma cells is reduced, so that the ratio of internal to external surface is reduced.

Two years after lime-sulfur was introduced as an apple spray, P. J. PARROTT and W. J. SCHOENE (1910) showed that it may cause fruits to fall. On the other hand, J. B. DEMAREE and J. R. LARGE (1934) reported that pecans hang longer than normal on bordeaux-sprayed trees, and the mixture tends to prevent the formation of the normal abscission layer in tomato fruits.

As early as 1895 LODEMAN said that bordeaux mixture might cause apple blossoms to die and fall. Fruit growers have been very careful not to "spray in bloom" if they could possibly avoid it, and yet vegetable growers continue to "spray in bloom" all summer, wondering sometimes why the sprayed vegetables seem to yield less than expected. Much of the loss in yield from spraying tomatoes with bordeaux is due to defloration. Sometimes as many as half of the open blossoms are destroyed during a single application. Probably most of deflora-tion is due to killing of the germinating pollen grains by a process analogous to killing spores, but part may be due to transpiration shock caused by the bordeaux mixture. Other copper sprays may also cause defloration.

Apples do not ripen with the normal red color if the bordeaux or lime-sulfur sprays destroy too many leaves (DUTTON, 1932b). This is parallel to the situation in tomatoes and cherries which do not redden normally if disease destroys too many leaves.

One of the most fascinating elements in the problem of the effects of sprays on plants is the so-called "delayed ripening" or "delayed maturity" dogma. As early as 1894 FAIRCHILD (1894) claimed that bordeaux mixture "delayed the ripening" of grapes and HALSTED made a similar claim for tomatoes (1895). HALSTED's observation was rediscovered later and introduced as a clear cut case into the literature by C. W. EDGERTON (1918) and the fallacy has persisted to the present. It has even influenced the recommendations to farmers. "Delayed maturity" is often claimed for bordeaux mixture on potatoes.

This general phenomenon has been investigated recently here and it has been found to be due primarily to two factors, dwarfing and de-floration.

Tomato plants set fruits in accordance with their size If they are dwarfed by bordeaux or other sprays, they set their fruit load late in the season. When the blossoms do appear, many are destroyed by sprays. Of course, if the fruit load is set late in the season it is picked late in the season. Often the frost catches a portion of the crop. This is said to be due to "delayed ripening".

Actually it is delayed picking. This was demonstrated in a simple experiment tagging blossoms. Although many of the tags on sprayed plants were carried to the ground with dead blossoms, enough remained to show that the tagged fruits were picked just as quickly on sprayed as on unsprayed plants.

Sometimes the other tack is proposed that defoliation on unsprayed plants accelerates ripening. This seems reasonable because fruits on naked plants are warmed more by the sun than those on leafy plants, but a tagging experiment in 1941 showed that the two types of fruit ripened equally fast. The raised temperature might have accelerated all ripening processes except that of reddening which has a temperature ceiling at about 75° F.

The explanation for the "delayed maturity" of potatoes is similar according to HORSFALL and TURNER (1943). Since no blossoms are concerned in the potato crop, the effect is one of dwarfing. Whether bordeaux actually dwarfs potatoes was long debated, but it now seems reasonably clear that bordeaux is primarily deleterious to potatoes. It distinctly dwarfs the young potato plants just as young tomato plants. Since the potato sets tubers in accordance with its size, it sets tubers late when dwarfed by bordeaux.

If no pests come along, the sprayed plants remain smaller than the checks all season and the yield is reduced. If, however, insects and diseases attack the checks and reduce their growth, the sprayed plants may overtake them and actually yield more.

In most cases the persistence of green foliage on the sprayed potato as compared with the check is due to the prevention of foliage destruction by pests. Part of it may be due to chlorophyll fixation with attendant slow breakdown. Part of it seems to be due to the fact that the plant dwarfed by the spray reaches its production peak late.

Processes Affected: — The plant carries on various processes that may be adversely affected by fungicides. The ones known to be affected are transpiration, photosynthesis, translocation. The sum of these is reflected in growth. Some phases of growth may be affected directly.

Transpiration: — Transpiration is a function of the leaves, and leaves are sprayed directly. Here then is a prime function that should be affected.

The effect of spray materials on transpiration is one of those fascinating biological problems which will yield almost any type of data desired by any investigator. Many of these data appear at first glance to be mutually exclusive. This has led more or less inevitably into controversy where no cause for controversy exists. Most of the data are only bits of data, like field stones of all sizes, shapes, and colors. They need a little sorting and mortar to make a structure, such as that attempted by J. G. HORSFALL and A. L. HARRISON (1939).

Some investigators stemming back historically to CUBONI (see FAIRCHILD, 1894) in the early nineties have contended that bordeaux mixture, for instance, increases transpiration. Others notably E. C. MILLER (1938, p. 468) have contended equally vehemently that bordeaux mixture has no effect on transpiration. Others, as F. W. SOUTH-WICK and N. F. CHILDERS (1941), have held that bordeaux mixture reduces transpiration. All are probably right because bordeaux mixture sometimes increases, sometimes decreases transpiration, and sometimes does neither.

Transpiration has two elements, cuticular transpiration and stomatal transpiration. In general bordeaux mixture and other materials increase cuticular transpiration and reduce stomatal transpiration. The mean transpiration from a given plant is a resultant of these two opposite forces. Obviously, it depends upon the relative importance of each under any given set of conditions.

The simplest experimental design first used by B. M. DUGGAR and J. S. COOLEY (1914) to measure cuticular transpiration is to spray the plants, cut them off, and hang them out to dry like so much laundry. Stomata can be expected to close as soon as wilting sets in, and from then on, the water goes through the cuticle. J. D. WILSON and H. A. RUNNELS (1933) first suggested that the accelerating effect of spray material on transpiration was largely an effect on the cuticle.

Evidence that sprays accelerate cuticular transpiration are: (1) Water loss increases in proportion to the amount of material applied to the leaf, probably because of the capillary activity of the dry residues; (2) they produce effects at night when stomata are normally closed; (3) they accelerate water loss of leaves sprayed on the upper surface where stomata are practically absent; (4) the effect seems to be more prominent on thin cuticles than on thick cuticles; (5) the leaves tend to wilt more readily when sprayed below where the cuticles are thin than when sprayed above where they are thicker; (6) nighttime water loss, when stomatal transpiration can be neglected, is higher for leaves sprayed below than for leaves sprayed above; (7) transpiration is less likely to be accelerated on out-of-door plants (see E. C. MILLER, 1938) than on greenhouse plants where cuticles are thin. Most of the experimental work has been done with greenhouse plants.

YARWOOD (1943) suggested that frost injury to bordeaux-sprayed foliage may be due to excessive transpiration losses. If potato foliage near O°C. were sprayed with bordeaux, it wilted immediately. YARWOOD's conclusion is supported (*1*) by the fact that frost damage seems to be due to a species of desiccation and (*2*) by the fact that water movement in the plant is slowed at cool temperatures.

The mechanism of accelerated cuticular transpiration has been deduced from indirect evidence by HORSFALL and HARRISON (1939) who showed that the acceleration increases markedly with alkalinity and it can be produced by lime water alone without copper. Burgundy mixture prepared with sodium hydroxide caused much more water loss than when prepared with sodium carbonate according to J. D. WILSON and H. A. RUNNELS (1935*a*). This type of evidence suggests immediately a saponification of the fatty or waxy cuticular layer, with formation of soaps, and attendant lessening of resistance to water passage. BELL (1941) reported that he could find no cytological evidence favoring a theory of saponification of cuticle.

H. FAES and M. STAEHELIN (1930) suggested that excessively alkaline bordeaux should be avoided as it may cause leaf injury by destroying the cuticle.

K. K. KRAUSCHE and B. E. GILBERT (1937) assumed a deep-seated reduction in tissue permeability on account of the copper and calcium. Time works against this hypothesis. When sprayed tissue is cut and hung out to dry, it begins immediately, *i.e.*, within a matter of minutes, to lose water more rapidly than the checks. There has not been enough time for penetration to tissues below. Other evidence is available on the matter of the internal effect of copper and calcium on rate of water loss. There is little doubt of the penetration of the materials. W. H. MARTIN and E. S. CLARKE (1929), J. D. WILSON and H. A. RUNNELS (1935*b*), and HORSFALL and HARRISON (1939) agree that second applications of bordeaux to leaves do not increase transpiration as much as the first application. This suggests that the copper and calcium that have gone before reduce the water-losing ability of the leaf.

Applications to leaves heated by the sun are much more effective than applications made to cold or cool leaves in the shade. This accounts in part for the results of SOUTHWICK and CHILDERS (1941) who obtained little evidence of accelerated transpiration. They applied the sprays at night under an artificial light of relatively low intensity. Moreover, water must be present at the time of application, if cuticular transpiration is to be increased. These effects of temperature and moisture lend support to the saponification theory.

It should be mentioned that the plants slowly recover from the accelerating effect of bordeaux on transpiration. E. C. WAGNER (1939) thinks that this may be due to growth in area of the tissue after spraying. This effect was cancelled out of the work of HORSFALL and HARRISON (1939) who measured leaves on alternate days and expressed data on leaf area basis. It seems more probable that the recovery is a matter of laying down a new layer of cuticle under that saponified. Further saponification does not proceed if the leaves are kept dry. The upper leaf surface seems to recover more rapidly than the lower, probably because new cuticle is normally laid down more rapidly on the upper surface than on the lower.

The effect of acid materials on transpiration cannot be explained, of course, on the basis of saponification. More probably this is to be explained on the basis of hydrolysis or oxidation.

Of course, stomata constitute the normal outlet for water in the leaf. Stomata receive their share of material during spraying. They are therefore fit subjects for speculation on the question of the effects of sprays on transpiration.

The effect of spray materials on stomatal transpiration can be examined by contrasting the effects of spraying the upper surface of a leaf where stomata are absent with the effects of spraying the lower surface where stomata occur. Cuticle occurs, of course, on both sides although it is thinner below.

There is good agreement on the data, disagreement on the explanation. If the spray produces no effect on the stomata, the sprayed lower surface should lose more than the sprayed upper surface because the cuticle is thinner.

If the spray props the stomata open, the total transpiration of leaves sprayed below should be greater than that of leaves sprayed above, because the stomata would lose water at night as well as in the daytime.

If, however, the spray clogs the stomata, the total transpiration of leaves sprayed below should be greater than that of leaves sprayed above, because the stomata should lose less water than normal in the daytime.

The latter proved to be the case in our experiments. Leaves sprayed below lost much less water than those sprayed above in two tests. In fact, in one test those sprayed below lost less water than the non-sprayed leaves. Clearly, the stomata were plugged shut as G. P. CLINTON (1910) had suggested. The magnitude of the stomatal plugging effect can be calculated. In the data of HORSFALL and HARRISON (1939), the transpiration difference due to the effect of bordeaux (treated minus check) during the first 24 hours after spraying the upper surface of bean leaves was 24.5 mg. per square centimeter per day. The sprayed lower surface should have transpired as much or more than the upper since the cuticle was thinner, but actually the transpiration difference was only 16.1 mg. per square centimeter per day. These data mean that the stomata transpired 34 percent less water than expected. A 23.6 percent difference appears in similar data of J. D. WILSON and H. A. RUNNELS (1933).

KRAUSCHE and GILBERT (1937) observed that "stomatal pores (of the tomato) appeared to be clogged or sealed by minute particles of dried spray". Further they say, "In fact where the stomata are more numerous, the spray film on the lower surface significantly depressed transpiration during the day".

A significant experimental design in this matter of stomatal versus cuticular transpiration is spray load. Data from H. A. RUNNELS and J. D. WILSON (1934) show that as the quantity of material per unit of leaf area is increased, the water loss from potted plants with functional stomata was generally decreased. On the other hand, the water loss from plants hung up to dry increased as spray load increased. In one case increasing spray load probably plugged more and more stomata, whereas in the desiccation experiments, increasing spray load increased the possibility of saponification and capillary surface exposed to evaporation.

BEASLEY (*née* WAGNER, see under both names) (1939, 1942) is the chief exponent of the theory that pesticides increase transpiration by propping stomata open. To her the fact that the effect occurs largely at night indicates that the stomata are open at night. One can say with equal justice as SOUTHWICK and CHILDERS (1941) have said that light reflectance in the daytime from the white residues may lower leaf temperature and therefore lower transpiration sufficiently to offset the extra cuticular transpiration.

She noted that the effect was produced only by fine dusts capable of entering the stomata. On the other hand, fine dusts are more active chemically than coarse dusts. In her tests afternoon applications were more effective than night applications. She looked at this as evidence that stomata were open in the afternoon and not at night. Actually stomata are often closed in the afternoon. Moreover, temperatures are higher in the afternoon than at night and hence cuticular saponification is more likely to occur.

She examined the openings and found in them the particles which she thought were acting as props. CLINTON (1910) and KRAUSCHE and GILBERT (1937) seeing the same things thought of them as plugs rather than as props.

BEASLEY-WAGNER'S best evidence for her stomatal-propping theory is that such apparently chemically inert substances as washed silicon dioxide increased transpiration. This probably could not saponify cuticle.

Oil-containing sprays reduce transpiration as first pointed out by V. W. KELLEY (1930). Little evidence is available on the mode of this action. HORSFALL and HARRISON (1939) obtained no evidence that the oil bridges the stomata and closes them. Perhaps it simply acts to repair cracks in the cuticle.

Photosynthesis: — If bordeaux mixture plugs stomata as the transpiration evidence indicates, this effect should be reflected also in lowered photosynthesis, because exchange of carbon dioxide and oxygen should be interfered with. A. AMOS (1907) first suggested that spray materials may reduce photosynthesis of leaves. He suggested even ahead of the transpiration people that the particles of spray materials probably plugged the stomata. M. B. HOFFMAN (1932 *et seq.*) has done much good work in this field. Most of the work on photosynthesis has been done with sulfur fungicides and bordeaux mixture. Probably any heavy spray deposit applied to the lower leaf surface would reduce the photosynthesis.

Lowered photosynthesis, of course, would be reflected in reduced growth, and this factor is undoubtedly involved in dwarfing from sprays.

EWERT (1905) showed that potato leaves sprayed with bordeaux mixture are still heavily loaded with starch in the morning, while most of that in the check leaves is removed during the night. EWERT thought that this starch was present, not because an excess had been manufactured the day before by the sprayed leaves, but because it had not been translocated away. He felt that the copper in the leaf had affected the diastase action.

Growth: — Sprayed potato tubers grow more slowly than checks according to G. F. MACLEOD and W. DICKISON (1936), and to E. O. MADER and M. T. MADER (1937b). This is especially true early in the season before pest damage confuses the situation. This could be explained by sluggish translocation of elaborated foodstuffs outward from the sprayed leaves toward the tubers. Other evidence in support of this hypothesis is the fact that more leaves per tuber are required for sprayed than for unsprayed plants. It seems probable also that the slower growth of plants from sprayed tubers already mentioned is due to sluggish translocation of food materials outward from the tuber.

Growth often is reduced by fungicides and insecticides. We have already seen how reduced photosynthesis and translocation plus increased transpiration may reduce growth of certain organs. Apparently, sprays may influence growth even more directly.

Growth is a composite of cell division and cell enlargement. HORSFALL and HEUBERGER (1942) suggest that bordeaux mixture and other copper materials produce dwarfing because the calcium and, to a smaller extent, the copper enter the tissues, combine with the ingredients of the middle lamella and harden it. As a result, the expansion phases of growth are depressed. From the few studies that have been made on the effects of bordeaux mixture in dwarfing the growth of young cherries, it would seem that the cell number is not affected, but rather that cell enlargement is curtailed.

Sprayed tissues, whether leaf or fruit, are known to be hardened and toughened. It seems probable that such hardened tissues may resist the forces of enlargement, perhaps not mechanically, but rather because the affected colloids are not as hydrophilic as normal. Imbibition is depressed and expansion is thereby reduced.

Permeation: — Although NÄGELI (1893) concocted some 50 years ago a theory of oligodynamic action postulating that chemicals, especially copper, can induce injury in tissue without penetration, it is usually held that the toxic substance must enter host tissue if it is to be poisonous (see CRANDALL, 1909). Evidence for entry is plentiful. MADER and MADER (1937a) were able to recover more copper from the tubers of bordeaux-sprayed than from check potatoes. Many mineral deficiency diseases can be corrected by spraying a salt of the missing element onto foliage.

The methods by which fungicides enter the leaf have been speculated upon freely. Perhaps the most widely held theory, proposed apparently by R. SCHANDER (1904), is that penetration is through abrasions or rents in the cuticle. CRANDALL (1909) kept copper sulfate on apple leaves for two weeks without injury even with daily moistening but no injury occurred unless the cuticle were pricked. He examined 6,000 apple leaves and found that less than one percent were free of injury by cracking, insect punctures, or other injuries.

CURTIS (1944a) has proposed a new and intriguing theory that spray materials, collecting at the margins of the leaves in the vicinity of the hydathodes, are solubilized there by compounds, probably ammonium compounds, present in guttation water. The drops of guttation water may be sucked back into the leaf tissues if conditions change suddenly from positive internal pressure favoring guttation to lower internal pressure favoring transpiration.

BAIN (1902) recognized hydathodal secretion in 1902 and the possibility that injury from copper was associated with it, but he did not suggest that copper could be sucked in with guttation water. In fact, physiologists had never suggested that guttation water was sucked back in. BAIN thought that the cuticle was much thinner over the hydathodes than elsewhere, and that this accounted for the penetration in that area.

The probability has been discussed under transpiration that lime often used in sprays may partially saponify the cuticle. If so, it should encourage penetration of copper or other toxic ingredient.

U. P. HEDRICK (1907) showed that copper penetrates through the trichomes on young apple fruits.

Toxicity of Copper: — Copper probably kills host cells in much the same fashion as it kills fungal cells as discussed in Chapter XI. It is probably solubilized by host cell secretions as BARTH (1894) first showed. CRANDALL (1909) and many other investigators have made much of the necessity for moisture, so called meteoric moisture, in copper solubilization. Probably this is largely a case that any chemical reaction requires moisture to proceed. HORSFALL and HARRISON (1939) have shown that the accelerating effect of bordeaux on transpiration is dependent upon moisture in the first stages.

Copper appears to interfere with diastase action as SORAUER (1899) and EWERT (1905) held. This action probably retards photosynthesis and translocation and probably accounts for dwarfing. Copper may also fix chlorophyll somewhat. BARKER and GIMINGHAM (1914b) showed that chlorophyll in treated leaves is difficult to extract. This fixation is probably similar to that involved in color fixation by copper salts of museum specimens and formerly used for holding the color in canned peas.

Toxicity of Lime: — Until fairly recently lime was considered an inert filler in fungicides and insecticides and it was used extensively as a diluent in dusts. The evidence has piled up according to HORSFALL and SUIT (1938) that lime is distinctly deleterious to many plants especially herbaceous plants. LUTMAN (1910) presented data from which the deleteriousness of lime on potatoes can be extracted, although apparently he did not recognize what he had. F. C. COOK (1923) obtained similar data but he made no use of the fact.

The primary symptoms of lime injury are dwarfing and leaf deformation as illustrated by HORSFALL, HERVEY, and SUIT (1939). Since dwarfing from cuprous oxide is much less severe than that from calcium oxide, it may be deduced that the dwarfing is a function of the calcium. Calcium oxide is more soluble, however, and more alkaline, and these factors may account for the difference. The stiffening and hardening of bordeaux-sprayed plants can be shown to be caused by lime alone, although copper and zinc can also cause it. This probably indicates heavy metal poisoning of the tissue, but whatever the explanation, it takes lime definitely out of the class of inert fillers, especially for herbaceous plants.

There are some interesting examples of antagonism between metallic oxides in the causation and alleviation of injury. The antagonistic action between calcium and potassium in the plant is an elementary demonstration in plant physiology. Modern nutrition research indicates that potassium nutrition cannot be divorced from calcium nutrition and *vice versa,* although sometimes they are not considered together. O. Loew (1903) in his classical early paper· on mineral nutrition of plants suggested that potassium is concerned in synthesis and translocation of carbohydrates. Excess calcium, then, from bordeaux mixture would be expected to overbalance the action of potassium on translocation so that it would be reduced as the evidence indicates.

M. D. Sweetman (1936) reports that high potash reduces the mealiness of potatoes, and Mader and Mader (1937b) note that bordeaux mixture improves mealiness. Possibly this is because the calcium or the copper antidote the potassium effect.

Calcium and magnesium also seem to antidote each other inside the plant because S. F. Trelease and H. M. Trelease (1931) have shown that calcium will reduce magnesium injury. It has been found here that magnesium oxide reduces calcium oxide injury. Bonde (1934) and others have observed that high calcium bordeaux mixture is less injurious in the presence of magnesium. Bonde demonstrated that a part of the effect, at least, is due to magnesium deficiency in his potato soils, but this explanation is probably incomplete because Bonde stated in correspondence that potato plants that were on the brink of magnesium deficiency could be thrown into it by spraying with high-calcium bordeaux mixture. In other words the calcium may antidote what little magnesium there is and cause the plant to suffer from a deficiency.

Horsfall, Hervey, and Suit (1939) observed that cuprous oxide reduces lime injury to cucurbits, presumably by antidoting it, in the same way that calcium is able to antidote copper injury to rosaceous foliage. To make this particular triangle complete, Suit and Horsfall (1938) have shown that magnesium is able to antidote copper injury. Hence we have antagonism between calcium oxide and copper oxide, between calcium oxide and magnesium oxide, and between magnesium oxide and copper oxide. Injury from any one of the three may be antidoted by any of the others.

Effect of Sulfur: — Sulfur had hardly been re-introduced as a foliage protectant in the early part of the century when its injuriousness began to be evident. E. WALLACE (1910) devoted an entire publication to the subject. Much sulfur injury is aggravated by high temperature according to YOUNG and WALTON (1925). If sprayed foliage takes a long time to dry, of course, injury is more prominent as one would expect since the reaction is chemical and such reactions require moisture. WALLACE (1910) noted that vigorous trees were less susceptible to injury than trees that have been weakened by deficiency diseases or winter injury.

V. I. SAFRO (1913) and many others have shown that polysulfide sulfur is more phytotoxic than elemental sulfur just as it is more fungicidal (see Chapter XII). Following their work on the relation of H_2S to fungicidal action of sulfur, McCALLAN et al. (1936) showed that many higher plants produce H_2S when sulfur is applied to them. Since H_2S injury is similar to sulfur injury they suggest that injury from sulfur is caused by the H_2S produced.

G. E. SANDERS (1922) concluded that the sulfur passed through the stomata of an apple leaf because injury was more severe when the material was applied to the under surface of the leaves where the stomata are then on the upper surface where they are not. Later McCALLAN et al. (1936) found that sulfur was more injurious to turgid than to flaccid leaves presumably because the stomata are more likely to be open on turgid than on flaccid leaves.

F. M. TURRELL et al. (1943) have shown that citrus fruit is injured at high temperatures because the sulfur volatilizes and penetrates the rind. In the spring the penetrating sulfur is changed to H_2S which is injurious. In the summer the sulfur is oxidized to sulfate.

Much of the injuriousness of sulfur materials, especially lime-sulfur, is badly confounded with injury from arsenate of lead in the mixture. Mention of this subject sets entomologists and plant pathologists to verbal battle. The preponderance seems to favor the conclusion that the injury comes from the arsenate of lead. (1) Lime reduces the injury as R. H. ROBINSON (1919) found but SAFRO (1913) showed that lime will not safen lime-sulfur damage, whereas metals are known to safen arsenate of lead. (2) Dilution of the lime-sulfur ingredient increases the injury as YOUNG (1930) found. Presumably this is because the free lime available to neutralize the arsenic is reduced.

Mineral oil emulsions increase injury from sulfur. Apparently, this was first reported by T. J. TALBERT et al. (1926). The nature of this injury has not been elucidated, but one wonders if the oil does not encourage permeation.

PICKETT and BIRKELAND (1941) think that the cells of the apple leaf are so dwarfed and pushed together that the intercellular spaces are reduced when lime-sulfur is applied repeatedly. Possibly, they think, this accounts for some of the loss in photosynthetic ability.

Effect of Safeners: — Although the dictionary does not recognize such a word as safener, the Committee on Standardization of Fungicide Tests in the American Phytopathological Society defines a safener as a chemical that reduces the phytotoxicity of another, *i.e.*, makes it more nearly safe. DREISCH (1873) uncovered this area of fungicide work when he observed in 1873 that copper sulfate-treated wheat seed is less injured in soil than in a moist chamber. Thinking that the lime was the important soil factor, he recommended that lime be used in the mixture to reduce injury. The fact that protein and colloidal absorption in the soil are probably more important than the lime detracts in no way from DREISCH's discovery of the safening action of lime.

Of course, lime is what distinguishes MILLARDET's mixture from the spray recommended by RADCLYFFE on roses twenty years ahead of MILLARDET. At any rate the usefulness of lime led fruit growers to lean heavily on it to safen bordeaux until fantastically high ratios of lime to copper sulfate were recommended. The fact that atmospheric CO_2 soon reduces the whole mass to relatively inert carbonate, whatever the ratio, discouraged few. HEDRICK (1907) even demonstrated experimentally that the ratio of copper sulfate to lime had little to do with injury. This fact has been reported repeatedly since HEDRICK's time.

Lime is used to safen arsenates and other spray materials. Usually, of course, it reduces the effectiveness of the safened ingredient.

HORSFALL and HAMILTON (1935) showed that glyceride oils safened copper spray materials. The explanation appears to be that the oil surrounds each particle of copper material with a semi-drying paint-like film which reduces the injurious activity of the particle. It has been shown in the chapter on copper that the fungicidal property is reduced as well. Of course, the oil spreads the particles better than otherwise over the sprayed surface and this reduces in effect the concentration over any given area.

Stimulation from Sprays: — According to the Arndt-Schutz law any toxicant in low dose is stimulatory. Undoubtedly, some fungicides are stimulatory to plants. It is very difficult to demonstrate this phenomenon in specific cases, however. When organic mercuries were new they were held to stimulate seedling growth. Seedlings from seed treated with copper salts in many cases appear to be greener, taller, and thriftier than checks. It is a common observation that copper-sprayed plants have a sleek healthful look. If bordeaux is the copper spray concerned, much of the apparent greenness is due to an optical illusion because the blue film acts as a filter to screen out the yellow rays coming from a green leaf. This effect can be observed immediately after the leaf dries.

Sometimes, however, leaves sprayed with copper materials may definitely be greener than checks. BARKER and GIMINGHAM (1914) hold that leaves, which unfold after spraying, may be greener than normal.

In part this greenness is associated with chlorophyll fixation, as already discussed. Fixation of chlorophyll probably is more deleterious than beneficial to the plant. After producing the initial greening, the copper may then injure the leaves, causing them to fall badly.

In the early work on chloranil in 1939, it was observed to induce more rapid growth of pea epicotyl than that of the checks. This could be observed even on blotters in the seed laboratory.

The so-called stimulation of potatoes by bordeaux mixture is a terribly overemphasized phenomenon, if indeed it ever occurs. This matter has been considered in detail recently by HORSFALL and TURNER (1943). The roots go far back. Many cannot be traced. Possibly the first clear-cut statement was made by STURGIS (1895) who said that the phenomenon was well known then. F. C. STEWART and his collaborators (1912) in New York State perhaps did more to freeze the concept than any other group. The following statement of theirs is widely quoted. "Plainly we have here a striking example of the beneficial influence of bordeaux in the absence of insects and diseases."

Careful reading of the paper concerned, however, brings to light the fact that, in the example cited, the checks died early from tipburn. In 1910 when the experiment was made, the Pasteurian theory of disease etiology so dominated the field, that the authors almost certainly excluded tip-burn from the category of disease. Hence they could say "in the absence of insects and diseases". Probably, however, the so-called stimulation was due to tip-burn control, as LUTMAN (1922) suggested, rather than to any beneficent influence.

There are no iron-clad data to support the theory of bordeaux stimulation to potatoes. At Pittsford, New York, where the soils have a high pH and where copper should be short, it may be that some nutritive purpose is served by the copper. Even there, however, tubers are delayed in growth by bordeaux mixture as shown by MADER and MADER (1937b) who are exponents of the theory of bordeaux stimulation.

Like many words in biology, stimulation is a big word to cover ignorance. The problem really should be to explain the stimulation. Many cases of so-called copper stimulation are cases of copper starvation in the checks. These cases often occur in high calcium soils where copper cannot penetrate the plant normally.

The detractors of the hypothesis of stimulation with seed treatments have held that the apparent stimulation is a result of disease control and not an effect on the host itself. The chloranil evidence sidesteps this criticism.

The film of such a fungicide as bordeaux mixture over a leaf may shade it and protect it somewhat from strong rays of the sun. If the residue is light colored it reflects sunlight also. P. E. TILFORD and C. MAY (1929) have demonstrated that a layer of bordeaux mixture over a leaf reduces the temperature of the leaf, when it is in bright sunlight. Without direct experimental evidence, LUTMAN (1922) holds that this shading and cooling effect is important for the potato which cannot, like other plants, turn the edges of its leaves to the hot sun to escape heat damage.

BIBLIOGRAPHY

ABBOTT, W. S., 1925: A method of computing the effectiveness of an insecticide (Jour. Econ. Ent. 18: 265-267).

ALEXANDER, L. J., H. C. YOUNG & C. M. KIGER, 1931: The causes and control of damping-off of tomato seedlings (Ohio Agr. Exp. Sta. Bull. 496 : 1-38).

American Phytopath. Soc. Comm. on Standardization of Fungicidal Tests, 1943: Definitions of fungicide terms (Phytopath.: 33: 624-626). The slide-germination method of evaluating protectant fungicides (Phytopath. 33: 627-632).

AMOS, A., 1907: The effect of fungicides upon the assimilation of carbon dioxide by green leaves (Jour. Agr. Sci. 2: 257-266).

ANDERSON, P. J., 1940: Diseases and decays of Connecticut tobacco (Connecticut Agr. Exp. Sta. Bull. 432: 89-161).

ANGELL, H. R., A. V. HILL & J. M. ALLAN, 1935: Downy mildew (blue mould) of tobacco: Its control by benzol and toluol vapours in covered seed-beds (Jour. Council Sci. and Industr. Res. (Australia) 8: 203-213).

Anon., 1936: *Oidium* leaf disease (Bul. Rubber Res. Scheme, Ceylon 53. 23 pp.). Abs. in Rev. Appl. Myc. 16: 202-203, 1937.

ANSON, M. L., 1939: The denaturation of proteins by detergents and bile salts (Science 90: 256-257).

APPEL, O., 1917: (Flugbl. biol. Reichsanst. Bull. 63). Cited by MARTIN, 1940.

ARK, P. A., 1941: Chemical eradication of crown gall on almond trees (Phytopath. 31: 956-957).

ARMET, H., 1930: Action coagulante du cuivre sur le mildiou (Prog. Agr. et Vitic. 94: 137-140). Abs. in Rev. Appl. Myc. 10: 156, 1931.

ARNOLD, E. I. & J. G. HORSFALL, 1936: Use of graphite to prevent clogging of drills when sowing dusted pea seed (New York State Agr. Exp. Sta. Bull. 660: 1-23).

ARTHUR, J. C., 1897: Formalin for prevention of potato scab (Indiana Agr. Exp. Sta. Bull. 65: 19-36).

AUDOYNAUD, A., 1885: Le mildiou et les composees cupriques (Prog. Agr. et Vitic. 6). Cited by MARTIN, 1940).

BAECHLER, R. H., 1939: Toxicity of normal aliphatic alcohols, acids, and sodium salts (Amer. Wood-Pres. Assoc. 35: 1-8). Cited by RIGLER and GREATHOUSE, 1940.

BAIN, S. M., 1902: The action of copper on leaves. With special reference to the injurious effects of fungicides on peach foliage (Tennessee Agr. Exp. Sta. Bull. 15: 2: 21-100).

BARKER, B. T. P., 1926: Discussion on "the fungicidal action of sulfur" (Ann. Appl. Biol. 13: 311-313).

—— & C. T. GIMINGHAM, 1911: The fungicidal action of bordeaux mixtures (Jour. Agr. Sci. 4: 76-94).

—— & —— 1914a: Further observations on the fungicidal action of bordeaux mixtures (Jour. Agr. Sci. 6: 220-232).

—— & —— 1914b: The action of bordeaux mixture on plants (Ann. Appl. Biol. 1: 9-21).

——, —— & S. P. WILTSHIRE, 1920: Sulfur as a fungicide (Univ. Bristol, Agr. and Hort. Res. Sta. Ann. Rept. 1919: 57-75).

BARRATT, R. W., 1945: Intra seasonal advance of disease to evaluate fungicides or genetical differences (Phytopath. 35. *In press*).

BARTH, 1894: Einige neue Beobachtungen über die Blattfallkrankheit der Reben

(Landwirt. Zeit. für Elsass-Lothringen 34 : 265).   Abs. Bot. Centralbl. 61 : 268, 269, 1895.

BATEMAN, E., 1922 : Theory on the mechanism of protection of wood by preservatives, III. Experimental proof of the theory by means of the toxicity and solubility partition of a number of tar acids (Amer. Wood-Pres. Assoc. 18 : 70-80).

—— 1933 : The effect of concentration on the toxicity of chemicals to living organisms (U.S.D.A. Tech. Bull. 346 : 1-54).

—— & R. BAECHLER, 1937 : Some toxicity data and their practical significance (Amer. Wood-Pres. Assoc. 33 : 91-104).

—— & C. HENNINGSEN, 1923 : Theory on the mechanism of protection of wood by preservatives. IV. Experiments with hydrocarbons (Amer. Wood-Pres. Assoc. 19 : 136-145).

BEASLEY (née WAGNER), E. W., 1942 : Effects of some chemically inert dusts upon the transpiration rate of yellow coleus plants (Plant Phys. 17 : 101-108).

BELL, H. P., 1941 : The origin and histology of bordeaux spray russeting on the apple (Canadian Jour. Res., Ser. C., 19 : 493-499).

BERGER, C. A., E. R. WITKUS & B. J. SULLIVAN, 1944 : The cytological effects of benzene vapor (Torrey Bot. Club. Bul. 71 : 620-623).

BERGMAN, 1852 : (Gard. Chron. 1852 : 419). Cited by MARTIN, 1940.

BERKSON, J., 1944 : Application of the logistic function to bio-assay (Jour. Amer. Statistical Assoc. 39 : 357-365).

BERTOLET, E. C., 1943 : Observations on soil burial procedure (Symposium Amer. Soc. Test. Materials, October 1943, 8 pp. mimeo.).

BEWLEY, W. F., 1921 : (Jour. Min. Agr. 28 : 653). Cited by MARTIN, 1940.

BLANK, I. H., 1933 : Studies in the physiology of molds, IV. Moulding of chrome tanned skins (Jour. Amer. Leather Chem. Assoc. 28 : 583-593). Abs. in Rev. Appl. Myc. 13 : 486-487.

BLANK, L. M. & P. J. TALLEY, 1941 : Are ammonium salts toxic to the cotton root of fungus? (Phytopath. 31 : 926-935).

BLISS, C. I., 1934 : The method of probits — a correction (Science 79 : 409-410).

—— 1935a : The calculation of the dosage-mortality curve (Ann. Appl. Biol. 22 : 134-167).

—— 1935b : Estimating the dosage-mortality curve (Jour. Econ. Ent. 28 : 646-647).

—— 1939 : The toxicity of poisons applied jointly (Ann. Appl. Biol. 26 : 585-615).

—— 1940 : The relation between exposure time, concentration and toxicity in experiments on insecticides (Ann. Ent. Soc. Amer. 33 : 721-766).

—— & M. CATTELL, 1943 : Biological assay (Ann. Rev. Physiol. 5 : 479-539)

—— & H. P. MARKS, 1939 : The biological assay of insulin. II. The estimation of drug potency from a graded response (Quart. Jour. Pharm. Pharmocol. 12 : 182-205).

BLODGETT, F. M., 1913 : Hop mildew (Cornell Agr. Exp. Sta. Bull. 328 : 277-310).

—— & E. O. MADER, 1934 : A method of recording the distribution of copper dusts or sprays on leaves (Phytopath. 24 : 418-422).

BODNAR, J. & A. TERENYI, 1930 : Biochemie der Brandkrankheiten der Getreidearten, II. Mitteilung. Biophysikalische und biochemische Untersuchungen über die Kupferadsorption der Weizensteinbrandsporen (*Tilletia tritici* (Bjerk) Winter) (Hoppe-Seyler's Zeitschr. f. Physiol. Chem. 186 : 157-182).

BOLLEY, H. L., 1891 : Potato scab and possibilities of prevention (North Dakota Agr. Exp. Sta. Bull. 4 : 1-14).

—— 1897 : New studies upon the smut of wheat, oats, and barley, with a résumé of treatment experiments for the last three years (North Dakota Agr. Exp. Sta. Bull. 27 : 109-162).

—— 1906 : Tree feeding (North Dakota Agr. Exp. Sta. Rept. 17 : 104-105).

BONDE, R., 1934 : Potato spraying — the value of late applications and magnesium-bordeaux (Amer. Pot. Jour. 11 : 152-156).

——, D. FOLSOM & E. R. TOBEY, 1929 : Potato spraying and dusting experiments 1926-1928 (Maine Agr. Exp. Sta. Bull. 352 : 97-140).

BOURCART, E., 1913 : Insecticides, fungicides, and weedkillers (Trans. by DONALD GRANT; Scott, Greenwood & Son, London, 431 pp.)

BOYD, O. C., 1926 : The relative efficiency of some copper dusts and sprays in the control of potato diseases and insect pests (Cornell Agr. Exp. Sta. Bull. 451 : 1-68).

BRANAS, J. & J. DULAC, 1935. Sur quelques effets des produits ajoutes aux bouillies cupriques (Rev. Path. Veg. et Ent. Agr. 22 : 13-18).

BRAUN, H., 1920 : Presoak method of seed treatment : A means of preventing seed injury due to chemical disinfectants and of increasing germicidal efficiency (Jour. Agr. Res. 19 : 363-392).

BROOKS, M. A. & H. H. STOREY, 1923 : Silver leaf disease, IV (Jour. Pomol. & Hort. Sci. 3 : 1-25).

BROWN, G. T. & W. M. HOSKINS, 1939 : Factors concerned in the deposit of sprays, V. The effects of pH upon the deposit of the oil and water phases of oil emulsions (Jour. Econ. Ent. 32 : 57-61).

BROWN, J. G. & A. M. BOYLE, 1944 : Penicillin treatment of crown gall (Science 100 : 528).

BROWN, W., 1922a : On the germination and growth of fungi at various temperatures and in various concentrations of oxygen and carbon dioxide (Ann. Bot. 36 : 257-283).

—— 1922b : Studies in the physiology of parasitism, IX. The effect on the germination of fungal spores of volatile substances arising from plant tissues (Ann. Bot. 36 : 285-300).

—— 1935 : On the Botrytis disease of lettuce, with special reference to its control (Jour. Pomol. & Hort. Sci. 13 : 247-259).

BUTLER, O., 1914 : Bordeaux mixture, I. Physico-chemical studies (Phytopath 4 : 125-180).

—— & T. O. SMITH, 1919 : Relative adhesiveness of the copper fungicides (Phytopath. 9 : 431-444).

—— & —— 1922 : On the use of the acetates of copper as fungitides (Phytopath. 12 : 279-289).

CADE, A. R., 1944 : The use of diphenyl dihydroxymethanes as disinfectants. (Paper given before Nat. Assoc. Insect. & Disinfect. Mfgrs. Dec. 1943. Givaudanian, New York. Mar.-April, p. 1-4.)

CARSWELL, T. S. & I. HATFIELD, 1939 : Pentachlorophenol for wood preservation (Ind. Eng. Chem. 31 : 1431-1435).

CARTER, W., 1943 : A promising new soil amendment and disinfectant (Science 97 : 383-384).

CHAINE, E., 1929: L'action catalytique des bouillies cupriques (Prog. Agric. et Vitic. 91: 380-385). Abs. in Rev. Appl. Myc. 8: 659-660, 1929.

CHURCHMAN, J. W., 1923: The mechanism of selective bacteriostasis (Proc. Nat. Acad. Sci. 9: 78-81).

CLARK, A. J., 1933: The mode of action of drugs on cells (Edward Arnold & Co., London).

—— 1937: General Pharmacology (Sonderabdruck Hand. Exp. Pharm. 4, Julius Springer, Berlin, 228 pp.).

CLARK, J. F., 1901 : On the toxic value of mercury chlorid and its soluble salts (Jour. Phys. Chem. 5: 289-316).

—— 1902: On the toxic properties of some copper compounds with special reference to bordeaux mixture (Bot. Gaz. 33: 26-48).

CLAYTON, E. E., 1937: Spraying as a method of control for mildew (*Peronospora tabacina*) and wildfire (*Bacterium tabacum*) in tobacco plant beds (Phytopath. 27: 124).

CLINTON, G. P., 1910: Spraying potatoes in dry seasons (Connecticut Agr. Exp. Sta. Rept. 1909-1910: 739-752).

COHEE, R. F. & J. L. ST. JOHN, 1934: Lead ursolate in relation to fruit cleaning (Ind. & Eng. Chem. 26: 781-782).

COOK, F. C., 1923: The influence of copper sprays on the yield and composition of Irish potato tubers (U.S.D.A. Bull. 1146: 1-27).

CORDLEY, A. B., 1909: Lime-sulphur spray as a preventive of apple scab. (Better Fruit, April, 1909).

CRANDALL, C. S., 1909: Bordeaux mixture (Illinois Agr. Exp. Sta. Bull. 135: 200-296).

CRANE, H. L., 1919: A study of the factors governing the efficiency of distribution and rate of discharge of spray nozzles (West Virginia Agr. Exp. Sta. Bull. 169: 1-65).

CRESSMAN, A. W. & L. H. DAWSEY, 1934: Oil retention, oil-emulsifier ratio, and oil-water ratio as affecting the insecticidal efficiency of emulsions (Jour. Agr. Res. 49: 1-19).

CROWELL, I. H., 1941: Use of dichloricide in the control of scavenger mites in test tube cultures (Mycologia 33: 137).

CUBONI, G.: La transpirazione e l'assimilazione nelle foglie trattete con latte di calce (Malphighia Ann. 1, fasc. 8). Cited by FAIRCHILD, 1894.

CUNNINGHAM, G. H., 1925: *Corticium*-disease of potatoes (New Zealand Jour. Agr. 30: 14-21).

—— 1935: Plant protection by the aid of therapeutants (Dunedin, New Zealand).

CUNNINGHAM, H. S. & E. G. SHARVELLE, 1940: Organic seed protectants for lima beans (Phytopath. 30: 4).

CUPPLES, H. L., 1943: Proprietary surface-active agents of possible use in insecticide preparations (U.S.D.A. Bur. Ent. & Pl. Quar. Publ. Ser. E. 607: 1-49).

CURTIN, L. P. & M. T. BOGERT, 1927. Experiments in wood preservation. IV. Preservative properties of chlorinated coal-tar derivatives (Ind. & Eng. Chem. 19: 1231-1240).

CURTIS, L. C., 1944a: The influence of guttation fluid on pesticides (Phytopath. 34: 196-205).

—— 1944b: The exudation of glutamine from lawn grass (Plant Phys. 19: 1-5).

DAVIES, C. & G. R. B. SMYTH-HOMEWOOD, 1938: Investigations on machinery used in spraying, Part V. Tabulated results of nozzle tests (Jour. S.-E. Agric. Coll., Wye, 42:9-36).

DAY, L. H., 1928: Pear blight control in California (California Agr. Ext. Service Circ. 20:1-52).

DEANE, S., 1797: The New-England Farmer, or Georgical Dictionary (second edition). Cited by LODEMAN, 1896.

DEGRULLY, L., 1898: New copper fungicides (Prog. Agr. et Vitic. 29:445-447). Cited by Exp. Sta. Rec. 10:156, 1898.

DEMAREE, J. B. & J. R. LARGE, 1934: Some injurious effects of bordeaux mixture on pecan trees (Proc. S. E. Pecan Growers' Assoc. 28:20-29).

DEONG, E. R., H. KNIGHT & J. C. CHAMBERLIN, 1927: A preliminary study of petroleum oil as an insecticide for citrus trees (Hilgardia 2:351-384).

DIMOCK, A. W., 1944: Soil treatment with sodium selenate for control of foliar nematode of chrysanthemums (Phytopath. 34:999).

DIMOND, A. E., J. W. HEUBERGER & J. G. HORSFALL, 1943: A water soluble protectant fungicide with tenacity (Phytopath. 33:1095-1097).

—— & J. G. HORSFALL, 1942: Progress report by fungicide sub-committee on substitutes (Mimeographed Rept. to Amer. Phytopath. Soc.).

—— & —— 1943: Preventing the bacterial oxidation of rubber (Science N. S. 97:144-145).

—— & —— 1944: Synergism as a tool in the conservation of fungicides (Phytopath. 34:136-139).

——, ——, J. W. HEUBERGER & E. M. STODDARD, 1941: Role of the dosage-response curve in the evaluation of fungicides (Connecticut Agr. Exp. Sta. Bull. 451:635-667).

DOMAGK, G., 1935: (Deut. Med. Wochschr. 61:829). Cited by RAWLINS et al., 1942.

DORAN, W. L., 1922: Laboratory studies of the toxicity of some sulphur fungicides (New Hampshire Agr. Exp. Sta. Tech. Bull. 19:1-11).

—— 1923: Toxicity studies with some copper fungicides (Phytopath. 13:532-542).

—— 1928a: Acetic acid as a soil disinfectant (Jour. Agr. Res. 36:269-280).

—— 1928b: The growth of tobacco and brown root rot of tobacco as affected by timothy infusions of different ages (Jour. Agr. Res. 36:281-287).

DREISCH, F. E., 1873: Untersuchungen über die Einwirkung verdünnter Kupferlösungen auf den Keimprocess des Weizens (Dresden. Inaug. Diss., Rostock, 50 pp.).

DUBOIS, R., 1923: Sur la toxicité du cuivre à l'égard des moisissures (Compt. Rend. Acad. Sci. 176:1498-1500).

DUGGAR, B. M. & J. S. COOLEY, 1914: The effect of surface films and dusts on the rate of transpiration (Ann. Mo. Bot. Garden 1:1-22).

DUNLAP, A. A., 1943: Inhibition of *Phymatotrichum* sclerotia formation by sulphur autoclaved with soil (Phytopath. 33:1205-1208).

DUTTON, W. C., 1926: Concentration of materials and rate of application in the control of apple scab (Michigan Agr. Exp. Sta. Tech. Bull. 76:1-18).

—— 1932a: Spray injury studies, I. Injuries from summer applications on apples (Michigan Agr. Exp. Sta. Spec. Bull. 218:1-68).

—— 1932b: Spray injury studies, II. Secondary effects of spray injury to apple foliage (Michigan Agr. Exp. Sta. Spec. Bull. 219:1-38).

EDGERTON, C. W., 1918: Delayed ripening of tomatoes caused by spraying with bordeaux mixture (Louisiana Agr. Exp. Sta. Bull. 164:1-16).

ELMER, O. H., 1942: Dormant applications of lime sulphur for controlling raspberry anthracnose (Phytopath. 32:3-4).

EVANS, A. C. & H. MARTIN, 1935: The incorporation of direct with protective insecticides and fungicides, I. The laboratory evaluation of water-soluble wetting agents as constituents of combined washes (Jour. Pomol. & Hort. Sci. 13:261-292).

EWERT, R., 1905: Die wechselseitige Einfluss des Lichtes und der Kupferkalkbrühen auf den Stoffwechsel der Pflanze (Landw. Jahrb. 34:233-309).

EYRE, J. V. & E. S. SALMON, 1916: The fungicidal properties of certain sprayfluids (Jour. Agr. Sci. 7:473-507).

EZEKIEL, W. N. & J. J. TAUBENHAUS, 1934: Comparing soil fungicides with special reference to *Phymatotrichum* root rot (Science 79:595-596).

FAES, H. & M. STAEHELIN, 1930: La lutte contre les parasites de la vigne, insectes et champignons, en 1929 (Ann. Agr. Suisse 31:123-133). Abs. in Rev. Appl. Myc. 10:9, 1931.

FAIRCHILD, D. G., 1894: Bordeaux mixture as a fungicide (U.S.D.A. Div. Veg. Path. Bull. 6:1-55).

FAJANS, E. & H. MARTIN, 1937: The incorporation of direct with protective fungicides and insecticides, II. The effects of spray supplements on the retention and tenacity of protective deposits (Jour. Pomol. & Hort. Sci. 15:1-24).

—— & —— 1938: The incorporation of direct with protective insecticides and fungicides, III. Factors affecting the retention and spray residue of emulsions and combined emulsion-suspensions (Jour. Pomol. and Hort. Sci. 16:14-38).

FARGHER, R. G., L. D. GALLOWAY & M. E. PROBERT, 1930: The inhibitory action of certain substances on the growth of mould fungi (Shirley Inst. Mem. 9:37-52). Abs. in Rev. Appl. Myc. 9:783-784, 1930.

FARLEY, A. J., 1923: Dry mix sulfur lime. A substitute for self-boiled lime-sulfur, and summer-strength concentrated lime-sulfur (New Jersey Agr. Exp. Sta. Bull. 379:1-16).

FINDLAY, W. P. K., 1932: Laboratory methods for testing wood preservatives (Ann. Appl. Biol. 19:271-280).

FINNEY, D. J., 1942: The analysis of toxicity tests on mixtures of poisons (Ann. Appl. Biol. 29:82-94).

—— 1943: The statistical treatment of toxicological data relating to more

—— 1944: The application of the probit method to toxicity test data adjusted than one dosage factor (Ann. Appl. Biol. 30:71-79).

for mortality in the controls (Ann. Appl. Biol. 31:68-74).

FISHER, D. F., 1922: Effect of alkaline sprays on the size of sweet cherries (Phytopath. 12:104).

FITCH, R., 1906: The action of insoluble substances in modifying the effect of deleterious agents upon the fungi (Ann. Myc. 4:313-322).

FORBUSH, E. H. & C. H. FERNALD, 1895: The gypsy moth (*Porthetria dispar* L.) (Boston).

FOREMAN, F. W., 1910: The fungicidal properties of liver of sulphur (Jour. Agr. Sci. 3:401-416).

FORSYTH, D. D. & M. L. SCHUSTER, 1943: Abnormal leaf formation on flax seedlings caused by Spergon (Jour. Amer. Soc. Agron. 35:733-735).

FORSYTH, W., 1791: Observations on the diseases, defects and injuries of all kinds of fruit and forest trees, with an account of a peculiar method of cure (London, 1791, 71 pp.).

FREAR, D. E. H., 1944: Deposition and retention of sprays, III. Apparatus and methods for laboratory spraying (Pennsylvania Agr. Exp. Sta. Bul. 463: 1-18).

—— & H. H. WORTHLEY, 1940: Deposition and retention of sprays on apples, II. (Pennsylvania Agr. Exp. Sta. Bull. 400: 1-22).

FRENCH, O. C., 1934: Machinery for applying atomized oil spray (Agr. Eng. 15: 324-325). Cited by FRENCH, 1942.

—— 1942: Spraying equipment for pest control (California Agr. Exp. Sta. Bull. 666: 1-42).

FRON, G., 1936: La maladie de l'Orme (C. R. Acad. Agr. Fr. 22: 1081-1089). Abs. in Rev. Appl. Myc. 16: 350, 1937.

GADDUM, J. H, 1933: Reports on biological standards, III. Methods of biological assay depending on a quantal response (Med. Res. Counc., London, Spec. Rept. Series 183: 1-46).

GEGENBAUER, V., 1921: Studien über die Disinfektionswirkung des Sublimates (Arch. Hyg. 90: 23-81). Cited by LIN, 1940.

GEPPERT, 1889: (Berlin. klin. Wochenschr. 1809: 789 & 819). Cited by J. H. SMITH, 1921.

GEUTHER, T., 1895: Über die Eeinwirkung von Formaldehydelösungen auf Getreidebrand. (In Ber. Pharm. Gesell. Jahrg. 5: 325-329).

GIMINGHAM, C. T., A. M. MASSEE & F. TATTERSFIELD, 1926: A quantitative examination of the toxicity of 3,5-dinitro-o-cresol and other compounds to insect eggs under laboratory and field conditions (Ann. Appl. Biol. 13: 446-465).

GINSBURG, J. M., 1927: Investigation of stickers in dusting mixtures (New Jersey Agr. Exp. Sta. Rept. '25-'26: 206).

GLASGOW, R. D. & ROBERT BLAIR, 1944: The use of explosives for the application of insecticide dusts (Jour. Econ. Ent. 37: 230-234).

GOLDSWORTHY, M. C., R. H. CARTER & E. L. GREEN, 1942: The fungicidal and phytocidal properties of some copper xanthates (Phytopath. 32: 497-504).

—— & E. L. GREEN, 1933: Some promising fungicides (Phytopath. 23: 561-562).

—— & —— 1938: Effect of low concentrations of copper on germination and growth of conidia of Sclerotinia fructicola and Glomerella cingulata (Jour. Agr. Res. 56: 489-505).

—— & —— 1939: The fungicidal activity of phenothiazine and some of its oxidation derivatives (Phytopath. 29: 700-716).

GOODEN, E. L. & C. M. SMITH, 1940: Measuring average particle diameter of powders (Ind. & Eng. Chem., Anal. Ed. 12: 479-482).

GOODWIN, W., H. MARTIN & E. S. SALMON, 1926: The fungicidal properties of certain spray-fluids, IV. (Jour. Agr. Sci. 16: 302-317).

GREATHOUSE, G. A. & N. E. RIGLER, 1940a: The chemistry of resistance of plants to Phymatotrichum root rot, IV. Toxicity of phenolic and related compounds (Amer. Jour. Bot. 27: 99-108).

—— & —— 1940b: The chemistry of resistance of plants to Phymatotrichum root rot, V. Influence of alkaloids on growth of fungi (Phytopath. 30: 475-485).

GREEN, E. L. & M. C. GOLDSWORTHY, 1937: The copper content of residues from sprays containing adjuvants (Phytopath. 27: 957-970).

GREGORY, P. H., 1940: The control of narcissus leaf diseases, II. The effect of white mould on flower and bulb crop (Ann. Appl. Biol. 27: 472-488).

GRIES, G. A., 1943a: Juglone (5-hydroxy-1, 4-naphthoquinone) — a promising fungicide (Phytopath. 33: 1112).

—— 1943b: The effect of plant-decomposition products on root diseases (Phytopath. 33: 1111-1112).

—— 1944: Juglone—the active agent in walnut toxicity (Northern Nut Growers' Assoc. Proc. 34: 52-55).

GUILLON, J. M. & G. GOUIRAND, 1898: Recherches sur l'adhérence des bouillies cupriques (Rev. Vit. 10: 631-635). Cited by BUTLER & SMITH, 1919.

GUTERMAN, C. E. F. & L. M. MASSEY, 1935: A liquid formaldehyde treatment to control damping-off of flower seedlings (Phytopath. 25: 18).

HALLER, H. L., E. R. McGOVRAN, L. D. GOODHUE & W. N. SULLIVAN, 1942: The synergistic action of sesamin with pyrethrin insecticides (Jour. Organic Chem. 7: 183-184).

HALSTED, B. D., 1895: Experiments with tomatoes. Report of the botanist (New Jersey Agr. Exp. Sta. Rept. 16: 293-296).

—— & J. A. KELSEY, 1903: Some of the newer fungicides (New Jersey Agr. Exp. Sta. Bull. 167: 1-15).

HAMILTON, J. M., 1931: Studies of the fungicidal action of certain dusts and sprays in the control of apple scab (Phytopath. 21: 445-523).

—— 1932: Recent investigations on the control of apple scab in the Hudson Valley (New York State Agr. Exp. Sta. Bull. 604: 1-44).

—— 1935: Studies on apple scab and spray materials for its control in the Hudson Valley (New York State Agr. Exp. Sta. Tech. Bull. 227: 1-56).

——, G. L. MACK & D. H. PALMITER, 1943: Redistribution of fungicides on apple foliage (Phytopath. 33: 5).

——, D. H. PALMITER & G. L. MACK, 1943: Particle size of sulphur and copper fungicides in relation to apple scab and cedar-apple rust control. (Phytopath. 33: 533-550).

——, D. H. PALMITER & L. O. WEAVER, 1943: Evaluation of fermate for the control of apple scab and cedar apple rust fungi (Phytopath. 33: 5).

HANNA, W. F., H. B. VICKERY & G. W. PUCHER, 1932: The isolation of tri-methyl amine from spores of *Tilletia levis,* the stinking smut of wheat (Jour. Biol. Chem. 97: 351-358).

HARRISON, F. C., 1898: The effect of spraying bordeaux mixture on foliage (Ontario Agr. Col. Ann. Rept. 23: 125-128).

HASKELL, R. J., 1917: The spray method of applying concentrated formaldehyde solution in the control of oat smut (Phytopath. 7: 381-383).

HASTINGS, E. B. & J. H. PEPPER, 1939: Studies on some of the factors involved in the use of sodium arsenite against the Mormon cricket (Montana Agr. Exp. Sta. Bull. 370: 1-25).

HATFIELD, I., 1935: Toxicity in relation to the position and number of chlorine atoms in certain chlorinated benzene derivatives (Amer. Wood-Pres. Assoc. 31: 57-66).

HAWKINS, L. A., 1913: The influence of calcium, magnesium, and potassium nitrates upon the toxicity of certain heavy metals toward fungus spores (Physiol. Researches 1: 57-92).

HEALD, F. D., 1921: The relation of spore load to the per cent of stinking smut appearing in the crop (Phytopath. 11: 269-278).

HEDRICK, U. P., 1907: Bordeaux injury (New York State Agr. Exp. Sta. Bull. 287: 217-286).

HENSILL, G. S. & W. M. HOSKINS, 1935: Factors concerned in the deposit of sprays, I. The effect of different concentrations of wetting agents (Jour. Econ. Ent. 28: 942-950).

—— & V. J. TIHENKO, 1939: Mechanical and other factors affecting oil spray deposits (Jour. Econ. Ent. 32: 36-40).

HERANGER, S. F., 1935: Pulvérisations et mouillabilité (Rev. Vitic. (Paris) 82: 21-25, 37-46, 56-61, 72-79, 90-94, 105-108, 117-121). Abs. in Rev. Appl. Myc. 14: 556, 1935.

HEUBERGER, J. W., 1940: A laboratory biological assay of tenacity of fungicides. (Phytopath. 30: 840-847).

—— 1942a: Effect of copper content, completeness of admixture of copper and diluent, and nature of diluent on field performance of copper dusts (Phytopath. 38: 8).

—— 1942b: Improved control of *Alternaria solani* (Early Blight) on tomatoes by controlling flea beetles (Phytopath. 32: 8).

—— & J. F. ADAMS, 1936: Another role of zinc-lime in combination peach sprays (Trans. Pen. (Del.) Hort. Soc. 26: 55-59).

—— & J. G. HORSFALL, 1939: Relation of particle size and color to fungicidal and protective value of cuprous oxides (Phytopath. 29: 303-321).

—— & —— 1942: Reduction in fungicidal value of copper compounds by organic materials (Phytopath. 32: 370-378).

—— & T. F. MANNS, 1943: Effect of zinc sulphate-lime on protective value of organic and copper fungicides against early blight of potato (Phytopath. 33: 1113).

—— & N. TURNER, 1942: A laboratory apparatus for studying settling rate and fractionation of dusts (Phytopath. 32: 166-171).

HILTNER, L., 1914: Über die Wirkung von Chinosol und Formaldehyd als Beizmittel gegen dem Fusariumbefall des Getreides (Prakt. Blätter 12: 77-80).

—— 1915: Seed treatment tests (Prakt. Bl. Pflanzenbau u. Schutz, N. Ser. 13: 65-90), Abs. Exp. Sta. Rec. 35: 651-652, 1916).

HOFFMAN, C., T. R. SCHWEITZER & G. DALBY, 1939: Fungistatic properties of the fatty acids and possible biochemical significance (Food Research 4: 539-545).

——, —— & —— 1940: The effect of chlorine substitution on the fungistatic properties of acetic and propionic acids (Jour. Amer. Chem. Soc. 62: 988-989).

HOFFMAN, M. B., 1932: The effect of certain spray materials on the carbon dioxide assimilation by McIntosh apple leaves (Amer. Soc. Hort. Sci. Proc. 29: 389-393).

HOLLAND, E. B., C. O. DUNBAR & G. M. GILLIGAN, 1929: Supplements for copper fungicides (Massachusetts Agr. Exp. Sta. Bull. 252: 94-112).

HOOD, C. E., 1926: Fish oil, an efficient adhesive in arsenate-of-lead sprays (U.S.D.A. Bull. 1439).

HOOKER, H. D., 1924: Copper hydroxide as a substitute for bordeaux (Amer. Soc. Hort. Sci. Proc. 21: 173-176).

HOPPERSTEAD, S. L., M. W. GOODWIN & K. J. KADOW, 1943: Bitter rot of apples and its control in Delaware (Delaware Agr. Exp. Sta. Bull. 241: 1-23).

HORSFALL, J. G., 1930: A study of meadow-crop diseases in New York (Cornell Agr. Exp. Sta. Mem. 130: 1-139).

—— 1932a: Dusting tomato seed with copper sulfate monohydrate for combating damping-off (New York Agr. Exp. Sta. Tech. Bull. 198: 1-34).

—— 1932b: Red oxide of copper as a dust fungicide for combating damping-off by seed treatment (New York Agr. Exp. Sta. Bull. 615: 1-26).

—— & R. W. BARRATT, 1945: An improved grading system for measuring plant diseases (Phytopath. 35. *In press*).

—— & J. M. HAMILTON, 1935: Some fungicidal possibilities of red copper oxide (Phytopath. 25: 21).

—— & A. L. HARRISON, 1939: Effect of bordeaux mixture and its various elements on transpiration (Jour. Agr. Res. 58: 423-443).

——, G. E. R. HERVEY & R. F. SUIT, 1939: Dwarfing of cucurbits sprayed with bordeaux mixture (Jour. Agr. Res. 58: 911-928).

—— & J. W. HEUBERGER, 1942: Measuring magnitude of a defoliation disease of tomatoes (Phytopath. 32: 226-232).

—— & —— 1942: Causes, effects and control of defoliation on tomatoes (Connecticut Agr. Exp. Sta. Bull. 456: 183-223).

——, J. W. HEUBERGER, E. G. SHARVELLE & J. M. HAMILTON, 1940: A design for laboratory assay of fungicides (Phytopath. 30: 545-563).

——, R. O. MAGIE & R. F. SUIT, 1938: Bordeaux injury to tomatoes and its effect on ripening (New York Agr. Exp. Sta. Tech. Bull. 251: 1-39).

——, R. W. MARSH & H. MARTIN, 1937: Studies upon the copper fungicides, IV. The fungicidal value of the copper oxides (Ann. Appl. Biol. 24: 867-882).

—— & A. D. McDONNELL, 1943: The coverage factor in fungicidal efficiency (Phytopath. 33: 1114).

—— & R. F. SUIT, 1938: The lime factor in bordeaux injury (Phytopath. 28: 9).

—— & N. TURNER, 1943: Injuriousness of bordeaux mixture (Amer. Pot. Jour. 20: 308-320).

—— & G. A. ZENTMYER, 1941: Chemotherapy for vascular diseases of trees (Nat. Shade Tree Conf. Proc. 17: 7-15).

—— & —— 1942: Antidoting the toxins of plant diseases (Phytopath. 32: 22-23).

—— & —— 1944: Fungicidal action of reagents for amino acids, amines, aldehydes, and other reactive cell constituents (Phytopath. 34: 1004).

HOSKINS, W. M. & E. L. WAMPLER, 1936: Factors concerned in the deposit of sprays, II. Effect of electrostatic charge upon the deposit of lead arsenate (Jour. Econ. Ent. 29: 134-143).

HOWARD, F. L., 1941: Antidoting toxin of *Phytophthora cactorum* as a means of plant disease control (Science, N.S. 94: 345).

—— & H. L. KEIL, 1943: Cationic quaternary ammonium compounds as fungicides (Phytopath. 33: 1115).

—— & M. B. SORRELL, 1943: Cationic phenyl mercury compounds as specific apple-scab eradicants on foliage (Phytopath. 33: 1114).

HUMPHREY, C. J. & R. M. FLEMING, 1915: The toxicity to fungi of various oils and salts, particularly those used in wood preservation (U.S.D.A. Bull. 227: 1-38).

HUNT, G. M. & G. A. GARRATT, 1938: Wood preservation (McGraw-Hill Book Co., Inc., 457 pp.).

HUTCHINSON, C. M., 1913: Rangpur tobacco wilt (Mem. Dept. Agr. India, Bact. Ser., 1: 67-84). Abs. Exp. Sta. Rec. 30: 50, 1914.

HYRE, R. A., 1942: Relation of particle size to fungicidal value and tenacity of two "insoluble" copper fungicides (Phytopath. 32: 388-393).

INMAN, M. T., Jr., 1929: Sulfonated oxidation products of petroleum as insecticide activators (Ind. and Eng. Chem. 21: 542-543).

IPSEN, J., 1941: Contribution to the theory of biological standardization (Copenhagen).

IRONS, F., 1943: A laboratory study of crop duster problems (Agr. Eng. November, 1943, pp. 383-384.)

ISELY, D. & W. R. HORSFALL, 1943: Effect on arsenical deposits of accessory materials in the spray mixture (Jour. Econ. Ent. 36: 751-756).

JACOBS, H. L., 1929: Injections of shade trees for the control of insects and diseases (Davey Tree Expert Co. Res. Dept. Bull. 3: 1-4).

JENKINS, G. L. & W. H. HARTUNG, 1943: The chemistry of organic medicinal products (John Wiley & Sons, Inc., New York).

JENSEN, J. L., 1888: The propagation and prevention of smut in oats and barley (Jour. Roy. Agr. Soc. England Series 2, 24: 397-415).

JOHNSON, F. H., 1942: Mechanism of p-aminobenzoic acid action and the parallel effects of ethyl carbamate (urethane) (Science N.S. 95: 104-105).

JOHNSON, G. F., 1935: The early history of copper fungicides (Agr. History 9: 67-79).

JOHNSON, J., 1941: Chemical inactivation and the reactivation of a plant virus (Phytopath. 31: 679-701).

JOHNSON, S. W., 1891: Fungicides and their application. Note by the director on p. 113 (Connecticut Agr. Exp. Sta. Rept. 1890: 104-113).

JOHNSON, T. B. & F. W. LANE, 1921: The preparation of some alkyl derivatives of resorcinol and the relation of their structure to antiseptic properties (Jour. Amer. Chem. Soc. 43: 348-360).

KADOW, K. J., M. W. GOODWIN & S. L. HOPPERSTEAD, 1939: The relation of copper fungicides to lead arsenate-lime and fixed nicotine-oil sprays (Phytopath. 29: 12-13).

KAGY, J. F. & G. L. McCALL, 1941: Dust mixtures of a phenol salt for control of mites (Jour. Econ. Ent. 34: 119-120).

—— & C. H. RICHARDSON, 1936: Ovicidal and scalicidal properties of solutions of dinitro-o-cyclo-hexylphenol in petroleum oil (Jour. Econ. Ent. 29: 52-61).

KAHLENBERG, L. & R. H. TRUE, 1896: On the toxic action of dissolved salts and their electrolytic dissociation (Bot. Gaz. 22: 81-124).

KEITT, G. W., 1935: Progress in the development of eradicant fungicides (Phytopath. 25: 23).

—— 1939: Toxicity of the sodium salt of dinitro-o-cresol to *Venturia inaequalis* (Science 90: 139-140).

—— & E. E. WILSON, 1926: Studies on the development of the ascigerous stage of *Venturia inaequalis* in nature (Phytopath. 16: 77).

KELHOFER, W., 1907: Über die Ausführung und die Ergebnisse von Haftfestigkeitversuchen kupferhaltiger Bekämpfungsmittel gegen die *Peronospora* (Zeitschr. Pflanzenkr. 17: 1-12).

KELLERMAN, K. F. & T. D. BECKWITH, 1906: The effect of copper upon water bacteria (U.S.D.A., B.P.I. Bull. 100: 1-19).

KELLERMAN, W. A. & W. T. SWINGLE, 1890: Additional experiments and observations on oat smut, made in 1890 (Kansas Agr. Exp. Sta. Bull. 15: 93-133).

KELLEY, V. W., 1930: Effect of certain hydrocarbon oils on the transpiration rate of some deciduous tree fruits (Illinois Agr. Exp. Sta. Bull. 353: 579-600).

KERLING, L. C. P., 1928: De anatomische bouw van bladvlekken (Meded. Landbouwhoogeschool Wageningen 32: 1-107). Abs. in Rev. Appl. Myc. 8: 118-120, 1929.

KIESEL, A., 1913: Recherches sur l'action de divers acides et sels acides sur le développement de l'Aspergillus niger (Ann. l'Inst. Pasteur 27: 391-420). Cited by RIGLER & GREATHOUSE, 1940.

KITAJIMA, K. & J. KAWAMURA, 1931: Antiseptic action of higher fatty acids against wood-attacking fungi (Imp. Forestry Exp. Sta. Tokyo Bull. 31: 108-113).

KOZLOVA, E. N., 1935: Amount of added benefactor depending on the specific surface of the dust insecticide (Plant Protection 1935: 404-406). Abs. in Rev. Appl. Ent. 25: 157-158 Ser. A., 1937.

KRAUSCHE, K. K. & B. E. GILBERT, 1937: Increase of transpiration rates of tomato leaves due to copper sprays (Plant Phys. 12: 853-860).

KRÖNIG, B. & T. PAUL, 1897: Die chemischen Grundlagen der Lehre von der Giftwirkung und Disinfektion (Ztschr. Hyg. u. Infektionskrank. 25: 1-112). Cited by LIN, 1940.

LARGE, E. C., 1940: The advance of the fungi (Henry Holt & Co., New York).

LEACH, R., 1940: Banana leaf spot investigations, I. The basis of control (Jour. Jamaica Agric. Soc. 44: 499-502). Abs. in Rev. Appl. Myc. 20 : 265, 1941.

LEE, H. A. & J. P. MARTIN, 1927: The development of more effective dust fungicides by adding oxidizing agents to sulphur (Science 66: 178).

LENARD, P., 1915: Über Wasserfallelektrizität und über die Oberflachenbeschaffenheit der Flüssigkeiten (Ann. Physik 47: 463-524). Cited by WAMPLER and HOSKINS, 1939.

LE PELLEY, R. H. & W. N. SULLIVAN, 1936: Toxicity of rotenone and pyrethrins, alone and in combination (Jour. Econ. Ent. 29: 791-797).

LEUTRITZ, J. JR., 1939: Acceleration of toximetric tests of wood preservatives by the use of soil as a medium (Phytopath. 29: 901-903).

LIN, C. K., 1940: Germination of the conidia of Sclerotinia fructicola, with special reference to the toxicity of copper (Cornell Agr. Exp. Sta. Mem. 233: 1-33).

LODEMAN, E. G., 1895: The spraying of orchards, apples, quinces, plums (Cornell Agr. Exp. Sta. Bull. 86: 45-76).

—— 1896: The spraying of plants (Macmillan & Co., New York, 399 pp.).

LOEW, O., 1903: The physiological rôle of mineral nutrients in plants (U.S.D.A., B.P.I. Bull. 45: 1-70).

LUTMAN, B. F., 1910: Plant diseases; potato spraying (Vermont Agr. Exp. Sta., Bull. 153: 619-629).

—— 1916: Some studies on bordeaux mixture (Vermont Agr. Exp. Sta. Bull. 196: 1-80).

—— 1922: The relation of the water pores and stomata of the potato leaf to the early stages and advance of tipburn (Phytopath. 12: 305-333).

MACH, E. & K. PORTELE, 1884: (Weinlaube 16:433). Cited by MARTIN, 1940.

MACHT, D. I., 1929: Pharmacological synergism of stereoisomers (Proc. Nat. Acad. Sci. 15:63-70).

MACLEOD, G. F. & W. DICKISON, 1936: Bordeaux spraying in relation to growth rate and yield of potatoes in Nassau County, L. I. (Am. Pot. Jour. 13:180-184).

—— & H. F. SHERWOOD, 1937: Grenz radiographs of sulfur dispersion on foliage (Jour. Econ. Ent. 30:395-398).

MADER, E. O., 1943: Some factors inhibiting the fructification and production of the cultivated mushroom, *Agaricus campestris* L. (Phytopath. 33:1134-1145).

—— & F. M. BLODGETT, 1935: Effects of modifications of the potato-spray program (Cornell Univ. Agr. Exp. Sta. Bull. 621:1-34).

—— & M. T. MADER, 1937a: The composition of tubers of sprayed and unsprayed potato plants in relation to cooking quality (Amer. Pot. Jour. 14:56-59).

—— & —— 1937b: Effect of bordeaux mixture on three varieties of potatoes with respect to yields, composition of tubers, and control of scab (Phytopath. 27:1032-1045).

MAGIE, R. O., 1942: The epidemiology and control of downy mildew on hops (New York State Agr. Exp. Sta. Tech. Bull. 267:1-48).

—— & J. G. HORSFALL, 1936: Relative adherence of cuprous oxide and other copper fungicides (Phytopath. 26:100-101).

MARCILLE, N., 1911: Sur le mode d'action des soufres utilisés pour combattre l'oidium (Compt. Rend. 152:780-783). Cited by DORAN, 1922.

MARES, H. H., 1869: Manual for the sulphuring of diseased vines and results (In three seasons in European vineyards by W. J. FLAGG, New York: 209-283). Cited by DORAN, 1922.

MARSH, P. B., 1945: Salts as antidotes to copper in its toxicity to the conidia of *Sclerotina fructicola* (Phytopath. 35:54-61).

MARSH, R. W., 1929: Investigations on the fungicidal action of sulphur, III. Studies on the toxicity of sulphuretted hydrogen and on the interaction of sulphur with fungi (Jour. Pom. & Hort. Sci. 7:237-250).

—— 1936: Notes on a technique for the laboratory evaluation of protective fungicides (Trans. Brit. Mycol. Soc. 20:304-309).

—— 1937: Some recent American work on the copper fungicides (Sci. Hort. 5:60-66).

—— 1938: Some applications of laboratory biological tests to the evaluation of fungicides (Ann. Appl. Biol. 25:583-604).

MARSHALL, J., 1937: Inverted spray mixtures and their development with reference to codling moth control (Wash. Agr. Exp. Sta. Bull. 350:1-88).

MARTIN, H., 1932: Studies upon the copper fungicides, I. The interaction of copper sulphate with calcium hydroxide (Ann. Appl. Biol. 19:98-120).

—— 1940: The scientific principles of plant protection with special reference to chemical control (Edward Arnold & Co., London, third edition).

—— & E. S. SALMON, 1931: The fungicidal properties of certain spray-fluids, VIII. The fungicidal properties of mineral, tar and vegetable oils (Jour. Agr. Sci. 21:638-658).

—— & —— 1932: The fungicidal properties of certain spray fluids, IX. The fungicidal properties of the products of hydrolysis of sulphur (Jour. Agr. Sci. 22: 595-616).

—— & —— 1933: The fungicidal properties of certain spray fluids, X. Glyceride oils (Jour. Agr. Sci. 23: 228-251).

——, R. L. WAIN & E. H. WILKINSON, 1942: Studies upon the copper fungicides, V. A critical examination of the fungicidal value of copper compounds (Ann. Appl. Biol. 29: 412-438).

MARTIN, W. H., 1920: Studies on tomato leaf-spot control (New Jersey Agr. Exp. Sta. Bull. 345: 1-43).

—— & E. S. CLARKE, 1929: Influence of bordeaux mixture on transpiration (New Jersey Agr. Exp. Sta. Rept. 50: 249-255).

MASON, A. F., 1928: Spraying, dusting, and fumigating of plants (Macmillan Co., 539 pp.).

MASSON, E., 1887: Nouveau procédé bourquinon contre le mildiou (Jour. Agr. Prat. 51: 814-816). Cited by MARTIN, 1940.

MAY, C., 1941: Methods of tree injection (Trees 4: 7, 10-12, 14, 16).

McCALLAN, S. E. A., 1930a: Studies of fungicides, II. Testing protective fungicides in the laboratory (Cornell Agr. Exp. Sta. Mem. 128: 8-24).

—— 1930b: Studies on fungicides, III. The solvent action of spore excretions and other agencies on protective copper fungicides (Cornell Agr. Exp. Sta. Mem. 128: 25-79).

——, A. HARTZELL & F. WILCOXON, 1936: Hydrogen sulphide injury to plants (Contr. Boyce Thompson Inst. 8: 189-197).

—— & R. H. WELLMAN, 1942: Fungicidal versus fungistatic (Contr. Boyce Thompson Inst. 12: 451-463).

——, R. H. WELLMAN & F. WILCOXON, 1941: An analysis of factors causing variation in spore germination tests of fungicides, III. Slope of toxicity curves, replicate tests, and fungi (Contr. Boyce Thompson Inst. 12: 49-77).

—— & F. WILCOXON, 1931: The fungicidal action of sulphur, II. The production of hydrogen sulphide by sulphured leaves and spores and its toxicity to spores (Contr. Boyce Thompson Inst. 3: 13-38).

—— & —— 1934: Fungicidal action and the periodic system of the elements (Contr. Boyce Thompson Inst. 6: 479-500).

—— & —— 1936: The action of fungous spores on bordeaux mixture (Contr. Boyce Thompson Inst. 8: 151-165).

—— & —— 1938: Laboratory comparison of copper fungicides. Contr. Boyce Thompson Inst. 9: 249-263).

—— & —— 1939: An analysis of factors causing variation in spore germination tests of fungicides, I. Methods of obtaining spores (Contr. Boyce Thompson Inst. 11: 5-20).

—— & —— 1940: An analysis of factors causing variation in spore germination tests of fungicides, II. Methods of spraying (Contr. Boyce Thompson Inst. 11: 309-324).

McCLINTOCK, J. A., 1931: The relation of canker treatment to fireblight control (Phytopath. 21: 901-906).

McWHORTER, F. P., 1927: Fungicidal value of oil sprays (Phytopath. 17: 201-202).

—— & J. PRYOR, 1937: Onion mildew in Oregon and the advisability of testing malachite green as a control agent for downy mildews (Plant Disease Reporter 21: 306).

MELHUS, I. E. & G. C. KENT, 1939: Elements of plant pathology (Macmillan Co.).

MENZEL, K. D., 1935: Untersuchungen der schädigenden Wirkungen Kupferhaltiger Spritzmittel (Angew. Bot. 17: 225-253).

MEYER, C. F., 1753: Abhandlung von dem Brand im Getreide, und den Mitteln solchem zu wehren (In Hannoversche Anst., Gelehrte Anz. Stück 78: 1022-1026). Cited by WOOLMAN and HUMPHREY, 1924.

MILLARDET, P. M. A., 1885: Traitement du mildiou par le mélange de sulphate de cuivre et de chaux (Jour. Agr. Prat. 2: 707-710). Phytopath. Classic 3: 12-17, 1933. Traitement du mildiou et du rot (Jour. Agr. Prat. 2: 513-516). Phytopath. Classic 3: 7-11, 1933. Sur l'histoire du traitement du mildiou par le sulphate de cuivre (Jour. Agr. Prat. 2:801-805). Phytopath. Classic 3: 18-25, 1933. Trans. by F. J. SCHNEIDERHAN.

MILLER, B. F. & Z. BAKER, 1940: Inhibition of bacterial metabolism by synthetic detergents (Science 91: 624-625).

MILLER, E. C., 1938: Plant physiology (McGraw-Hill Book Co., Inc., 1201 pp.).

MILLER, H. J., 1943: A comparison of laboratory and field retention and protective value of certain copper fungicides (Phytopath. 33: 899-909).

MILLER, L. C., C. I. BLISS & H. A. BRAUN, 1939: The assay of ... I. Criteria for evaluating various methods using frogs (Jour. Amer. Assoc. 28: 644-657).

MONTGOMERY, H. B. S. & M. H. MOORE, 1938: A laboratory method for testing the toxicity of protective fungicides (Jour. Pomol. & Hort. Sci. 15: 253-266).

MOORE, W., 1921: Spreading and adherence of arsenical sprays (Minnesota Agr. Exp. Sta. Tech. Bull. 2: 1-50).

MORGAN, M. F., 1941: Chemical soil diagnosis by the universal soil testing system (Connecticut Agr. Exp. Sta. Bull. 450: 574-628).

MORRIS, H. I., L. J. KLOTZ & V. P. SOKOLOFF, 1941: Brown rot control and copper injury (California Citrograph, August, 1941).

MUIR, R. M., 1940: Effect of bile salts and oleates on the structural viscosity of protoplasm (Bot. Gaz. 102: 357-365).

NÄGELI, 1893: Über oligodynamische Erscheinungen in lebenden Zellen, mit einem Vorwort von S. SCHWENDENER und einem Nachtrag von C. CRAMER (Separatabdruck aus den Denkschriften der Schweizerischen naturforsch. Ges. 33: 1-51. Kommiss.-Verlag v. H. Georg, Basel). Cited by SWINGLE, 1896.

NIELSON, L. W., 1942: Studies with silver compounds and mixtures as fungicidal sprays (Cornell Agr. Exp. Sta. Mem. 248: 1-44).

NIKITIN, A. A., 1937: Zeolitic copper compounds as fungicides (Diss. Columbia Univ. 1937: 1-71).

O'KANE, W. C., W. A. WESTGATE, & L. C. GLOVER, 1934: Studies of contact insectides, VII. Methods of expressing toxicity (New Hampshire Agr. Exp. Sta., Tech. Bull. 58: 1-35).

——, ——, —— & P. R. LOWRY, 1930: Surface tension, surface activity, and wetting ability as factors in the performance of contact insecticides (New Hampshire Agr. Exp. Sta. Tech. Bull. 39: 1-44).

——, L. C. GLOVER & R. L. BLICKLE, 1941: An insect toximeter. Studies of contact insecticides, XV (New Hampshire Agr. Exp. Sta. Tech. Bul. 76: 1-10).

PARKER-RHODES, A. F., 1941: Studies on the mechanism of fungicidal action,

I. Preliminary investigation of nickel, copper, zinc, silver and mercury (Ann. App. Biol. 28: 389-405).

—— 1942: Studies on the mechanism of fungicidal action, II. Sulphur (Ann. Appl. Biol. 29: 136-143).

PARKINSON, J., 1629: "Paradisus", the ordering of the orchard (Chap. 8: 550). Cited by LODEMAN, 1896.

PARROTT, P. J. & W. J. SCHOENE, 1910: Experiments with home-made concentrated lime-sulphur mixtures (New York State Agr. Exp. Sta. Bull. 330: 349-382).

PECK, S. M. & H. ROSENFELD, 1938: The effects of hydrogen ion-concentration, fatty acids and vitamin C on the growth of fungi (Jour. Invest. Dermatology 1: 237-265).

PETERSON, P. D., 1941: The spore-germination method of evaluating fungicides (Phytopath. 31: 1108-1116).

PETIT, A., 1930: Energie fongicide de certains sels halogénés de cuivre (Ann. Serv. Bot. Tunisie 6: 57-70).

PICKERING, S. U., 1907: The interaction of metallic sulfates and caustic alkalis (Jour. Chem. Soc. London 91: 1981-1988).

—— 1912: Copper fungicides (Jour. Agr. Sci. 4: 273-281).

PICKETT, W. F. & C. J. BIRKELAND, 1941: Common spray materials alter the internal structure of apple leaves (Amer. Soc. Hort. Sci. Proc. 38: 158-162).

PIERCE, N. B., 1900: Peach leaf curl, its nature, and treatment (U.S.D.A. Div. Veg. Phys. and Path. Bull. 20: 1-204).

PINCKARD, J. A. & R. McLEAN, 1940: A laboratory method for determining the fungicidal value of vapors and its application to paradichlorobenzene in the control of tobacco downy mildew (Phytopath. 30: 19).

PIRONE, P. P., 1942: Mercury substitutes for turf disease control (Nursery Dis. Notes 15: 1-4).

PLAKIDAS, A. G., 1938: The mode of action of bordeaux on *Mycosphaerella fragariae* (Phytopath. 28: 307-329).

POLLACCI, E., 1875: Della ragione per cui il solfo uccide l'oidio della vite, e sulla emissione d'idrogeno libero dalle piante (Gazz. Chim. Ital. 5: 451-460). Abs. Justs Bot. Jahrb. 4: 125, 1876.

POLYAKOV, I. M., 1941: A new method for controlling agricultural crop diseases (Bul. Plant Protect. U.S.S.R. No. 1, 92-99). Abs. in Chemical Abs. 36: 2073, 1942.

POSNJAK, E. & G. TUNELL, 1929: (Amer. Jour. Sci. 18: 1). Cited by MARTIN, 1940.

POTTER, C., 1941: A laboratory spraying apparatus and technique for investigating the action of contact insecticides. With some notes on suitable test insects (Ann. Appl. Biol. 28: 142-169).

POTTS, S. F., 1939: A method for determining the quantity of foliage per acre of woodland (Jour. Forestry 37: 922-923).

—— 1940: Concentrated spray mixtures and their application by ground and aerial equipment as compared with standard spraying and dusting methods (U.S.D.A. Bur. Ent. & Plant Quar. Publ., Circ. E-508: 1-21).

—— & D. F. BARNES, 1931: Adhesives and carriers for insecticidal dusts (Jour. Econ. Ent. 24: 1110-1111).

PREVOST, B., 1807: Memoire sur la cause immédiate de la carie ou charbon des blés, et de plusieurs autres maladies des plantes, et sur les préservatifs de la carie (Phytopath. Classic 6: 1-94). Trans. by G. W. KEITT, 1939.

PROUST, J. L., 1800: Recherches sur le cuivre (Ann. Chim. et Phys. (1) 32: 26-54). Cited by HOLLAND et al., 1929.

QUASTEL, J. H., 1930: (Trans. Farad. Soc. 26: 853). Cited by CLARK, 1933.

RADCLYFFE, W. F., 1861: (Gard. Chron. pg. 967). Cited by LODEMAN, 1896.

RAHN, O., 1929: The size of bacteria as the cause of the logarithmic order of death (Jour. Gen. Phys. 13: 179-205).

RALEIGH, W. P., 1933: A homemade colloidal copper spray (Phytopath. 23: 29).

RAWLINS, A. L., L. A. SWEET & D. A., JOSLYN, 1942: Relationship of chemical structure to germicidal activity of a series of quaternary ammonium salts (Jour. Amer. Pharm. Assoc. 32: 11-16).

REED, H. S., 1942: A short history of the plant sciences (Chronica Botanica Co., Waltham, Mass.).

REMNANT, R., 1637: A discourse or historie of bees . . . . Whereunto is added, the causes, and cure of blasted wheat. And some remedies for blasted hops, and rie, and fruit. Together with the causes of smutty wheat; all of which are very useful for this later age (London: 1-47). Cited by WOOLMAN and HUMPHREY, 1924.

RICHARDS, C. A., 1923: Methods of testing the relative toxicity of wood preservatives (Amer. Wood-Pres. Assoc. 19: 127-135).

RICHARDSON, C. H. & C. R. SMITH, 1923: Studies on contact insecticides (U.S.D.A. Bull. 1160: 1-15).

RIDEAL, S. & J. F. A. WALKER, 1903: Determination of the value of a disinfectant in terms of its carbolic coefficient (Jour. Roy. Sanitary Inst., London). Cited by YOUNG and COOPER, 1917.

RIEHM, E., 1913: Prüfung einiger Mittel zur Bekämpfung des Steinbrandes (Mitt. K. Biol. Anst.). Abs. Zentralbl. Bakt. II, 40: 424, 1914.

RIGLER, N. E. & G. A. GREATHOUSE, 1940: The chemistry of resistance of plants to Phymatotrichum root rot, VI. Fungicidal properties of fatty acids (Amer. Jour. Bot. 27: 701-704).

—— & —— 1941: Fungicidal potency of quinoline homologs and derivatives against Phymatotrichum omnivorum (Ind. & Eng. Chem. 33: 693-694).

ROACH, W. A., 1939: Plant injection as a physiological method (Ann. Bot., N.S., 3: 155-226).

—— & M. D. GLYNNE, 1928: The toxicity of certain sulphur compounds to Synchytrium endobioticum, the fungus causing wart disease of potatoes (Ann. Appl. Biol. 15: 168-190).

ROARK, R. C., 1934: A bibliography of chloropicrin, 1848-1932 (U.S.D.A. Misc. Publ. 176: 1-88).

ROBBINS, W. J. & V. KAVANAGH, 1942: Vitamin deficiencies of the filamentous fungi (Bot. Rev. 8: 411-471).

ROBERTSON, J., 1824: (Trans. Hort. Soc. London 5: 175). Cited by LODEMAN, 1894.

ROBINSON, R. H., 1919: The beneficial action of lime in lime sulfur and lead arsenate combination spray (Jour. Econ. Ent. 12: 429-433).

RUMBOLD, C., 1920: The injection of chemicals into chestnut trees (Amer. Jour. Bot. 7: 1-20).

RUNNELS, H. A. & J. D. WILSON, 1933: Control of Alternaria blight of ginseng with bordeaux mixture and injuries accompanying its use (Ohio Agr. Exp. Sta. Bull. 522: 1-16).

—— & —— 1934: The influence of certain spray materials, herbicides, and other compounds on the desiccation of plant tissue (Ohio Agr. Exp. Sta. Bi-mo. Bull. 19 : 104-109).

SAFRO, V. I., 1913: An investigation of lime-sulfur injury. Its causes and prevention (Oregon Agr. Exp. Sta. Res. Bull. 2 : 1-32).

SALMON, E. S. & W. M. WARE, 1931: The downy mildew of the hop in 1930 (Inst. Brew. Jour. 28 : 24-31). Cited by MAGIE, 1942.

SANDERS, G. E., 1922: Dusting and spraying the apple (Dosch Chem. Co., Louisville, Ky., Res. Bull. 8 : 1-11).

—— & A. KELSALL, 1918: A copper dust (Nova Scotia Ent. Soc. Proc. 4 : 32-37).

SAUNDERS, W., S. A. BEDFORD & A. MACKAY, 1894: Smut in wheat (Canada Exp. Farms Rept. 1893 : 41-42).

SAYRE, J. D. & R. C. THOMAS, 1927: New dust treatments for oat smuts (Science, N. S. 66 : 398).

SAZONOV, P. V., 1937: Influence of mineral oil added to dust insecticides. In summary of the scientific research work of the Institute of Plant Protection for the year 1935 (Plant Prot. 1935 : 401-403). Abs. in Rev. Appl. Ent. Series A 25 : 157, 1937.

SCHANDER, R., 1904: Über die physiologische Wirkung der Kupfervitriolkalkbrühe (Landw. Jahrb. 33 : 517-584).

SCHERER, C. M., 1927: Tree injection for the control of fungous diseases and insect pests (Phytopath. 17 : 51).

SCHULTHESS, H., 1761: Vorschlag einiger durch die Erfahrung bewährter Hilfsmittel gegen den Brand im Korn (In Abhandl. Naturf. Gesell. Zürich, Bd. 1 : 498-506). Cited by WOOLMAN and HUMPHREY, 1924.

SEIFRIZ, W. & M. URAGUCHI, 1941: The toxic effects of heavy metals on protoplasm (Amer. Jour. Bot. 28 : 191-197).

SELBY, A. D., 1900: Onion smut. Preliminary experiments. (Ohio Agr. Exp. Sta. Bull. 122 : 71-84).

SESSIONS, A. C., 1936: Fungicide adjustment (Ind. & Eng. Chem. 28 : 287-290).

SHEPARD, H. H., 1939: The chemistry and toxicology of insecticides (Burgess Publishing Co., Minneapolis).

—— & C. H. RICHARDSON, 1931: A method of determining the relative toxicity of contact insecticides, with especial reference to the action of nicotine against Aphis rumicis (Jour. Econ. Ent. 24 : 905-914).

SIEGLER, E. H. & C. H. POPENOE, 1925: The fatty acids as contact insecticides (Jour. Econ. Ent. 18 : 292-299).

SKAPTASON, J. B. & F. M. BLODGETT, 1941: Reduced toxicity of cuprous oxide to Phytophthora infestans (Mont.) De Bary by the addition of certain insecticides (Amer. Pot. Jour. 18 : 179-180).

SMITH, J. H., 1921: The killing of Botrytis spores by phenol (Ann. Appl. Biol. 8 : 27-50).

—— 1923: The killing of Botrytis cinera by heat with a note on the determination of temperature coefficients (Ann. Appl. Biol. 10 : 335-347).

SMITH, L. M., 1938: The relation of concentration of active ingredient to insecticidal efficiency of dusts (Jour. Econ. Ent. 31 : 598-602).

SMITH, M. A., 1930: The control of certain fruit diseases with flotation sulphurs (Phytopath. 20 : 535-553).

SMITH, R. H., 1926: The efficacy of lead arsenate in controlling the codling moth. (Hilgardia 1 : 403-453).

—— 1928: An investigation of spray coverage and arsenical residue in relation to the control of the codling moth (Jour. Econ. Ent. 21: 571-588).

SORAUER, P., 1899: Der "Vermehrungspilz." (Zeitschr. Pflanzenkr. 9:321-388).

SOSTEGNI, L., 1890: Sulla composizione chimica della casi detta poltigia bordolese (Staz. Sper. Agr. Ital. 19: 129-141). Cited by BUTLER, 1914.

SOUTHWICK, F. W. & N. F. CHILDERS, 1941: Influence of bordeaux mixture and its component parts on transpiration and apparent photosynthesis of apple leaves (Plant Phys. 16: 721-754).

STARKEY, R. L. & S. A. WAKSMAN, 1943: Fungi tolerant to extreme acidity and high concentrations of copper sulfate (Jour. Bact. 45: 509-519).

STARR, D. F., 1944: The theory of probits at high mortalities (Jour. Econ. Ent. 37: 850).

STEINBERG, R. A., 1940: Action of some organic compounds on yield, sporulation and starch formation of Aspergillus niger (Jour. Agr. Res. 60: 765-773).

STEWART, F. C., G. T. FRENCH & F. A. SIRRINE, 1912: Potato spraying experiments, 1902-1911 (New York State Agr. Exp. Sta. Bull. 349: 99-139).

STODDARD, E. M., 1942: Inactivating in vivo the virus of X-disease of peach by chemotherapy (Phytopath. 32: 17).

—— 1944: Immunization of peach trees to X disease by chemotherapy (Phytopath. 34: 1011).

—— & W. D. HENRY, 1943: The coverage effect of sulphur on the control of apple scab. (Phytopath. 33: 1119).

—— & J. W. HEUBERGER, 1943: Eradicant action of fungicides on spores on living plants (Phytopath. 33: 1190-1195).

—— & G. A. ZENTMYER, 1943: Possible chemical similarity of virus and fungous toxins. (Phytopath. 33:20).

STRONG, F. C. & DONALD CATION, 1940: Control of cedar rust with sodium dinitrocresylate (Phytopath. 30: 983).

STURGIS, W. C., 1895: Notes on the early blight of potatoes (Connecticut Agr. Exp. Sta. Rept. 18: 127-133).

SUIT, R. F. & J. G. HORSFALL, 1938: The copper factor in bordeaux injury (Phytopath. 28: 20).

SUTER, C. M., 1941: Relationships between structure and bactericidal properties of phenols (Chem. Rev. 28: 269-299).

SWEETMAN, M. D., 1936: Factors affecting the cooking qualities of potatoes (Maine Agr. Exp. Sta. Bull. 383: 296-387).

SWINGLE, W. T., 1896: Bordeaux mixture, its chemistry, physical properties, and toxic effects on fungi and algae (U.S.D.A. Veg. Phys. & Path. Bull. 9: 1-37).

TALBERT, T. J., H. D. HOOKER & H. G. SWARTWOUT, 1926: An investigation of sprays and spraying material (Missouri Agr. Exp. Sta. Bull. 236: 62-63).

TATTERSFIELD, F., 1927: The relationship between the chemical constitution of organic compounds and their toxicity to insects (Jour. Agr. Sci. 17: 181-208).

—— & C. T. GIMINGHAM, 1927a: Studies on contact insecticides, Part V. The toxicity of the amines and N-heterocyclic compounds to Aphis rumicis L. (Ann. Appl. Biol. 14: 217-239).

—— & —— 1927b: Studies on contact insecticides, Part VI. The insecticidal action of the fatty acids. Their methyl esters and sodium and ammonium salts (Ann. Appl. Biol. 15: 331-358).

—— & H. M. Morris, 1924: An apparatus for testing the toxic values of contact insecticides under controlled conditions (Bull. Ent. Res. 14: 223-233).

Taubenhaus, J. J. & P. Decker, 1935: Laboratory and field studies on sulphur as a fungicide (Phytopath. 25: 35-36).

Taylor, G. G., 1939: Application of orchard sprays (New Zealand Dept. Sci. & Ind. Res. Bull..22: 1-46).

Tehon, A. R., 1944: Experimental immunization of American elm from infection by *Verticillium albo-atrum* (Phytopath. 34: 1012).

—— & H. L. Jacobs, 1939: Experimental injection of hard maple saplings artificially infected with *Verticillium albo-atrum*, R. & B. (Davey Tree Expert Co. Res. Bull. 7).

Thatcher, R. W. & L. R. Streeter, 1925: The adherence to foliage of sulfur in fungicidal dusts and sprays (New York State Agr. Exp. Sta. Tech. Bull. 116: 1-18).

Thurston, H. W., Jr., & H. J. Miller, 1938: Experiments with liquid lime sulphur for spraying apples (Phytopath. 28: 823-832).

Tilford, P. E. & C. May, 1929: The effect of bordeaux mixture on the internal temperature of potato leaflets (Phytopath. 19: 943-949).

Tillet, M., 1755: Dissertation sur la cause qui corrumpt et noircit les grains de blé dans les épis et sur les moyens de prévenir ces accidens (Phytopath. Classic 5: 1-191, 1937). Trans. by H. B. Humphrey.

Tisdale, W. H. & I. Williams, 1934: U. S. Patent 1,972,961.

Townsend, G. R., 1942: Spraying and dusting for the control of celery early blight in the Everglades (Florida Agr. Exp. Sta. Bull. 366: 1-26).

Traube, J., 1913: Theorie der Narkose (Pflüg. Archiv. Phys. 153: 276-308).

Trelease, S. F. & H. M. Trelease, 1931: Magnesium injury of wheat (Bull. Torrey Bot. Club, 58: 127-148).

Trevan, J. W., 1927: The error of determination of toxicity (Proc. Roy. Soc. London, Ser. B. 101: 483-514).

Tull, J., 1733: Horse-hoeing husbandry: or, an essay on the principles of tillage and vegetation (London, 269 pp.). Cited by Woolman and Humphrey, 1924.

Turner, N., 1943: Reversals in order of effectiveness of insecticides (Jour. Econ. Ent. 36: 725-728).

—— 1945: The coverage factor in the application of dusts (Jour. Econ. Ent. *In press*).

Turrell, F. M., F. Cuneo, D. Slack & H. Carns, 1943: Factors in injury to citrus by sulphur dusts (California Citrograph 28: 286-287, 302, 306-307, 310-311).

Upholt, W. M. & W. M. Hoskins, 1940: Factors concerned in the deposit of sprays (Jour. Econ. Ent. 33: 102-107).

Uppal, B. N., 1926: Toxicity of organic compounds to the spores of *Phytophthora colocasiae* Rac. (Jour. Agr. Res. 32: 1069-1097).

Vermorel, V. & E. Dantony, 1910: Le mildiou de la grappe (Rev. Vit. 34: 71). Cited by Nielson, 1942.

—— & —— 1913a: (Le Progrès Agric. et Vitic. 30:745-746). Cited by Cunningham, 1935.

—— & —— 1913b: Notes on the wetting power of fungicides (Compt. Rend. Acad. Sci. (Paris) 156: 1475-1476). Abs. in Exp. Sta. Rec. 29: 451.

Villedieu, G. & Mme. Villedieu, 1923: Action des oxydes insolubles sur le mildiou de la pomme de terre (*Phytophthora infestans*) (Compt. Rend. Acad. Sci. (Paris) 176: 534-536). Abs. in Rev. Appl. Myc. 2: 374.

—— & —— 1924: D'action des solutions de sulfate de cuivre sur le mildiou (Compt. Rend. Acad. Sci. (Paris) 179: 1345-1348).

WADLEY, F. M. & W. N. SULLIVAN, 1943: A study of the dosage mortality curve (Jour. Econ. Ent. 36: 367-372).

WAGNER, E. C., 1939: Effects of certain insecticides and inert materials upon the transpiration rate of bean plants (Plant Phys. 14: 717-735).

WAIN, R. L. & E. H. WILKINSON, 1943: Studies upon the copper fungicides, VI. The solution of copper from Bordeaux and Burgundy mixtures (Ann. Appl. Biol. 30: 379-391).

WALKER, J. C. & K. P. LINK, 1935: Toxicity of phenolic compounds to certain onion bulb parasites (Bot. Gaz. 96: 468-484).

——, S. MORRELL & H. H. FOSTER, 1937: Toxicity of mustard oils and related sulfur compounds to certain fungi (Amer. Jour. Bot. 24: 536-541).

WALLACE, E., 1910: Spray injury induced by lime-sulphur preparations (Cornell Agr. Exp. Sta. Bull. 288: 103-137).

——, F. M. BLODGETT & L. R. HESLER, 1911: Studies on the fungicidal value of lime-sulphur preparations (Cornell Agr. Exp. Sta. Bull. 290: 1-207).

WAMPLER, E. L. & W. M. HOSKINS, 1939: Factors concerned in the deposit of sprays, VI. The role of electrical charges produced during spraying (Jour. Econ. Ent. 32: 61-69).

WARD, H. M., 1880: Report on the coffee leaf disease (Colombo Sessional Paper No. 17, 1880, with continuations 1881, 1882). Cited by LARGE, 1940.

WATSON, R. W., 1942: The mechanism of elongation in palisade cells (New Phytol. 41: 206-221).

WEBER, A. L., H. C. McLEAN, B. F. DRIGGERS & W. J. O'NEILL, 1937: Influence of different materials on coverage and adhesiveness of sprays and their effect on residue removal from apples (New Jersey Agr. Exp. Sta. Bull. 627: 1-16).

WEED, C. M., 1889: Notes on experiments with remedies for certain plant diseases (Ohio Agr. Exp. Sta. Bull. Ser. 2, 2: 186-189).

WEISS, FREEMAN & E. L. EVINGER, 1932: The toxicity of naphthalene for fungi of the *Sclerotium rolfsii* type (Phytopath. 22: 30).

WELLMAN, R. H. & S. E. A. McCALLAN, 1942: An analysis of factors causing variation in spore germination tests of fungicides, IV. Time and temperature. (Contr. Boyce-Thompson Inst. 12: 431-450).

WHETZEL, H. H., 1918: An outline of the history of phytopathology (W. B. Saunders Co., Philadelphia, 1918).

—— & S. E. A. McCALLAN, 1930: Studies on fungicides, I. Concepts and terminology (Cornell Agr. Exp. Sta. Mem. 128: 1-7).

WHIPPLE, G. C., 1916: The element of chance in sanitation (Jour. Franklin Inst. 182: 37-59).

WILCOXON, F. & S. E. A. McCALLAN, 1930: The fungicidal action of sulphur, I. The alleged rôle of pentathionic acid (Phytopath. 20: 391-417).

—— & —— 1931: The fungicidal action of sulphur, III. Physical factors affecting the efficiency of dusts (Contr. Boyce Thompson Inst. 3: 509-528).

—— & —— 1935: Fungicidal action of organic thiocyanates, resorcinol derivatives, and other organic compounds (Contr. Boyce Thompson Inst. 7: 333-339).

—— & —— 1938: The weathering of bordeaux mixture (Contr. Boyce Thompson Inst. 9 : 149-159).

—— & —— 1939: Theoretical principles underlying laboratory toxicity tests of fungicides (Contr. Boyce Thompson Inst. 10 : 329-338).

WILLIAMS, R. C., 1929: Laboratory method for measuring relative adhesive qualities of fungicidal dusts (Ind. & Eng. Chem. Anal. ed., 1 : 81-82).

WILSON, E. E., 1942: The effect of certain added materials on bordeaux mixture in the control of peach blight and leaf curl (Hilgardia 14 : 491-515).

WILSON, J. D. & H. A. RUNNELS, 1933: Some effects of bordeaux mixture on transpiration (Ohio Agr. Exp. Sta. Bi-Mo. Bull. 18 : 147-151).

—— & —— 1935a: The influence of various copper-containing fungicides on the transpiration rate (Ohio Agr. Exp. Sta. Bi.-Mo. Bull. 20 : 13-16).

—— & —— 1935b: The relation of time to the effect of bordeaux mixture on transpiration (Ohio Agr. Exp. Sta. Bi-Mo. Bull. 20 : 120-124).

—— & F. IRONS, 1942: Specifications of some of the ingredients commonly used in fungicidal dust mixtures (Ohio Agr. Exp. Sta. Bi-Mo. Bull. 27 : 26-41).

WÖBER, A., 1920: Die fungizide Wirkung der verschiedenen Metalle gegen *Plasmopara viticola* Berl. et de Toni und ihre Stellung im periodischen System der Elemente (Zeitschr. Pflanzenkr. 30 : 51-59).

WOLF, F. A., R. A. McLEAN, J. A. PINCKARD, F. R. DARKIS & P. M. GROSS, 1940: Volatile fungicides, benzol and related compounds and the principles involved in their use (Phytopath. 30 : 213-227).

WOODS, D. D., 1940: The relation of *p*-amino-benzoic acid to the mechanism of the action of sulphanilamide (Brit. Jour. Exp. Path. 21 : 74-90).

WOODWARD, G. J., L. B. KINGERY & R. J. WILLIAMS, 1934: The fungicidal power of phenol derivatives, I. Effect of introducing alkyl groups and halogens (Jour. Lab. & Clin. Med. 19 : 1216-1223). Abs. Rev. Appl. Myc. 14 : 105, 1935.

WOOLLEY, D. W., 1944: Some new aspects of the relationship of chemical structure to biological activity (Science 100 : 579-583).

WOOLMAN, H. M. & H. B. HUMPHREY, 1924: Summary of literature on bunt, or stinking smut, of wheat (U.S.D.A. Bull. 1210 : 1-44).

WRIGHT, C. W. B. & R. M. WOODMAN, 1932: Problems confronting the sprayer, II. The volume of spray passing through nozzles of varying diameter at varying spraying pressures (Chem. News 144 : 146-147). Abs. in Rev. Appl. Myc. 11 : 523-524, 1932.

WÜTHRICH, E., 1892: Über die Einwirkung von Metallsalzen und Säuren auf die Keimfähigkeit der Sporen einiger der verbreitetsten parasitischen Pilze unserer Kulturpflanzen (Zeitschr. Pflanzenkr. 2 : 16-31, 81-94).

YARWOOD, C. E., 1937: Sulphur and rosin as downy mildew fungicides (Phytopath. 27 : 931-941).

—— 1941: Sporulation injury associated with downy mildew infections (Phytopath. 31 : 741-748).

—— 1943a: The function of lime and host leaves in the action of bordeaux mixture (Phytopath. 33 : 1146-1156).

—— 1943b: Bordeaux injury to foliage at low temperatures (Plant Physiol. 18 : 508-516).

YOUNG, H. C., 1922: The toxic property of sulfur (Ann. Mo. Bot. Gard. 9 : 403-435).

—— 1930: Water soluble arsenic in spray material (Ohio Agr. Exp. Sta. Bull. 448: 1-21).

—— & J. R. BECKENBACH, 1936: Spreader materials for insoluble copper sprays. (Phytopath. 26: 450-455).

—— & E. H. COOPER, 1917: A method for determining the fungicidal coefficient of lime sulphur and other common fungicides (Michigan Acad. Sc. Rept. 19: 221-236).

—— & L. E. TISDALE, 1929: Adhesiveness of sulfur mixtures. (Phytopath. 19: 89).

—— & R. C. WALTON, 1925: Spray injury to apple (Phytopath. 15: 405-415).

—— & R. WILLIAMS, 1928: Factors affecting the fungicidal property of sulphur (Phytopath. 18: 147).

ZENTMYER, G. A., 1942a: Toxin formation and chemotherapy in relation to Dutch elm disease (Phytopath. 32: 20).

—— 1942b: Toxin formation by *Ceratostomella ulmi* (Science 95: 512-513).

—— 1943: Mechanism of action of 8-hydroxyquinoline (Phytopath. 33: 1121),

—— 1944: Inhibition of metal catalysis as a fungistatic mechanism (Science 100: 294-295).

—— & J. G. HORSFALL, 1943: Internal therapy with organic chemicals in treatment of vascular diseases (Phytopath. 33: 16-17).

——, P. WALLACE & J. G. HORSFALL, 1944: Distance as a dosage factor in spread of Dutch elm disease (Phytopath. 34: 1025-1033).

GENERAL INDEX

—— plus bordeaux mixture, 169
—— redistribution, 87
—— resurgence of popularity of, 110
—— synergist for metallic oxides, 169
—— synergist for thiuramsulfides, 170-171
Sulfur deposits, rate of loss in field, 91
Sulfur dioxide, fungicidal action of, 121-122
Sulfur dust, tenacity of, 93
Sulfur injury, effect of oil on, 185
—— effect of tree vigor on, 185
Sulfur and oxygen in toxicity, 170
Sulfur-lead arsenate injury, symptoms of, 172
Sulfur materials, effect on palisade cells, 175
—— reduce growth, 173
Sulfur ointments, history of, 3
Sulfur protectants, 51
Sulfur spray, detergents in, 99
Sulfuric acid, toxicity of, 122
Sulfurous acid, toxicity of, 122
Sulsol, 124
Supplementary synergism, 159-160, 163-168
Surfaces, adherence of fungicides to, 9
—— adsorption of toxicants on, 163
—— effect on coverage, 69
—— effect on tenacity, 88
—— multiple, coverage of, 75-87
—— retention of fungicides by, 9
—— significance in bioassay, 20
—— single, coverage of, 62-74
—— standardized, 20
Surface-active compounds, *see* also Detergents, Soaps
—— antagonism of, 164
—— toxicity of, 137-139
Surface adsorption, effect on tenacity, 92-93
Surface of cells, action of toxicants at, 115
Surface of particle, effect on toxicity, 50-51, 111-112
Surface tension, 70
—— effect on bioassay, 20
—— effect on deposition, 56
—— effect on droplet size, 57

—— effect on toxicity, 154, *see* also Soap, Detergents
—— of leaf, 58
Symptoms, of phytotoxicity, 172
Synchytrium endobioticum, 122
Synergism, 159-171
—— between OH and CO, 148
—— between organisms, 123, 170
—— definition of, 159
—— in phytotoxicity, 171
—— of potassium permanganate, 122
—— of zinc oxide, 121
Synergy, definition of, 159

TMTD, ACTION OF, 121, 124-126
Tar acids, effect of chlorination on toxicity, 151
Tar oil, toxicity of, 151
Techniques of fungicide assay, 15
Tellurium, 118
Temperature, effect on availability of sulfur, 119-120
—— effect on sulfur injury, 185
—— effect on transpiration, 178
Tenacity, 88-96
—— assay of, 24
—— effect of synergism on, 160
—— resistance of protectants to weathering, 49
Tenacity coefficient, 24
Test organism, admixture of strains of, 35
Tests, committee on standardization of fungicidal, 9
Tetrachloronaphthalene, toxicity of, 151
Tetrachloroquinone, *see* also Chloranil and Spergon
—— first research on, 7
—— seed treatment, 3
—— structure of, 147
—— toxicity of, 145-146, 157
Tetramethyl ammonium chloride, structure of, 138
—— toxicity of, 136
Tetramethylthiuram disulfide, 34, 121, 124-125
—— structure of, 124
—— toxicity curve, 125
Tetrathionic acid, toxicity of, 122
Tetravalent sulfur, toxicity of, 127
Texas root rot, of cotton, 106

AUTHOR INDEX

Thatcher, R. W., 91, 92, 93, 208
Thaxter, R., 1, 12
Thomas, R. C., 7, 45, 103, 206
Thurston, H. W., Jr., 82, 208
Tihenko, V. J., 55, 56, 197
Tilford, P. E., 188, 208
Tillet, 2, 3, 208
Tisdale, L. E., 92, 211
Tisdale, W. H., 7, 124, 208
Tobey, E. R., 173, 191
Townsend, G. R., 166, 169, 170, 208
Traube, J., 154, 208
Trelease, H. M., 184, 208
Trelease, S. F., 184, 208
Trevan, J. W., 15, 26, 208
Trillat, 6, 145
True, R. H., 117, 199
Tucker, 3
Tull, J., 2, 6, 208
Tunell, G., 109, 204
Turner, N., 22, 31, 55, 57, 58, 85, 173, 176, 187, 197, 198, 208
Turrell, F. M., 185, 208

UPHOLT, W. M., 70, 208
Uppal, B. N., 143, 145, 148, 208
Uraguchi, M., 108, 206

VERMOREL, V., 94, 108, 208
Vickery, H. B., 114, 196
Villedieu, G., 50, 116, 208
Villedieu (Mme.), 50, 116, 208

WADE, 6
Wadley, F. M., 32, 209
Wagner, E. C., 179, 209
Wagner, 180, 190, *see* Beasley
Wain, R. L., 51, 65, 202, 209
Waksman, S. A., 116, 207
Walker, J. C., 18, 97, 126, 144, 209
Walker, J. F. A., 17, 23, 205
Wallace, E., 14, 185, 209
Wallace, P., 13, 68, 211
Walton, R. C., 173, 174, 185, 211
Wampler, E. L., 21, 60, 95, 198, 200, 209

Ward, H. M., 6, 11, 209
Ware, W. M., 86, 206
Warren, G. F., 9
Watson, R. W., 174, 209
Weaver, L. O., 171, 196
Weber, A. L., 80, 86, 87, 90, 209
Weed, C. M., 6, 159, 209
Weiss, F., 143, 209
Wellman, R. H., 17, 22, 33, 35, 202, 209
Westgate, W. A., 20, 203
Whetzel, H. H., 1, 44, 51, 209
Whipple, G. C., 28, 209
Wilcoxon, F., 15, 19, 22, 24, 30, 37, 51, 55, 64, 66, 67, 89, 93, 95, 108, 114, 120, 121, 122, 123, 141, 145, 168, 202, 209
Wilkinson, E. H., 51, 65, 202, 209
Williams, I., 7, 124, 208
Williams, R., 122, 211
Williams, R. C., 24, 210
Williams, R. J., 7, 152, 210
Wilson, E. E., 45, 60, 89, 91, 92, 95, 164, 199, 210
Wilson, J. D., 55, 174, 177, 178, 180, 205, 210
Wiltshire, S. P., 120, 189
Witkus, E. R., 44, 190 -
Wober, A., 108, 210
Wolf, F. A., 101, 210
Woodman, R. M., 77, 210
Woods, D. D., 156, 168, 210
Woodward, G. J., 152, 210
Woolley, D. W., 156, 210
Woolman, H. M., 5, 6, 108, 203, 205, 206, 208, 210
Worthley, H. H., 89, 195
Wright, C. W. B., 77. 210
Wüthrich, E., 108, 116, 210

YARWOOD, C. E., 42, 43, 44, 69, 70, 174, 178, 210
Young, H. C., 23, 45, 92, 95, 121, 122, 173, 174, 185, 189, 205, 210

ZENTMYER, G. A., 3, 13, 68, 97, 104, 105, 106, 107, 154, 155, 161, 167, 198, 207, 211

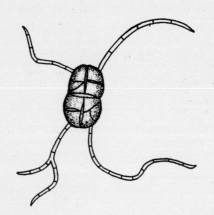